PROGRAMMING AND CODING DIGITAL COMPUTERS

PROGRAMMING

AND CODING

DIGITAL COMPUTERS

PHILIP M. SHERMAN

BELL TELEPHONE LABORATORIES
MURRAY HILL, NEW JERSEY

JOHN WILEY AND SONS, INC.

NEW YORK AND LONDON

73268

~

Library of Congress Catalog Card Number: 63-12290
Printed in the United States of America

TO DORIS,

JUDITH, ALAN, AND EMILY

PREFACE

Many thousands of problems, from dozens of professions, that must be answered quickly and accurately exist today. There are many methods for solving these problems, but none of them is as fast and precise as that of using the digital computer.

Every method of problem solution has a number of steps. For computer solution, the most important step is the writing of a *computer program,* a list of the operations that are to be performed to solve the problem.

This book is about writing programs. It is written in the belief that programming is best learned by doing, where "doing" means actually writing and running programs on the computer. The book covers a wide range of topics in program writing, beginning with first computer concepts. Related topics, such as computer design and numerical analysis, although not developed, are referenced in many chapters. The reader is urged to read further on the topics that interest him. An understanding of the book requires no prior knowledge of digital computers and no mathematical background beyond that which is ordinarily a part of the high-school curriculum. A few examples involve calculus, but the solutions of these problems, as of all the others, are approached by arithmetic means and offer little mathematical difficulty.

The book is organized into three parts. Part I is an introduction to digital computers. Its four chapters are general and do not pertain to any specific computer. Part II, consisting of seven chapters, is concerned with the details of *coding*—the actual writing of programs for a computer. This material is best illustrated by specific examples, so a hypothetical computer that has characteristics similar to those of most real computers is described. These characteristics were selected to provide a pedagogically sound object of study. The eight chapters of Part III are concerned with the nature and types of problems solved on computers rather than with the details of coding.

As a textbook for a programming course, this book provides material for at least 90 class hours, perhaps a third of which are to be spent writing programs. If the book is used in conjunction with computer manuals or the booklets described in a later paragraph, it will aid the programmer still further in his work with the computer. If program debugging time is included in the course, at least 120 hours are required to cover all the material. The material divides naturally after Chapter 11, so that Parts I and II together can be used for a one-semester course.

Since this book contains material of both a general and a specific nature, different sizes of type are used to distinguish between them. Usually, material that refers specifically to the hypothetical computer, including all the examples, appears in small type. General material that applies to most computers is in standard type. There are exceptions, since occasionally it is difficult to classify a particular topic.

The problems in each chapter range from simple exercises paralleling examples in the text to complex exercises that require considerable original work. The problems are designed both to provide the reader with a test of his knowledge of the text and to extend the subject matter of the book. Many problems are speculative: "What would happen if . . . ?"

There are two appendices. One summarizes all the information on the hypothetical computer that is scattered throughout the book. The description of each instruction is listed, as are the characteristics of the associated assembly program. The other appendix is bibliographical.

The hypothetical computer, the DELTA 63, incorporates features common to most computers, plus a selection of special features. If the DELTA 63 is compared with any real medium- or large-size computer, the following would be noted: the 63 is simpler, it has fewer instructions, and it is easier to code. It is perhaps most similar to medium-size computers, though its capacity and speed match those of many large ones.

A series of programming booklets is to be published for use with this book. Each booklet deals with one computer that is on the market and includes the following: (1) A listing of all the instructions and other characteristics of the computer, (2) a set of the examples appearing in this book, rewritten in the language of the real computer, and (3) text material to provide continuity. If the book is used with one of these booklets, the pair serves as a text for the particular real computer.

Since the DELTA 63 is hypothetical, the reader may wonder, as he reads the text, why there is so much specific information. For example, details on the manner in which data are read into the computer are given, although no data will ever be read into the DELTA 63. This approach is taken for illustrative purposes. Although the computer is imaginary, it is assumed to have the same problems as the real computers it typifies. Data will be read into real computers in much the same way they are "read" into the DELTA 63.

Although this book touches on areas not directly concerned with programming, it cannot do more than skim these fields. It cannot, for example, delve into the reasons for selecting a particular numerical method for the solution of algebraic equations. The reader must refer to a text on numerical analysis if he desires that information. Such omissions are unfortunate, because programming is closely allied with these topics, but space limitations force them.

Murray Hill, N.J.
January 17, 1963

PHILIP M. SHERMAN

ACKNOWLEDGMENTS

I wish to express my deep gratitude to those people of the Bell Telephone Laboratories whose cogitation and labors have helped me immeasurably. I can do no more than briefly sum up their efforts. Richard M. Brownell painstakingly showed me where my writing became unclear, inconsistent, or not to the point. Berkeley A. Tague pondered the matter of the book's organization and helped in the formulation of many important concepts. M. Douglas McIlroy widened my viewpoint on many points of fact. Others who critically read all or parts of the manuscript include Clarissa J. Kinnaman, Joe F. Traub, and A. Jay Goldstein. Appreciation is due also to the Systems Research Department, particularly to Thomas H. Crowley and H. Earle Vaughan, for support of much of my work. I wish to thank Elizabeth Jenkins for her help in the preparation of the manuscript.

Many people outside the Bell Telephone Laboratories deserve mention, but I wish to name only three. Daniel D. McCracken of McCracken Associates and Professor Herbert Teager of The Massachusetts Institute of Technology offered much critical help in the early stages of writing. Harriet Popham of John Wiley and Sons provided invaluable aid in the preparation and overall improvement of the manuscript.

Finally, to my wife I owe special thanks for her continuous patience and encouragement during the writing of this book.

CONTENTS

PART ONE

PROBLEM SOLVING

AND PROGRAMMING

IF A PROGRAMMER is to appreciate fully the job of writing a program, he must understand how a computer is organized and how it is operated to perform computations. Part I attempts to provide the programmer with this understanding.

The following topics are discussed. First, an introduction to the concepts of computers and programming and to the role of the computer in the business and scientific worlds is presented. Next, the job of analyzing a program for its solution by computer is described. Three aspects of a digital computer then provide an introduction to the machine: its organization, its operation, and its language. Finally, computer arithmetic is explained; the manner in which numbers are handled by the computer is described.

Before specific details of program writing are studied in Part II, the chapters in Part I provide a background in several areas that is independent of particular computers.

1

COMPUTERS
AND THEIR USE

The complexities of modern living and technology have produced mathematical, scientific, and engineering problems in great quantity. These problems increase so rapidly in number and scope that man has turned to mechanical and electronic devices for help in solving them. The increase has been continuous and will continue in the foreseeable future. Modern electronic computers provide the means for solving many of these problems rapidly and accurately. For computers to be able to accomplish this task, the problems must be translated into a form suitable for interpretation and solution by a computer.

In this chapter fundamental questions about computers and programming are answered. The answers provide an introduction to the concepts that are treated at length in this book. An introduction to the computer solution of problems and to the steps involved in preparing problems for a computer is given.

1.1 COMPUTER CONCEPTS

The Growth of Problems

Problems that people have to solve are becoming more complex and more numerous; the need to solve them is becoming more acute. Before the advent of computers, many problems were solved only approximately; this situation had to be accepted because no means for more accurate solutions were available.

Scientific discoveries yield vast amounts of data in great variety. In the areas of medicine, biology, and space technology, for example, there are many data, which require sorting, filing, and being kept up to date. Many areas of research such as weather, astronomy, and literature can progress only by the analysis of thousands or millions of items. Some complex problems require rapid answers, for example, the problem of whether or not a high-speed object in the atmosphere is an enemy missile.

Paperwork increases too, as the following quotation indicates:

> During the eight years of the Eisenhower administration, the amount of information processing done by the government increased several hundredfold. Within a few years it will have increased so much that the entire population of the country working full time would not be able to handle manually the paperwork involved in its own government.*

The "information" mentioned in this quotation refers to both people and property. Records about people, their bank and charge accounts, social-security records, income tax records, and business transactions increase not only because more information per person is kept, but also because the number of people increases. Complex questions in business may sometimes demand fast answers; an example is a question about the current status of a stock inventory.

The following aspect of problem solving emerges here: the need for fast and accurate results. Fast results are needed because the number of questions to be answered is so large; slow methods of solution cannot keep up with the demand. The requirement of accuracy, which we have not spelled out, is self-evident. With these concepts in mind, let us look at the digital computer to see what help it can offer.

Questions That Come to Mind

What is a digital computer? What are programming and coding? Why are computers so widely used today? Why weren't they available before? What kinds of problems can they handle? How have they been used?

Each of these questions, which probably have come to the reader's mind, will be examined in turn.

What Is a Digital Computer?

A computer can be viewed as a machine that performs the basic operations which deal with problems from mathematics and related areas. If a problem of any kind can be stated in mathematical terms and can be considered to consist

---

* "Government by Computers?" D. Bergamini, *The Reporter Magazine,* August 17, 1961.

of a number of distinct operations, those operations can be performed by a computer.

A definition of a computer presented before structure, operation, and use are described must be vague. It must serve us at the start, but as computer concepts are developed, the picture becomes clearer.

Computers are of two distinct types: *analog* and *digital*. Analog computers operate on numbers by representing them with a measure or analog of some sort; for example, 1 volt may represent 1 inch. As a quantity changes during the course of a calculation, the amount of its analog quantity changes proportionately and continuously. The accuracy with which a number can be represented depends on the precision of the mechanical or electronic components of the analog computer. Accuracies better than within 0.01% are rare; usually they are much poorer. Since this book is concerned only with digital computers, we shall say nothing further about analog computers.

Digital computers operate on numbers directly. Every digit of every number is stored as a separate entity. By the use of enough storage devices, each number can have as many digits as desired. Accuracies thus can be arbitrarily high; usually 8- to 15-decimal-digit accuracy is available. The operations that can be performed are not only arithmetic in nature; many other types can be performed to permit the solution of a variety of problems.

What Are Programming and Coding?

A digital computer is constructed to perform calculations. It does so by executing a sequence of operations called *instructions;* the sequence of instructions is called a *program*. For a problem to be solved on a computer, it must be analyzed into its component processes and these processes must be translated into a form suitable for execution, that is, into a sequence of instructions. The first of these tasks, analysis of the problem, is called *programming*. The second, translation into instructions, is called *coding*. These definitions oversimplify the job; there are other, associated tasks that must be done. In Section 1.2 the several steps in *program writing* (the combined tasks of programming and coding) are discussed.

A note of caution is required. The term *programming* is generally used in two different ways: to refer to the entire job of program writing and to refer to the job of problem analysis. In this book the latter, more restricted sense, is intended.

Why Are Computers So Widely Used?

Computers are widely used because they have at least four characteristics that are very useful for solving the problems we want them to solve. They are extremely fast, they are accurate, they can store large amounts of information to which they have rapid access, and they are capable of executing long, complex sequences of operations automatically.   We discuss these characteristics by comparison with similar features on a desk calculator, the machine that the digital computer has largely replaced.

Because of their speed, computers permit the solution of many problems that would otherwise remain unsolved because of the time required for their solution.   A desk calculator takes about half a million times as long to solve a given problem as a modern digital computer.*   A problem that a computer can solve in 10 minutes would therefore take 40 years on a desk calculator operated for 40 hours a week.   Clearly no one would have a person work so long on one problem, since its solution would probably then be of no value.   The comment in the quotation at the start of the chapter—that everyone would be needed to solve our government problems—is an unrealistic extrapolation.   Without computers, we simply would not attempt to solve more than a small fraction of the problems we do now solve.

A direct comparison between the accuracies of a desk calculator and a computer is unfair.   As we see later in this section, the computer performs all the operations within a problem without human intervention.   In contrast, nearly every operation on a desk calculator must be preceded and followed by a human action: entering operands onto the keyboard and reading and writing results on paper.   Therefore a comparison of accuracies should be made between the human-calculator combination and the computer.   A reasonable guess is that a person makes an error every thousand operations when operating a desk calculator.   Mechanical errors in the desk calculator are so infrequent by comparison that they can be neglected.   Digital computers usually run error-free for several hours or days; in 1 hour a large computer can perform a billion operations.

It is important to note here that computers do make mistakes; no machine can run forever without malfunctioning.   When a computer is used to solve a problem, there is always a possibility (although it is extremely small) that an error will occur in the machinery.   Errors are usually easily detected (although their causes are generally hard to track down) because they almost always lead to results that are obviously wrong.   By regular maintenance and performance tests engineers can prevent most troubles.   Little more can be said on the subject, aside from warning the reader of the situation.

Errors that people make in programming, on the other hand, are very likely to occur.   Part of the job of problem preparation is the elimination of these errors.   The subject is discussed several times in this book.

Computers have very fast access to large amounts of stored information; the

---

*For example, multiplication of two 10-digit numbers on a desk calculator takes about 10 seconds.   On the fastest computers, this operation takes about 10 microseconds.   The time ratio is not as high for other operations.

storage area is referred to as *memory*. Specifically, on some computers, up to about a quarter of a million numbers, each having 12 or more decimal digits, can be individually obtained for processing in 1 to 2 microseconds per number. By contrast, a desk calculator can store four or five numbers. These numbers appear on the visible registers (dials) and the keyboard; they can be stored only until the next operation that uses the same register is performed. The primary memory used with a desk calculator is the paper on which the calculator operator writes.

The existence of a program for a digital computer is in direct contrast with problem solution on a desk calculator. In the latter machine a list of the operations to be performed remains on paper or in the mind of the operator. A computer program, however, is stored within the memory of the machine. This feature permits the automatic execution of the program and associated processing of data entirely within the computer, without any human assistance. The process is automatic once the "start" button has been pushed. On a desk calculator only individual arithmetic operations are automatic; each such operation must be triggered by the operator.

A desk calculator is built to perform four arithmetic operations: addition, subtraction, multiplication, and division. Sometimes a fifth, square-root extraction, is available. By contrast, a computer has a large repertoire of instructions —anywhere from twenty to four hundred. The types of instruction generally available are described in Section 3.3.

Why Weren't Computers Available Before?

Digital computers, in their present form, could not have been built before the early 1950's. Only with electronic components could present speeds have been achieved; only with solid-state devices could present reliability have been obtained. Solid-state devices have been available in quantity only since the late 1940's. The basic computer concepts and designs, however, have been available for over a century.

The first device used to help man perform calculations was the abacus. The first mechanical digital computers were built in the seventeenth century by Pascal and Leibnitz. Towards the end of that century, Jacquard devised a loom controlled by punched cards which wove complex patterns. In 1812, Charles Babbage, a British mathematician, designed a machine he called a "Difference Engine," which was to aid in the computation of mathematical tables. This machine was completed in 1822. Later, in 1833, Babbage designed an "Analytical Engine," which was to be completely automatic. The machine was not built because the machined parts it required could not be built with sufficient precision, but it had all the elements of a modern digital computer. The series of operations required to solve a problem was to be punched on cards and supplied to the machine with the data. The memory was to hold

1000 words of 50 digits each, all in wheels. The ability to modify the course of calculations, depending on results obtained in the calculation, was to be incorporated by skipping cards or by moving back to earlier cards. The principles of the Analytical Engine form the basis of many present computer designs.

In 1937, Professor Howard Aiken of Harvard University conceived of an electromechanical computer that would be completely automatic and use the principles set down by Babbage. The computer, the Automatic Sequence Controlled Calculator (also known as the Mark I), was completed in 1944 by the joint effort of Harvard and the International Business Machines (IBM) Corporation. It could perform any specified sequence consisting of the four basic arithmetic operations and references to tables of previously computed results. Information was supplied on punched cards and by the setting of switches. Answers were punched on cards or written on a typewriter. A typical multiplication required about 3 seconds. The Mark I was in use for over 15 years.

In 1946, J. P. Eckert and J. W. Mauchley at the University of Pennsylvania were faced with the problem of processing rapidly increasing volumes of data on weather studies and ballistics. It was clear that high computing speeds were required. They became convinced that electronic techniques were essential for this purpose and so designed the ENIAC (the Electronic Numerical Integrator and Computer). This machine contained 18,000 vacuum tubes. Having no internal moving parts, it represented a great advance in computer technology. Addition required 0.2 millisecond, and multiplication required 2.8 milliseconds. Numbers were of 10 decimal digits. A program was established by the wiring of boards on the machine; this wiring was a slow process and limited the usefulness of the ENIAC.

The IBM 604 Electronic Calculator was the first computer built in quantity; 4000 were built between 1946 and 1960. The machine has a capacity of sixty instructions, set in a plug-board. The IBM Card-Programmed Calculator (CPC) incorporates the 604 in an accounting machine. Its program is stored on cards; alternate sequences of cards are used, depending on the results obtained. Because there is no limit to the size of programs, the CPC is a very flexible computer.

In 1945, Dr. John von Neumann proposed a different type of electronic computer, one that had its program stored internally. Internal storage, which is used in all modern computers, offers far greater flexibility in the use of a computer. The computer, completed in 1950, is called the EDVAC (Electronic Discrete Variable Automatic Computer). It has twelve different instructions. Addition requires about 0.9 millisecond; multiplication requires about 2.9 milliseconds.

In 1945 the Digital Computer Laboratory at the Massachusetts Institute of Technology was assigned the job of building an aircraft simulator. The Whirlwind I computer was designed as a result; it was completed in 1951. It contains 5000 vacuum tubes and 11,000 semiconductor diodes. Addition requires 3 microseconds, and multiplication takes 16 microseconds. These speeds are comparable to modern-computer speeds. Programs are stored in memory;

there are 27 distinct instructions and 2048 numbers may be stored internally. Because of checking features, Whirlwind I is extremely reliable. Many of the concepts incorporated in it are used in modern computers.

Other computers built in the late 1940's and early 1950's include the UNIVAC I (completed in 1951), the IAS (Institute for Advanced Study) Computer (completed in 1952), the IBM 701, and the IBM 650. The last of these computers, the 650, was considered the "workhorse" of the industry in recent years.

Recent computers are much more similar to one another than were older machines.[1]* Most modern computers use semiconductors (diodes and transistors) and magnetic cores for memory storage; magnetic tapes are used as auxiliary storage. All computers now being built have internally stored programs; all use automatic checking features. It is because of these devices and characteristics that computers have been able to attain their current level of computational speed, storage capacity, and reliability.[2]

What Kind of Problem Can Computers Handle?

If a problem can be written as a sequence of explicit mathematical operations, it can be solved on a computer. The question usually asked is not whether a problem *can* be solved on a computer, but rather whether it is economically feasible to do so. Programming time can be expensive, and problems that are readily solved manually or with a desk calculator may better be done by those means.

Some problems are too small for computer solution, such as the balancing of a single checking account or the computation of one person's income tax. Nevertheless banks and the Bureau of Internal Revenue use computers to perform these computations because thousands or millions of repetitions of the same problem occur. A computer is particularly useful in such situations, because one program can be reused indefinitely, processing new data each time.

Another type of repetitious problem is quite frequent. It is concerned with a series of operations each of which computes a result that is successively closer to the true answer to a problem. For example, one way to solve a quadratic algebraic equation is to guess at an answer, substitute it in the equation, and note whether the guess is too large or too small. This guess is followed by a "better" guess and further substitution. In this manner a series of guesses is produced which hopefully approaches the desired answer. This procedure is an *iterative* one.

Some problems are much more easily programmed for computer solution than others, although they may seem more difficult. For example, the problem of evaluating a seventh-order polynomial at each of 5000 values of the inde-

---

* Superscript numerals in the text refer to notes at the end of the chapter. All such material is bibliographical and may be skipped with no loss in continuity.

pendent variable is easily programmed, whereas the problem of translating a paragraph of Russian text into English is considerably more difficult to program. The reason for this is that the first problem can be readily stated explicitly in terms of a sequence of operations, whereas the second cannot without a great deal of difficulty.

Certain operations can be quickly executed on a computer, whereas others that appear simpler require more time. For example, consider the problems of (1) determining the largest number of a given set of 100 4-digit numbers and (2) finding their sum. It probably takes a person about fifteen times as long to solve the second problem as the first, whereas a computer takes two to three times as long to solve the first as the second. This is a disparity in human-to-computer-time ratios of at least 30 to 1. The rules for addition are simpler than the rules for determining the largest number. This fact affects both the manner of computer construction and the ease of programming these problems.*

How Have Computers Been Used?

The specific ways in which computers have already been used to solve problems would fill a book if fully documented. Here we consider some applications of computers as an indication of the broad scope of their use.

One of the most valuable large-scale applications of computers has been in the process control field. The processing of raw materials requires the maintenance of a number of parameters, such as temperature, pressure, and rate of flow, which depend on dozens of other factors. The decisions that must be made to maintain them can be stated explicitly, and programs have been written to make them. The result is a more efficient and reliable system than would be possible under human control; changes can be monitored more rapidly by computers.

An area similar to the process control field is that of inventory control. Data on current stock, cost of storage, customers' orders, and seasonal variations in the cost of materials can be quickly processed by computers to provide information on the purchase of raw material. Because the time delay between the assessment of the current situation and the purchase time can be made very small, it is possible to maintain inventories at relatively low levels and with great sensitivity to sudden changes in demand.

Certain problems require the processing of large amounts of data so vast in scope that noncomputer processing is almost out of the question. For example,

---

* Because arithmetic operations are so common and are intrinsically simple, computers are built to execute them as single instructions. A computer designer must make a decision on just which operations are to be so treated; different designers make different decisions. Economics must enter into the decision; it is not feasible to incorporate two thousand distinct instructions, since the required circuitry would be prohibitively expensive.

in meteorology, attempts to predict and perhaps control weather must be based on the analysis of thousands of map-like pictures.[3]   In astronomy, theories are based on many observations; the validity of these theories is checked by using them to make predictions into the future.   In both fields computers are used to perform the thousands of required calculations.

Information retrieval and medical diagnosis are two areas that accumulate large amounts of data from which particular selections must be made.   The problem in both instances is the identification of items having a set of specified characteristics.   It is often difficult to describe the desired information precisely, since too much specificity results in an incomplete answer, whereas too much generality results in the retrieval of extraneous material.   Computers, by virtue of their speed, permit repeated searching; if the wrong answers are returned, the specification can be modified and the process repeated.

The design of machines is a prerequisite to their being built.   It is often economically advantaneous to set up mathematical models in the form of equations and then to perform the design on a computer.   Motors, airplane guidance systems, nuclear reactors, and even new computers have been so designed.   Since a computer can produce a design rapidly, the designer often varies several parameters of the model so that a number of designs are produced, from which the best is selected.

Chess and checkers have recently been studied by computer methods in an attempt to gain insight into the strategies of problem solving.   Computers have been programmed to play against a human opponent.   The computer plays by examining the existing board situation and considering all possible moves. After checking for essential moves, such as moving a piece out of danger, the computer looks ahead a number of plays, evaluates each possible move, and chooses the "best" by some criteria.   An interesting by-product of the work is the question whether computers can learn.   After playing a game many thousands of times and keeping track of the results of its decisions, cannot the computer better its future attack?   If so, is this learning?

Business and industry have found many uses for computers.   Clerical operations, common in payroll and billing processes, are well suited for computer solution.   Files of records can be searched, modified, and kept up to date at electronic speeds.   Results of computations can be printed directly in any form, such as checks, statements, or complicated reports, by the computer.   The result is a saving of clerical work and the avoidance of errors.   The net financial savings generally more than pay the cost of the computer.

1.2 THE USE OF COMPUTERS

Computation by machine, viewed generally, consists of three basic steps.

1. The program, with its data, must be loaded into memory.   The data con-

sist of the numbers on which computations are to be performed; the term *input data* is sometimes used.

2. The computations are performed. This process is usually internal to the machine although sometimes memory outside the computer is used temporarily.

3. The results of the computation are removed from memory and supplied to the programmer.*

These three steps are examined in far greater detail from a number of points of view in later chapters.

The Need to Be Explicit

In preparing a problem for a computer it is necessary to be explicit. The program must contain no errors, because it is executed exactly as written. Furthermore, all eventualities must be considered in advance. If, for example, the square roots of each of a set of numbers are to be computed, and some of the numbers may be negative, the program must include directions for dealing with them. Because there is normally no human intervention during the running of the computer and because the computer cannot exercise judgment, all decisions required during the execution of the program must be set up explicitly in advance. Whether it is performing meaningful operations or not, the computer will blindly follow the instructions written. It cannot know, for example, that data should have been supplied in inches instead of feet or that the programmer intended negative and positive numbers to be processed differently. It cannot know these things unless it is specifically "told" about them.

Because programs must be written explicitly, the programmer is forced to think about his problem in precise terms. He often gains insight into his problem that he otherwise might have missed. New points of view or even new methods of solution frequently result.

Writing a Program

At least five distinct steps in writing a computer program can be listed. Sometimes the distinction between steps is not clear, since some operations overlap two or more steps. Frequently it is more convenient, and it may even be necessary, to proceed with a later step on one phase of the problem while holding back on another at an earlier step. Nevertheless, it is almost certainly true that each portion of a problem must proceed from the start to the finish of this list, going through all the indicated steps:

---

* The term *programmer* is used in this book to mean "the person who either programs a problem for a computer or uses a program written by someone else." The usual meaning is simply "one who writes a program."

1. Definition of the problem.
2. Selection of a method for solution.
3. Problem analysis.
4. Writing the instructions of the program.
5. Testing and checkout.

These steps are considered briefly in the following pages. Later chapters, as we have indicated, further expand the considerations.

Problem definition.   Before a program for solving a problem can be written, the problem must be clearly defined. Strictly, this step does not lie entirely within the scope of program writing, but it is a vital preliminary step.

We have seen that an explicit problem statement is required. The following information must be provided: (1) a statement of what information is given; (2) a statement of what answers are wanted; (3) if applicable, a statement of how accurate the results must be; (4) the precise manner in which data are supplied; and (5) the precise manner in which the answers are to be produced.

Chapter 12, on program planning, considers the matter of problem definition in more detail. The topic is deferred until then so that a number of fundamental computer and programming concepts can be studied first.

Selection of a method.   In selecting a method for the solution of a problem, several choices are generally available. If a programmer has a thorough knowledge of the organization and operation of a computer and of the methods of programming and coding, he is more likely to choose an optimum approach. Several criteria for making a choice are given in Chapter 12; at that point the reader will be familiar enough with the computer to make a reasonable choice.

Problem analysis.   After a method for solution has been selected, it is necessary to analyze the problem in order to identify its component operations and their interconnection. Problem analysis varies considerably. It may be extremely informal, and in fact be entirely mental; the programmer need not actually write down his analysis. It may be written as a list of steps in mathematical form. Finally, a picture of the process may be drawn; this is a diagram indicating the parts of the problem and their sequence.

The degree of analysis depends on both the programmer and the problem. Some people desire more detail in their analyses, and complex problems require more breakdown than simple problems. In any event, it is very common for a programmer, particularly a beginner, to spend too little time on problem analysis.

A problem is first analyzed with little attention paid to computers in general and virtually none to the particular computer on which the problem will be run. Therefore the resulting analysis is applicable to any computer. The next step is to take the computer at hand into account, analyzing the problem in more detail. Now the analysis becomes more closely allied to a particular computer and utilizes the features available. Problem analysis is discussed in Chapter 2.

Writing the instructions.   When the analysis is complete, coding the problem is the next step.   Coding involves writing a specific, detailed list of instructions in terms of the operations that the particular computer can perform.   Two approaches are possible.   First, the actual instructions executed may be written. The term *machine language* is used to describe the form of these instructions, which might be as follows:*

3518700390

Second, a more convenient form that is subsequently transformed into machine language may be used:†

ADD   NUMBER

This instruction is an example of a special *coding language;* further discussion of such languages is given in Chapter 3.

Testing and checkout.   After a program is written it must be checked for accuracy. If it does not run correctly, the errors that are present must be found and eliminated; this process is called *debugging.*   Errors may be introduced at any step in program writing, although the most susceptible stage is coding.   The subject of debugging is considered in Chapters 11 and 19.

To test a program it is necessary to apply a set of test data to it.   Such data are generally simple, so that hand calculations can be used for verification.   If a problem requires that a number of decisions be made, each possibility must be checked.   Continued, satisfactory use of the program serves as a final checking procedure.

Limitations

Because a computer serves a useful purpose only when coded to solve a problem, its potential value is limited by the ability of its programmers to code it. This book is an attempt to provide a detailed understanding of the nature of computers and of the problems involved in programming and coding them for efficient use.   We have taken a quick look at the present scope of computer applications.   The future range of applications depends on our abilities to code computers and thereby realize more of their tremendous potential.

Summary

To help him solve an ever-increasing number of problems, man has built the electronic digital computer.   This machine has proven very useful because of its speed, accuracy, rapid access to vast amounts of stored information, and ability

---

* This is an instruction for the IBM 650 computer.

† This instruction might be for any of a dozen computers.

to execute programs automatically. An examination of any list of the applications to which computers have been put reveals the vast scope of the problems that can be solved by machine.

To solve a problem on a computer it is necessary to proceed through a series of five steps: defining the problem, selecting a method of solution, analyzing the problem, coding the computer, and checking out the program.

Notes

1. The following two books each have one chapter devoted to a more extensive history of computers than is given here.

B. V. Bowden (ed.), *Faster Than Thought,* Pitman, 1953, Chapter 1.

G. R. Stibitz and L. A. Larrivee, *Mathematics and Computers,* McGraw-Hill, 1957, Chapter 4.

Another source of historical information is the following.

R. Serrell, M. M. Astrahan, G. W. Patterson, and I. B. Pyne, "The Evolution of Computing Machines and Systems," *Proc. IRE* **50** (1962), pp. 1039–1058.

2. The following book describes some of the devices used in modern computers.

I. Flores, *Computer Logic: the Fundamental Design of Digital Computers,* Prentice-Hall, 1960, Chapter 13.

3. A report on numerical calculations in weather data processing is given in the following.

N. A. Phillips, "Numerical Weather Prediction," in *Advances in Computers,* Academic Press, Vol. 1 (ed. by F. Alt), 1960, pp. 43–90.

PROBLEMS

Section 1.1

1.1. It has been said that almost any problem can be solved on a digital computer. Comment on the extent to which this is true. What are the limitations of digital computers—in theory and in practice?

1.2. Digital computers, on both small and large scales, can commonly be found around us. Give some examples.

1.3. Computers could be faster, have more storage, and be more reliable. Why are they not? What conditions must exist for them to be so? When, if ever, will they be so?

1.4. The questions asked in the text about computers and programming do not exhaust the curious reader's mind. Anticipate others that might be asked—and answer them.

1.5. Consider the following operations: alphabetizing a list of 50 words, finding the square root of a given number, raising a number to the tenth power, and multiplying two polynomials together. Write down the rules for performing these operations, and compare the human approach to the computer approach in each case. Such a comparison is possible even with no knowledge of programming; the complexity of the rules for the operations largely determines the outcome of the comparison.

1.6. Mention areas, besides those listed in the text, where digital computers have had wide application.

Section 1.2

1.7. As noted in the text, the statement of a problem for a computer must be explicit. Write the steps in the solution of a quadratic algebraic equation, explicitly indicating what must be done. All possibilities must be taken into account.

1.8. Are the rules written down in Problem 1.5 suitable for solution by computer methods? If not, modify the rules so that they are.

1.9. What might affect the selection of a method of computer solution of a particular problem?

1.10. What kind of errors might a programmer make in preparing a problem for computer solution? Consider each step in the program-writing process.

1.11. What characteristics are required of a good programmer? What skills and training does he need? (At this point in the book these questions are difficult to answer. They are asked again later.)

1.12. A digital computer was defined early in this chapter. Give a more nearly complete and precise definition.

2

PROBLEM ANALYSIS

After the problem to be solved has been defined and a method for its solution on a digital computer has been selected, it must be analyzed into its component parts. The breakdown of the problem is generally done in stages. First a rough analysis is made, with perhaps half a dozen steps indicated. Next each step is further analyzed. In this manner any level of detail may be obtained.

The analysis of a problem is usually done graphically: a diagram of the parts of the computation and their interrelation is drawn. Operations are placed in boxes and arrows are drawn to connect them.

In this chapter some problems are analyzed to indicate their structure and illustrate the analysis techniques. Of particular interest is the repetitive nature of problems; a notation for counting and controlling repetitions is introduced. A graphic approach to problem analysis is considered in detail.

2.1 METHODS OF PROBLEM ANALYSIS

Reasons for Analysis

There are a number of reasons why a problem should be carefully analyzed before it is coded. First, a precise statement of the method of solution results from such an analysis. Second, because all steps of the procedure must be precisely stated, the programmer's thinking is forced to be accurate. Third, debugging of the program is facilitated by an analysis, and fourth, future study of the program is aided thereby.

A problem analysis may be given as a list of steps or procedures, or it may be given in graphic form. In this section the former method is examined. Section 2.3 is concerned with the graphic approach.

Throughout this chapter no thought is given to the way in which the structure and operation of a computer affect the analysis of a problem. After a general analysis has been performed, a programmer will modify his methods in order to utilize the characteristics of computers in general and the computer at hand in particular.

Analysis of a Problem

The problem of solving a cubic algebraic equation for its three roots will be analyzed to illustrate the manner in which a problem may be broken down to varying degrees of detail.

Consider the following general equation with real coefficients:

$$y^3 + py^2 + qy + r = 0 \tag{1}$$

Making the substitution

$$y = (x - p)/3 \tag{2}$$

in Eq. 1, we obtain

$$x^3 + ax + b = 0 \tag{3}$$

In Eq. 3,

$$a = (3q - p^2)/3 \tag{4}$$

$$b = (2p^3 - 9pq + 27r)/27 \tag{5}$$

The roots of Eq. 3 are given by

$$x_1 = A + B \tag{6}$$

$$x_2 = -(A + B)/2 + \tfrac{1}{2}(A - B)\sqrt{3}\,i \tag{7}$$

$$x_3 = -(A + B)/2 - \tfrac{1}{2}(A - B)\sqrt{3}\,i \tag{8}$$

where

$$A = \sqrt[3]{-b/2 + \sqrt{b^2/4 + a^3/27}} \tag{9}$$

$$B = \sqrt[3]{-b/2 - \sqrt{b^2/4 + a^3/27}} \tag{10}$$

If it is true that

$$b^2/4 + a^3/27 < 0 \tag{11}$$

which implies that a must be negative, a trigonometric solution yields the roots more readily. When Eq. 11 is true, all roots are real, and after making the substitution to yield Eq. 3 the following equation is solved:

$$s = \arccos\left(\frac{-b}{2\sqrt{-a^3/27}}\right) \qquad (12)$$

The roots of Eq. 3 are then given by

$$x_1 = 2\sqrt{-a/3}\,\cos(s/3) \qquad (13)$$

$$x_2 = 2\sqrt{-a/3}\,\cos(s/3 + 2\pi/3) \qquad (14)$$

$$x_3 = 2\sqrt{-a/3}\,\cos(s/3 + 4\pi/3) \qquad (15)$$

This is a reasonably complex algebraic problem, yet its solution is straight-forward. Every step of the process has been clearly indicated.* As a first analysis, the following steps can be listed:

1. Evaluate a and b, using Eqs. 4 and 5, given p, q, and r.
2. Evaluate $b^2/4 + a^3/27$. If this quantity is nonnegative, do steps 3a, 4a, and 5. If it is negative, do steps 3b, 4b, and 5.
3a. Evaluate A and B, using Eqs. 9 and 10 and the values of a and b.
4a. Determine the roots x_j ($j = 1, 2, 3$) of Eq. 3, using Eqs. 6, 7, and 8 and the values of A and B.
3b. Evaluate s from Eq. 12, using the values of a and b.
4b. Determine the roots x_j ($j = 1, 2, 3$) of Eq. 3, using Eqs. 13, 14, and 15 and the values of a and s.
5. Determine the roots y_j ($j = 1, 2, 3$) of Eq. 1, using Eq. 2 and the roots x_j.

Thus the problem has been formulated in five steps, in each of which a function of two or three variables is evaluated. The steps must be performed in the order given, for the arguments of each function depend on previous results.

Each step can be further analyzed into smaller operations. Consider steps 1 and 3a and their component parts.

Step 1:
  1.1 Evaluate the binomial $P_1 = (3q - p^2)$.
  1.2 Set $a = P_1/3$.
  1.3 Evaluate the trinomial $P_2 = (2p^3 - 9pq + 27r)$.
  1.4 Set $b = P_2/27$.

Step 3a:
  3a.1 Evaluate the radical $R_1 = \sqrt{b^2/4 + a^3/27}$.
  3a.2 Set $A = \sqrt[3]{-b/2 + R_1}$.
  3a.3 Set $B = \sqrt[3]{-b/2 - R_1}$.

A further breakdown is possible. Consider step 3a.1:

  3a.1.1 Evaluate $Q_1 = b^2/4$.

---

* To complete the statement of the problem, the desired accuracy of the results should also be given.

3a.1.2   Evaluate $Q_2 = a^3/27$.
3a.1.3   Form the sum $S_1 = Q_1 + Q_2$.
3a.1.4   Set $R_1 = \sqrt{S_1}$.

A still further degree of analysis is possible. Consider step 3a.1.2:

3a.1.2.1   Form $T_1 = a \times a$.
3a.1.2.2   Form $T_2 = T_1 \times a$.
3a.1.2.3   Form $T_3 = T_2/27$.

If the raising of one number to a power were considered to be a fundamental operation, step 3a.1.2 would not be formulated as three steps; two steps (cubing and dividing) would be sufficient.

The question of what to do with the square-root and cube-root operations arises. Does the computer that is to be used have instructions to perform these operations?* If not, it is necessary to determine these roots using the basic operations. An iterative method for determining the square root of a number is described in Section 2.2.

If the analysis of the cubic equation is carried out fully to the fourth level of detail, over a hundred basic operations are required in each of the two paths of the problem, even if the iterative steps in the root determination processes are not counted. This is a great deal of work, and even if the computer at hand may demand such a fine breakdown because of its construction, it is usually not necessary for the programmer to so detail his analysis. Instead, he will break down the problem until it becomes quite clear what basic operations are needed. To one individual, step 3a.1 is detailed enough for coding; to another, steps 3a.1.1 through 3a.1.4 may be desired. The degree of analysis is a personal choice.

Choice of a Computer Language

One other factor determines the amount of detail incorporated into a problem analysis: the choice of a coding language for the computer. Some languages are designed with the provision for writing formulas as "instructions," whereas others require as instructions the basic operations discussed in this section. For the former languages the first breakdown into five steps is sufficiently detailed. These coding languages are discussed in Chapters 3 and 14.

2.2 REPETITION IN PROBLEMS

Data Repetition

Problems that are repetitious are, as we have seen in Section 1.1, suited to computer solution. They may be repetitious either because calculations are

---

* On most computers instructions for square-root and cube-root extraction are not available.

performed repeatedly on many numbers or because the answers are arrived at in an iterative manner. Examples of both types of problem are considered in this section. The first problem concerns repetition of data.

Consider the problem of summing n numbers $a_1, a_2, \ldots, a_n$. The sum is given by

$$S = a_1 + a_2 + \cdots + a_n$$

$$= \sum_{i=1}^{n} a_i \tag{16}$$

This operation as it is performed manually is essentially a simultaneous summation over all the a_i, since numbers are usually added one column at a time. A digital computer, however, performs such operations as the addition of two numbers.* Therefore in preparing the problem for programming the summation must be analyzed so that each addition operation is of that type.

What are the steps we would follow if we were to compute the sum manually by successively adding two numbers? We would write the first number down and add the second number to it. Then to that sum we would add the third, and proceed in this manner until the last number were added.

The need for being explicit in writing a program was explained in Section 1.2. Since the problem will eventually be translated into a computer program, statements like "until the last number is added" are useless. Rather, statements like "... until the nth number is added," where n is a number known at the start of the computation, are required. Thus we keep a running count of the numbers as they are added and stop the addition when the count is n. The count must be checked after each addition.† For simplicity, we might say that each new number is added to the old sum, which is initially set equal to zero.

The following steps can be listed in the analysis of this problem.

1. Set the sum equal to zero; set the count equal to 1.
2. Add to the sum the first number not yet added.
3. Add 1 to the count.
4. Check the count; if it is n or less, continue at step 2; if it is greater than n, stop.‡

This procedure is explicit, and when it is translated into machine language the computer can perform the summation. The manner in which step 2 is phrased permits its use both initially (to sum the first number) and after each return to that step (to sum all succeeding numbers). The problem has been formulated repetitively; the same sequence of operations is performed on all the data (the a_i).

* Computer instructions are described in Chapter 3 and the chapters of Part II. For the present, the reader can accept the fact that two numbers only can be added with one instruction.

† Throughout this chapter, n is assumed to be greater than 0 in this and similar problems.

‡ Because the count is initially set equal to 1, the process terminates when the count exceeds n as step 4 is about to be performed. If the count is initially set equal to 0, termination occurs when the count equals n.

As a second example of a problem involving the performance of the same operations on a sequence of data, consider the problem of solving 1000 cubic equations. The steps in the problem (in a first analysis) are these:

1. Set the count equal to 1.
2. Solve the first equation not yet solved.
3. Add 1 to the count.
4. Check the count; if it is 1000 or less, continue at step 2; if it is greater than 1000, stop.

These steps are identical in structure to those given earlier for the summation problem. Step 2 here will of course expand in the manner described in Section 2.1. It should be clear now that many problems involving the repetition of a calculation or set of calculations can be analyzed into a list of steps similar to these two.

Indexing

The four steps we have outlined, which constitute the analysis of the summation problem, must be translated into a form appropriate for a computer. As a significant move in this direction it is very helpful to be able to restate these steps in mathematical terms. Step 2, the heart of the process, is concerned with "the current number," that is, the one being processed "now." If the ith number, a_i, is the one under consideration, the count of the number already summed is i at the conclusion of step 2. With this notation, the four steps become

1. Set the sum equal to zero; set the count (i) equal to 1.
2. Add a_i to the sum.
3. Add 1 to the count.
4. Check the count; if it is n or less, continue at step 2; if it is greater than n, stop.

This is a more concise statement of operations. By changing the value of the subscript i, the significance of step 2 changes automatically to permit sequencing through the entire list of numbers. The use of a count which is associated with a subscripted variable (a_i) is termed *indexing*. The *index* is the subscript, and its value is not only important in permitting repetitious operations but also in providing initialization and allowing termination of the process. In this problem the initial value of the index is 1 and the final value is n; a check is made of the index against the constant n.

The four steps of the problem can be rewritten still more concisely in terms of the index. For this purpose a special symbol is introduced. The expression

$$a \rightarrow b$$

means "substitute the value of the expression a for the quantity b." Thus

$$28 \rightarrow y$$

means "set y equal to 28." Using this notation both for indexing operations and summation operations, the steps become

1. $0 \rightarrow S;\ 1 \rightarrow i.$
2. $S + a_i \rightarrow S.$
3. $i + 1 \rightarrow i.$
4. If $i \leqslant n$, continue at step 2; if $i > n$, stop.

A comment about steps 2 and 3 is perhaps needed. From the definition of the arrow, step 2 states " the value of $S + a_i$ replaces the value of S." In other words, "add a_i to S." Similarly, step 3 states "add 1 to i."

This last list of the steps in the summation process is not only concise and explicit; it also corresponds closely to the operations that a digital computer can perform. Because indexing is so useful in expressing the structure of repetitious problems, most computers have instructions (*indexing instructions*) that perform such operations on indices as setting them, modifying them, and checking them against constant values. Special registers (*index registers*) are generally available to hold index values. Index registers are considered in Chapter 8.

It is not necessary for an index to start at 1 or to be incremented by unity. For example, assume that the 34th, 37th, 40th, . . . , and 94th numbers in a list of one hundred numbers are to be multiplied together. The symbol a_i is used again to refer to these numbers. Instead of initializing a sum to zero, we initialize a product P to 1:

1. $1 \rightarrow P;\quad 34 \rightarrow i.$
2. $P \times a_i \rightarrow P.$
3. $i + 3 \rightarrow i.$
4. If $i \leqslant 94$, continue at step 2; if $i > 94$, stop.

Although an index may be modified by any amount, it is almost always modified by a constant during a particular repetitious process. A problem may occur in which the increment is a variable, depending perhaps on the value of the index, but this is a rare situation.

A more general indexing problem than the summation or multiplication of numbers occurs when indexing or counting is done *selectively*, that is, according to some criterion. For example, suppose the number of negative numbers in a set of n numbers is to be counted. If the index j is used to count negative numbers, the process is the following.

1. $1 \rightarrow i;\quad 0 \rightarrow j.$
2. If $a_i < 0$, continue at step 3; if $a_i \geqslant 0$, continue at step 4.
3. $j + 1 \rightarrow j.$
4. $i + 1 \rightarrow i.$
5. If $i \leqslant n$, continue at step 2; if $i > n$, stop.

In this process a test is performed (at step 2) before the main operation (counting negative numbers) is performed. If the test fails (if the number is nonnegative), the main operation (at step 3) is skipped. Counting the numbers processed and checking for problem termination proceed as before (at steps 4 and 5).

Iterative Problems

To illustrate the analysis of a problem involving iteration the computation of the square root of a positive number is considered here. The computation is based on the iterative formula

$$x_{i+1} = \frac{1}{2}\left(x_i + \frac{A}{x_i}\right) \tag{17}$$

where x_i is the ith estimate of the square root of A, a given positive number.[1] An initial nonzero estimate x_1 is made for $\sqrt{A}$, and a new estimate x_2 is calculated from Eq. 17. This value is substituted, and another estimate is calculated. The process continues until a sufficiently accurate value is obtained. One criterion for testing the accuracy of an estimate is to compare the square of the current estimate with A; when the difference is less than a predetermined value ϵ, the iteration stops.

The iterative process can be written as follows:

1. Assume a value x_i; $1 \rightarrow i$.

2. $\dfrac{1}{2}\left(x_i + \dfrac{A}{x_i}\right) \rightarrow x_{i+1}$.

3. $i + 1 \rightarrow i$.

4. Calculate $D = |A - (x_i)^2|$; if $D \geqslant \epsilon$, continue at step 2; if $D < \epsilon$, stop. The computed value of $\sqrt{A}$ is x_i when the process stops.

This iterative process is basically different from the repetitious examples considered earlier in a number of respects. First, the main operation is not performed on a sequence of data, but instead generates a sequence of estimates of a desired number. Second, the subscripted variable x_i does not represent a set of numbers but rather a set of estimates of the same number. Subscripting is therefore used for a different purpose than it was previously. Finally, the test to decide the termination of the computation is not a check on the value of the index but rather a check on the value of the current estimate of the computed number.

The examples given in this section were chosen to illustrate methods of analysis and indexing, and to illustrate two distinctly different types of repetition. Although these examples are simple, their structure is similar to more complex problems, which differ primarily in the nature of the "main operation." If, for example, ten functions were all to be evaluated for n sets of variable values, the steps given for the summation problem could be rewritten for use here, if instead of step 2 (the main operation) were written the ten functions to be evaluated.

The analyses studied in this section can all be summarized by listing four steps as follows.

1. Initialization of the index and constants.
2. Performance of the calculations of the problem.
3. Modification of the index.
4. Testing for the end of the process.

Not all problems require indexing, as is shown in Section 3.4.

2.3 FLOWCHARTING

Although it is always helpful to analyze a problem into a sequence of steps, the analysis is made considerably more useful by augmenting it with a *flowchart*, which is a graphical representation of the sequence of operations performed in a problem. All operations to be performed and all paths of processing are indicated.

Unless a problem consists primarily of a sequence of formulas to be evaluated (as in the solution of the cubic equation in Section 2.1), the flowchart of a problem is more valuable than a tabulation of steps. Its value is due primarily to its pictorial nature and to the fact that alternate paths are more vividly seen. If a flowchart is sufficiently detailed, the coding step can be made very simple, since it then involves little more than a translation of the indicated operations into instructions. It is possible, however, to fill a flowchart with too many details, resulting in extraneous information that obscures the structure of the problem.

There is another reason for the use of flowcharts. If a programmer reexamines a program he has written some time earlier or if another person studies the program, the job of understanding the coding is invariably made easier by an accompanying flowchart. Even the programmer may find it difficult to understand fully coding he has written some time in the past.

Flowcharts vary widely in the extent to which they are detailed, as do other forms of problem analysis. As a programmer prepares to write a program he frequently starts with a rough picture of the problem, with only the major portions drawn. As his plans become more precise, the flowchart indicates more details. At some point in this process he stops and proceeds to code the problem.

Flowcharts may be classified according to their general orientation. One type, primarily concerned with the structure of the problem, is the *problem flowchart*. A second type, a modification of the first, is drawn with considerations given to the characteristics of computers. It is a *computer flowchart*. After computers have been discussed in Chapter 3 the second type of flowchart will be described.

Flowcharts consist of a number of boxes with directed lines interconnecting them. Statements of operations to be performed are placed within the boxes.

The directed lines leaving these boxes indicate the paths of processing, that is, the boxes that follow in sequence.

Since a number of people may read the same flowchart, it is desirable to follow certain conventions in drawing. Unfortunately, no universal standards exist. As long as conventions are indicated and are consistent, however, any standard may be used. The conventions used here are representative.[2]

The following rules apply:

1. The statement of every operation (or other unit of computation, as determined by the degree and nature of the analysis) is placed in a box. In some circumstances several operations may be placed in one box.

2. The sequence of operations is indicated by directed lines between boxes.

3. Each box has one line entering it and one or more lines leaving it. The operation stated in a box represents a process to be performed at the time that the problem has proceeded to the entry point of the box. It is immaterial to that operation which process has just previously been performed. The points at which paths join before entering a box are *merge points*.

4. Several box shapes are used to identify a number of different types of operation.

These rules are illustrated by flowcharts for problems already analyzed.

The cubic-equation analysis of Section 2.1 is flowcharted in Fig. 2.1. The boxes are labeled to correspond to the steps in the analysis. Most of the characteristics we have listed are illustrated in this flowchart.

1. Operations are placed in boxes. Here the equations to be evaluated are omitted, so it is necessary to accompany the chart with the analysis. Alternately, the equations may be written within the boxes.

2. The lines between boxes with arrows indicate which operations follow other operations.

3. Since box 2 may be followed by either box 3a or box 3b, depending on the sign of the quantity computed in box 2, two lines leave that box. The operation in box 5 is performed on the same quantities (the x_j), using the same equation (Eq. 2), regardless of the preceding operation. Therefore only one line enters box 5, and the merge point just above it joins the paths of operation from boxes 4a and 4b.

4. Three box shapes, circular, rectangular, and hexagonal, have been used in this flowchart. The significance of the shapes is discussed below.

The summation problem of Section 2.2 is written as a sequence of four steps.

1. $0 \to S$; $1 \to i$.
2. $S + a_i \to S$.
3. $i + 1 \to i$.
4. If $i \leqslant n$, continue at step 2; if $i > n$, stop.

These steps are drawn in Fig. 2.2, where each step is placed in one box, num-

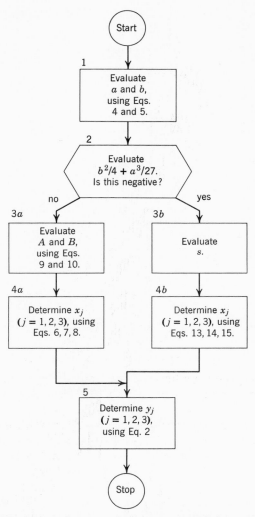

Fig. 2.1.   Flowchart for solution of a cubic algebraic equation.

bered as in this list. Since one of the two paths leaving box 4 is a return to box 2, an arrow is so drawn. The result of this return path is a closed path encompassing boxes 2, 3, and 4. The term *loop* applies to such a closed path in a flowchart. There must be a means for terminating the calculations in a loop. Here the test of the value of i serves this purpose; when i exceeds n, the path taken on leaving box 4 is downward.

Box 4 in Fig. 2.2 contains a new symbol, the colon (:). It indicates comparison and represents a relation between the expressions on both sides. The result of the comparison is one of at least two possibilities. These possibilities,

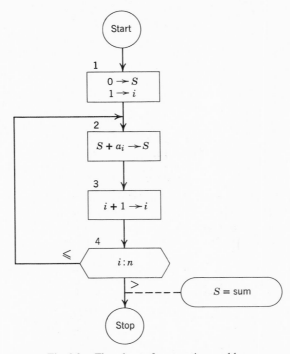

Fig. 2.2.   Flowchart of summation problem.

indicated by appropriate symbols, are written on the proper lines leaving the box. In Fig. 2.2 the result is either "$\leqslant$" or "$>$" for the comparison; these symbols are shown.

The four steps in a general analysis that were listed at the end of Section 2.2 apply here; the equivalent general flowchart has the same four parts.

Flowchart Boxes

The several kinds of boxes drawn in flowcharts are described next. As with other conventions, there is no standard set of box shapes. The boxes described here are typical of those most used, however.

The *operation box,* drawn as a rectangle, contains an operation or group of operations that perform some problem computations. Data are processed in some manner and the problem proceeds to the next box. There is only one output line from an operation box, indicating that there is only one possible next operation.

The statements contained within operation boxes may be of any form, provided they are explicitly given. In Figs. 2.1 and 2.2 the following statements are used:

"Evaluate a and b, using Eqs. 4 and 5."

"$S + a_i \rightarrow S$"

As indicated, an equation may be placed within an operation box:

"$P_2 = (2p^3 - 9pq + 27r)$"

For more consistency with the substitution notation, this operation should be rewritten as

"$(2p^3 - 9pq + 27r) \rightarrow P_2$"

The form of the statement is up to the programmer; any convenient and consistent notation is satisfactory.

The equals sign, as we have used it, does not indicate mere identity as in arithmetic or algebra, but rather a calculation to be performed to evaluate the quantity on the left. Hence the arrow notation is preferable. This concept can be clarified by considering that approximately a hundred boxes are required to detail completely the solution of a cubic equation. To state the problem as in algebra, however, with the equals sign having its usual significance, a single statement suffices:

"Solve the equation $y^3 + py^2 + qy + r = 0$."

Indeed, this might represent a single box in the flowchart of a larger problem, one that is not fully detailed.

Most operation boxes are used to contain the primary calculations in a problem, but they are also used for indexing operations. Boxes 1, 3, and 4 in Fig. 2.2 contain statements to set, increase, and test the index i, respectively.* Such operations are not strictly part of the problem, but in order to establish an iterative procedure they are required.

A convention sometimes used is that all the operations written within an operation box may be performed in any order. Where the order is significant, the operations are placed in separate boxes. For example, the two statements in box 1 of Fig. 2.2,

"$0 \rightarrow S$"

"$1 \rightarrow i$"

may be performed in either order and are drawn in one box. On the other hand, the statements in boxes 2 and 3 of that figure,

"$S + a_i \rightarrow S$"

"$i + 1 \rightarrow i$"

must be performed in that order and are placed in separate boxes.

---

* In the summation problem (Fig. 2.2) three out of four boxes are used for indexing purposes, whereas only one is used for summation. This proportion is not typical, of course, but it incidentally serves the purpose of indicating that frequently a considerable amount of computer time is spent in performing indexing operations.

The *decision box,* drawn as a hexagon, contains a statement of a test on which a decision is based.   The box has two or more lines leaving it, one for each alternative path that follows the decision.   Box 2 in Fig. 2.1 and box 4 in Fig. 2.2 are decision boxes containing the statements (paraphrased here)

$$\text{“Is } (b^2/4 + a^3/27) \text{ negative?”}$$
$$\text{“Is } i \text{ greater than } n?\text{”}$$

Depending on the answers to these questions, the next operation either evaluates A and B or s (in the first case) or returns to step 2 or stops (in the second case).
    A statement of the type

$$\text{“Test the value of } x\text{”}$$

may have several outcomes.   For example, after a calculation, if the quantity x is a positive integer, it may be necessary to take one of four courses of action, depending on the value of x:

$$
\begin{aligned}
&\text{If } 1 \leqslant x \leqslant 4, \quad &&\text{take action } Q1; \\
&\text{if } 5 \leqslant x \leqslant 10, \quad &&\text{take action } Q2; \\
&\text{if } 11 \leqslant x \leqslant 20, \quad &&\text{take action } Q3; \\
&\text{if } 21 \leqslant x, \quad &&\text{take action } Q4.
\end{aligned}
$$

The decision box corresponding to these alternatives is drawn in Fig. 2.3.   To specify the conditions under which each outgoing path is taken, comments about these conditions are placed next to these lines.   This is also done in Fig. 2.2, where the symbols that applied to the two results of the comparison were written.
    The *information box,* drawn as an oblong box with rounded ends, contains information not used directly in the computations but which is helpful in understanding the flowchart.   In Fig. 2.2, the box containing the statement

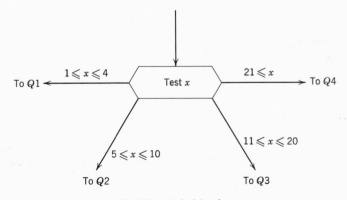

Fig. 2.3.   A decision box.

"S = sum"

is such a box. It is connected to the final arrow of the flowchart, following the decision box, by a dashed line. Its position indicates that when the problem progresses to that point (which is the end of this problem) the value of S is the desired sum. This box could not have been connected to the arrow leaving box 3, for example, because the value of S progresses through a sequence of partial sums.

Information boxes are useful in identifying variables or parameters of the problem, as in this statement:

"N_1 is the number of solutions with three real roots;
N_2 is the number of solutions with two complex roots."

This might refer to the cubic-equation problem.

The *conditions box,* drawn the same shape as an information box, also contains information incidental to the problem calculations. The condition under which each outgoing line of a decision box is taken is stated at each path. Often, however, the conditions at a point in the problem are fairly complex, as in this statement:

"$11 \leqslant x \leqslant 20$; y positive; z odd"

This set of conditions cannot be the outcome of a single decision. It indicates that, after a succession of several alternatives, the stated conditions are those met when the problem progresses to the point in question. Examples of conditions boxes appear in Fig. 5.5 (page 31).

The *terminal box,* drawn as a circle, contains either the word START or the word STOP (or equivalent words). These boxes merely serve to indicate the starting and stopping places of the flowchart. Occasionally there are several points at which the problem ends, unless these are merged to a single STOP. Terminal boxes appear in Figs. 2.1 and 2.2.

Remote connectors are sometimes used in a flowchart when it would be necessary to draw lines that would cross or be drawn across an entire page and thereby tend to clutter the diagram. The remote connector indicates that two separated points can be considered joined, that is, be the same point.

Consider the problem analyzed earlier, the multiplication of every third number in a list, starting with the 34th and ending with the 94th. In addition, assume that the numbers so multiplied are to be sorted in three lists, these being placed in turn in list 1, list 2, list 3, list 1, etc. A flowchart for this problem appears in Fig. 2.4. In that diagram, the points labeled α are to be joined; after the decision box, one path returns to box 2. These points are *fixed connectors.* The point labeled β_k represents a *variable connector;* it is joined to β_1, β_2, or β_3, depending on the current value assigned to k. This value is originally set equal to 1 (in box 7, near the start) and is then changed successively to 2, 3, 1, . . . by the boxes 6a, 6b, and 6c. The latest value determines the path taken at the connector marked β_k. In this way the numbers are sorted into the three lists.

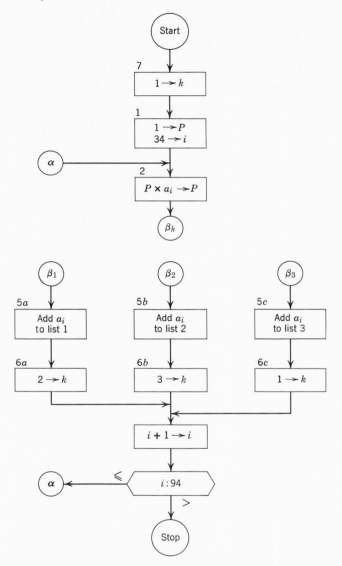

Fig. 2.4. Flowchart of multiplication and sorting into lists.

2.4 LOOPS

Loops, introduced in Section 2.3, are now given a closer examination. A loop is created in a flowchart whenever a repetitious process is present in the problem. In order to simplify the drawing of operation boxes, a return to an earlier operation is drawn. The action of performing each operation in one traversal of a loop is called a *loop cycle*.

Within a loop we must provide a means for its termination. Once in each cycle it is necessary to ask some form of the question, "should calculations within the loop be terminated?" The flowcharts already examined have such tests when they have loops.

Loops may be classified according to the manner in which the calculations contained therein are stopped. At least five types can be identified:

1. Loops having a number of cycles determined or implied by the statement of the problem.

2. Loops having a number of cycles that is a variable of the problem and is considered part of the data.

3. Loops having a number of cycles determined during the solution of the problem but prior to entry into the loop.

4. Loops that terminate on the successful completion of a searching or similar operation.

5. Loops that terminate when a specified characteristic is achieved by a quantity being processed.

Strictly, all loops must be classified under type 1, because when a problem is about to be run on the computer the number of cycles a loop will experience is already determined. Although the programmer cannot be aware of the outcomes of all future decisions, nevertheless these outcomes are "predetermined" once the program and its data have been placed in the computer memory. Thereafter, instructions will be executed and operations performed predictably. Despite this fact, it is meaningful to classify loops as indicated when the job of coding a problem is undertaken.

Loop type 1 is exemplified by the multiplication problem flowcharted in Fig. 2.4. In that problem it is known when the flowchart is drawn that exactly twenty-one numbers are to be multiplied together.

Loop type 2 differs from type 1 only in the fact that the number of loop cycles is part of the data. The problem of the summation of n numbers, flowcharted in Fig. 2.2, is type 2. When the n numbers are supplied to the computer with the program, the number n must also be supplied.

Loop type 3 can be illustrated by the following problem. Given a list of 100 numbers, determine the sum of those that are negative. This problem can be analyzed into two steps, performed in succession:

1. Sort the numbers by sign.
2. Sum the negative numbers.

When step 1 is finished, there are two lists, P (positive) and N (negative) in size; $P + N = 100$. The flowchart for step 2 is drawn in Fig. 2.5. It contains a loop of type 3, terminating after N cycles. The value of N is not known to the programmer when the problem is coded; rather, it is determined when a particular

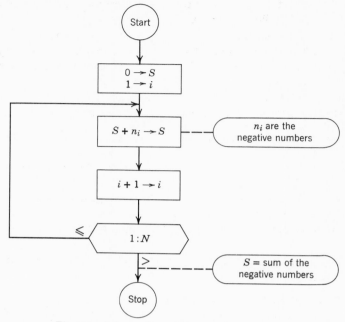

Fig. 2.5. A loop of type 3 (summation problem).

set of 100 numbers is chosen for processing. Since the flowchart applies to any set of 100 numbers, N is a variable of the problem.*

Loop type 4 is illustrated by a problem involving a search. Consider a number x and a list of n numbers (call them a_i) known to contain x as one number. Determine the location of x in the list. The problem is flowcharted in Fig. 2.6.

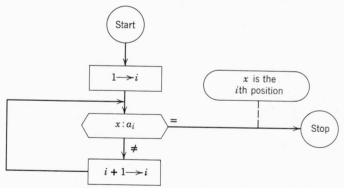

Fig. 2.6. A loop of type 4 (search for x).

---

* It is possible to solve this problem in a single step, testing each number and summing only those that are negative. Although this is a more reasonable approach, for purposes of illustration here the two-step approach is considered.

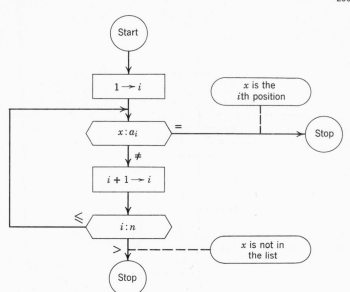

Fig. 2.7. A modified loop of type 4 (search for x).

Once each loop cycle, x is compared to a_i, and when a match is found, that is, when $x = a_i$, the search terminates. At that point, as indicated by the information box at the right, it is known that x occupies the ith position. An examination of the value of i reveals the position of x in the list.

Although this analysis is correct theoretically, it is also advisable to provide for termination of the loop after n cycles, that is, when the list is exhausted. There is the possibility that a particular value of x is *not* present in the list. Unless the loop is terminated in this way, the computer may run on indefinitely, attempting in vain to find a match. A modified flowchart is shown in Fig. 2.7, with this provision included.

Loop type 5 is exemplified by the iterative square-root problem already analyzed in Section 2.2. Its flowchart is drawn in Fig. 2.8. The loop is terminated when the absolute value of the difference between the square of the latest estimate of $\sqrt{A}$ and the value of A is less than ϵ. In other words, the loop is terminated when a specified characteristic has been attained. For a given value of A, the number of loop cycles depends on the original estimate.

Very often a loop must be classified under two types because it has two means of ending. The loop in Fig. 2.7, for example, terminates either when x is found in the list or after n cycles if x is not present in the list. There are two tests in this case, as seen in the flowchart. Thus this loop has to be classified as types 2 *and* 4.

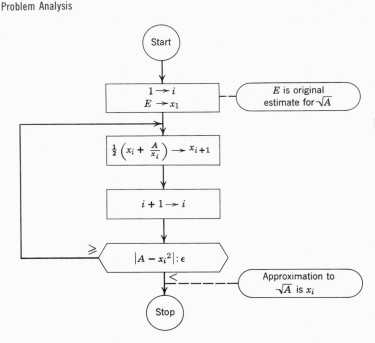

Fig. 2.8.   A loop of type 5 (iterative square-root computation).

Nested Loops

In many problems a small loop is *nested* within a larger one. This situation can readily be imagined when we picture a loop in which one of the boxes within the loop contains a repetitious process that can be drawn as a loop. It is a characteristic of nested loops that the inner loop is contained entirely within the outer loop.

Consider the following problem, which can be flowcharted with two nested loops. Given Z numbers, find the sum of the tenth powers of the numbers. As a first analysis this problem is flowcharted in Fig. 2.9, where the operation of computing p_i, the tenth power of a_i, is shown in a single box. The computation of this power is a repetitious problem and can be set up as a loop itself. This is shown in Fig. 2.10 as an inner nested loop. Box 2 in Fig. 2.9 has been expanded into boxes 2.1, 2.2, 2.3, and 2.4 of Fig. 2.10.*

Note that the inner and outer loops have the same structure; initialization, performance of the operation, index modification, and check for loop termination are all present in both. It is necessary to use a different index (j) for the

---

*For the general computation of powers this repetitious approach is unsatisfactory. The value of x^{10} can be computed in four multiplications, if x^2, x^4, and x^8 are initially computed, in that order. Similar techniques can be used for other powers.

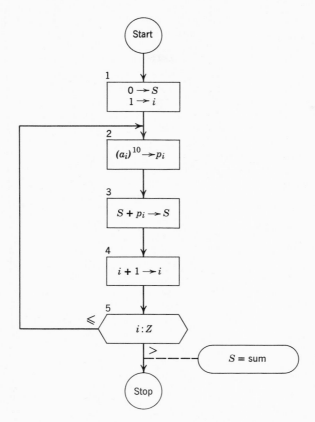

Fig. 2.9. First flowchart of nested-loop problem.

inner loop. This index must be initialized once each outer-loop cycle for the tenth power of each number to be properly computed. Thus the index j cycles from 1 to 10 between each unit increase of the index i, in the same manner that a digit position in a car odometer cycles through ten digits between changes in the digit to its left.

Some problems contain three or more nested loops. The flowchart techniques just explained can easily be extended to these cases. Generally one index per nested loop is necessary.

Summary

In preparing a problem for computer solution it is important to analyze the problem into its component parts. For this purpose drawing a flowchart or graphic analysis of the problem is extremely helpful. Drawing a flowchart tends

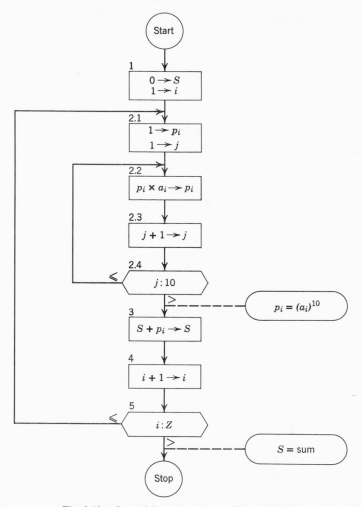

Fig. 2.10.   Second flowchart of nested-loop problem.

to clarify a programmer's thinking about his problem and helps him avoid errors in its analysis. Flowcharting also helps him to communicate his ideas to others, as well as back to himself at a later time.

It is usually unnecessary to carry analysis to the point of full detail, though this may make later coding an easier task. Groups of basic arithmetic operations, for example, may be considered as a larger "operation" and indicated as a single statement in a flowchart box. The extent of the detail depends on the problem and on the programmer.

Computer problems are invariably repetitious, and it is helpful to use indices to represent the sequential processing of data or the iterative calculations of certain problems.

Regardless of the way in which a loop is terminated, it usually has at least four identifiable parts: initialization of indices and constants, performance of the computations, modification of the index, and checking for the termination.

A flowchart is "universal" in its notation since it makes no reference to a particular computer. Programmers of different computers can apply it to their own machines, simply coding the problem in their computer languages. A general method for the solution of a problem, rather than a method for a specific computer, is provided by flowcharting.

Notes

1. Refer to the following book for a description of the Newton iteration method, from which Eq. 17 is derived.

R. G. Stanton, *Numerical Methods for Scientists and Engineers,* Prentice-Hall, 1961, pp. 84–88.

This reference also provides the following formula for the iterative solution of the cube root of a number A:

$$x_{i+1} = \frac{1}{3}\left(2x_i + \frac{A}{x_i^2}\right)$$

2. These books are useful for more detail on the techniques and conventions in flowcharting.

J. Jeenel, *Programming for Digital Computers,* McGraw-Hill, 1959.

H. D. Leeds and G. M. Weinberg, *Computer Programming Fundamentals,* McGraw-Hill, 1961, pp. 23–33 and 69–98.

IBM Corporation, *Flowcharting and Block Diagramming Techniques,* 1961 (C20-8008-0). IBM also provides a "Charting and Diagramming Template" of clear plastic (X24-5884-5).

PROBLEMS

Section 2.1

2.1. Analyze fully the listed steps for solving the cubic equation, breaking the entire problem down to the level of detail in the text.

2.2. In a particular problem, what factors will determine the degree to which the analysis of the problem is made?

2.3. Mention is made in the text that some computing languages are designed so that formulas may be written as instructions. Consider the utility of such a language in solving the cubic equation. What other features should the language have?

Section 2.2

2.4. Write analyses of the following problems, using indexing notation.
(*a*) Sum the squares of n numbers;
(*b*) sum the reciprocals of n numbers;

(*c*) sum the negative numbers and sum the positive numbers of a list of *n* numbers (form two sums);

(*d*) determine the first *n* odd powers of 2.

2.5. When a list of steps for a problem involving repetition is written down, the step that tells the reader to go back to an earlier step is important. Why?

2.6. The discrepancy that sometimes exists between human and computer solutions to problems is exemplified by the presence of steps 1, 3, and 4 in almost all the analyses in this section. Explain.

Section 2.3

2.7. What are the reasons for using flowcharts?

2.8. It is generally true that the degree of detail throughout a flowchart is consistent. Why is this so? When would it not be so?

2.9. A correctly drawn flowchart has certain features regardless of the problem it represents. What are they?

2.10. Draw flowcharts for the following problems.

(*a*) Determine why a car does not start.

(*b*) Find a given name in a telephone directory.

(*c*) Determine the next best move in a tic-tac-toe game, whatever the present situation.

(*d*) Find the largest number in a given set of numbers.

(*e*) Compute the sum of all the numbers in a given set that lie in the range from 0 to 1000 inclusively.

(*f*) Given four integers, determine if they are listed in either ascending or descending order.

(*g*) Given two dates in the year in numerical form, as "9-5" for September 5, determine the lesser time interval, in days, between them.

Section 2.4

2.11. Draw flowcharts for the summation and multiplication of two matrices, according to these formulas:

$$c_{ij} = a_{ij} + b_{ij} \quad c_{ij} = \sum_k a_{ik} b_{kj}$$

Assume that matrix **A** is order $m \times n$ and that matrix **B** is order $n \times p$.

2.12. Give examples, in addition to those in the text, of problems involving the five loop types.

2.13. What are some everyday devices or operations that, when flowcharted, would be seen to contain nested loops?

2.14. Compare the two approaches taken to analyze problems, those of Sections 2.2 and 2.3.

3

THE DIGITAL COMPUTER

In this chapter the digital computer is described in general terms. Four important aspects of the computer are studied: (1) the manner in which it is organized, and the manner in which each functional unit works with the others within the complete structure; (2) the manner in which the computer operates, both in detail at the level of each instruction execution and as a whole at the level of problem solution; (3) the language of the computer and the manner in which human beings communicate with the computer; (4) the preparation of flowcharts to reflect the organization, operation, and language of the computer.

As these topics are discussed, the role of the digital computer in solving problems becomes clearer. Problems analyzed by the techniques described in Chapter 2 can be translated into computer programs with the methods presented in this chapter. A study of specific computer languages is deferred until Parts II and III but the general nature of such languages is described.

3.1 COMPUTER ORGANIZATION

If a computer is to perform calculations, it must have a number of special units with which to work. The functions of and interactions among these units are perhaps best understood by analogy; the desk calculator considered in Section 1.1 serves well for this purpose.

Consider a clerk who solves an arithmetic problem on a desk calculator. To do his job he reads a set of instructions written on a piece of paper. Another piece of paper contains the data for the problem and special constants he needs.

On reading the instructions, he enters numbers into the calculator by pushing buttons on the keyboard. In the process of solving the problem, he reads the registers (dials) and may jot on scratch paper intermediate results for later use. When he is finished, he writes down final results.

The computer is organized similarly. An *arithmetic unit* performs addition, subtraction, and similar operations. A *program* lists the operations to be performed in proper sequence, and a *control unit* activates the proper circuitry to perform these operations. Data to be used, intermediate results for later use, and final results of the problem are stored in the *memory unit* (or *memory*). Just as the clerk prepares his final results for later use, so the computer provides results, by means of *output equipment,* in a form adapted to the programmer's needs. Analogously, *input equipment* accepts data provided by the programmer in a convenient form, converts them to the form used by the computer, and places them in the memory.

A block diagram of the structure of the computer, showing the interconnection of the units, is drawn in Fig. 3.1. In the diagram solid lines indicate the manner in which data are moved from unit to unit for processing; this movement is termed *flow of information.* Dashed lines indicate the exercise of control of some units over others. The program controls the control unit, which in turn controls the other units. By so doing, the control unit indirectly causes information to flow between units as needed for the calculations of the problem.

Although the program is shown as a separate unit, acting as the prime source of control in the computer, it is not structurally a part of the computer. It is loaded into memory with accompanying data by means of the input equipment. The manner in which this is done and the reasons for doing it are discussed in Chapters 7 and 11.

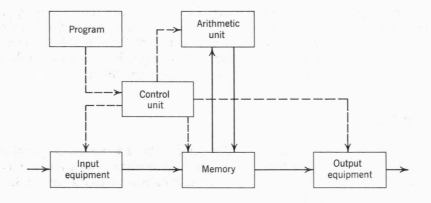

Fig. 3.1. Computer organization.

The Arithmetic Unit

The arithmetic unit performs arithmetic on receiving several pieces of information: (1) the operation to be performed and (2) the operand or operands to be operated on. Thus the information may be "add, x," "multiply, x, y," or something similar, depending on the instruction format of the computer. As the result of the operation, the arithmetic unit supplies the sum, the product, or what answer is called for. Computer instructions are described in Section 3.3.

Most computers have special registers to perform arithmetic within their arithmetic unit. One such register, the *accumulator*, is used for most arithmetic operations and "accumulates" the results. For example, a number in memory may be added to the number in the accumulator. The sum remains there until removed by a later operation. A second register, called by such names as the *M-register*, the *Q-register*, or the *MQ-register* (for *multiplier-quotient register*), aids in multiplication, division, and other operations.

The arithmetic unit is capable of performing a number of other operations and aiding in the execution of still others. Several chapters in Part II describe these instructions.[1]

The Control Unit

The control unit reads, interprets, and executes the instructions in a program; in this way, the program exercises its control. To execute instructions, the control unit removes data from memory, places them in the arithmetic unit, and returns the results to memory. It controls the several units by sending activating signals to these units.[2]

Special instructions are available to effect the alternate paths indicated in a flowchart at decision boxes. (These are studied in Chapter 5.) The control unit tests for the specified conditions and executes the appropriate instructions. The stages in the execution process are described in Section 3.2.

The control unit causes data to be read into the input equipment and read out of the output equipment, a process also under the control of the program.

The Memory Unit

The memory unit, known also as the *storage unit*, contains the program, data, and constants to be used by the program, and both intermediate and final results of calculations. The memory consists of individual *words*, each named and referred to by a number known as its *address*. Words are addressed sequentially, but each word may be individually referred to in any order. Each word can hold a single signed number or, if the programmer wishes, several numbers. In some computers the time required to obtain the number in each word is the same as the time to obtain any other, and the memory is termed *random-access*. In this type of memory the time to reference n words depends only on n and not on the sequence of reference addresses.[3]

The information contained within a word is called its *contents*.* The symbol $C(x)$ is used to mean the "contents of word x." Frequently a specific word is referred to as a *location;* the symbol $L(y)$ will mean the "location of the quantity y." Hence, if

$$C(p) = q$$

then

$$L(q) = p$$

Some statements that illustrate the usage of these terms are

"A group of 1000 words is used to store the data."
"Place this number at address 5000."
"The contents of location 500 is −2000."
"Locations 100 through 200 are used to store results."

The memory unit varies in capacity from one computer to another, but most memories consist of about 1000 to 250,000 words, 32,000 being perhaps the most common size. Each word is capable of holding numbers approximately 8 to 12 decimal digits in size. These numbers are not necessarily stored as decimal integers, however; they are most frequently stored as binary integers.

The memory units of many digital computers are composed of words of fixed length. Computers designed primarily for business purposes and a few other computers have a *variable-word-length* structure. In the latter type as much space as desired may be allotted to one word. The result is less wasted space but slightly more complex coding.

Internally, the contents of each word is a number. A word may contain many types of information, however: a constant, a variable, an instruction, or a sequence of English letters, or a place for a result. Each word may be likened to an egg box whose compartments are all always filled with eggs. Each egg represents one digit. To indicate a zero or "empty box," blank eggs are placed in the box. To indicate a nonzero number, eggs marked appropriately are placed in the box. If a number is to be stored in a box, the number that is already there must be removed, unless both numbers are small enough to fit simultaneously. Reading the number in the box does not affect its contents. Storing a number in a memory word destroys the old number (unless both fit). Reading a number to place it in a new word has no effect on the number. It is as though the

---

* The word *contents* may be singular or plural, and in this book its number varies with its usage. Occasionally it is more convenient to think of the contents of a word as a single piece of information; then we say "the contents is. . . ." At other times it is more reasonable to think of the contents of a word as several pieces of information, as when several numbers are stored in a word; then we say "the contents are. . . ."

marks on the eggs in the egg box were copied on a new set and the latter was placed in a new box. After the contents of one word is stored in another, the contents of both words are identical.

In addition to the memory we have described, other storage units are usually connected to a computer to store additional information. These are referred to collectively as *auxiliary storage*. Generally this memory has a longer *access time;* that is, it requires more time for an item of data to be taken from memory and placed into the arithmetic unit. Access times for *internal* or *high-speed memory*, the memory described earlier, run as low as 1 or 2 microseconds, whereas access times for auxiliary memory is usually many times greater. On the other hand, the capacity of auxiliary storage is invariably much higher. Throughout this book, the term "memory" is used to mean "internal memory."

Large modern computers have memories built of vacuum tubes, magnetic cores, or solid-state diodes, each such device holding one binary digit. Smaller computers usually have magnetic-drum memories on which are stored a number of words. Magnetic-core memories are, in most computers, random-access.

Auxiliary memory is usually provided by magnetic tape. Each reel of tape is capable of holding a large amount of information, about 10 to 200 times as much as high-speed memory. A reel of tape is mounted on a *magnetic-tape unit,* which resembles a large tape recorder. Reading and writing heads permit information to be read from or written on the tape; there are controls for rewinding the tape.

Magnetic disks are also used as auxiliary storage. These disks are coated with a magnetic material similar to magnetic tape, and they are stacked like a pile of phonograph records. Information on tapes and disks is stored as a series of magnetized spots.*

Input-Output Equipment

Information that is supplied to a computer in the form of a program and data is usually punched on cards. Figure 3.2 shows a card used with equipment of the IBM Corporation. It contains 80 columns, each of which has 12 positions for punching rectangular holes. Eighty characters (letters, digits, or punctuation marks) may be punched on each card. To represent a character, 1, 2, or 3 holes in 1 column are punched. Another type of card, used with equipment of the Remington Rand Corporation, is punched with round holes and has 45 columns. Each column can hold 2 characters, each represented by a set of holes, so that 90 characters may be punched on one card.

Cards are punched with *keypunch* machines, which have keyboards similar to those of typewriters. The keypunch prints the characters over the columns containing them, as shown in Fig. 3.2.

* The way in which information is stored on tape is studied in Chapter 7.

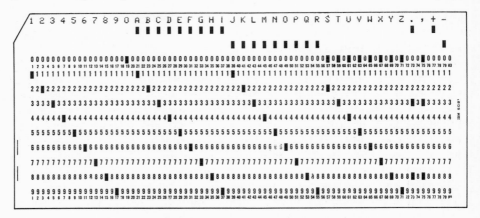

Fig. 3.2. An IBM card, punched with 40 characters.

Cards are read by *card readers,* which place the information read either directly into memory (termed *on-line* reading) or onto magnetic tape (*off-line* reading). Similarly, results of a computation may be punched on cards by the computer (*on-line* punching) or may be written on tape for later punching (*off-line* punching).

Magnetic tapes, in addition to providing auxiliary memory space, are a vital part of input-output equipment. They are used more than any other storage medium as the direct link between computer memory and the outside world. Information can be read from and written on tape much faster than cards. The use of tapes for this purpose is examined more closely in Section 3.2.

Operations that occur independently of computer processing are termed *off-line* operations. Operations that involve placing information into memory or removing information from memory are *on-line* operations. These processes are also examined further in Section 3.2.

The most common medium for storing final results is the printed page. The results of a program, written on tape, are later printed by *line printers,* mechanical devices that print 1 complete line at a time at a rate of up to about 1000 lines per minute, with about 130 characters per line. Printing wheels or chains that contain metal letters as on a typewriter are forced into contact with an inked ribbon and the paper. Electrical signals trigger the letters at the proper times. Some printers are not mechanical but print characters by photographic or chemical means.

Some small computers use punched paper tape as a medium for input-output operations. A strip of paper tape is shown in Fig. 3.3. The paper has 5 to 8 channels for information. One character is represented by a set of punched holes across the width of the tape. Paper tape may be punched by a typewriter that is connected to a punching mechanism. Conversely, the computer output, if on paper tape, can be printed by a typewriter. Some computers accept input directly from a typewriter keyboard and provide output by action of the keys on the same typewriter.[4]

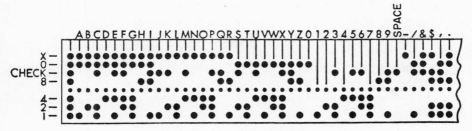

Fig. 3.3.   Punched paper tape (8 channels).

The Console

The *console* of a computer is the control and display unit. It does not take an active part in computer operations, but it provides a means of communication between the computer and the *operator,* the person who runs the computer.   The console has several functions.   (1) It contains the external controls of the computer, the means for starting and stopping it and running it "manually," that is, one instruction at a time at a slow rate.   (2) It displays the contents of the most important registers of the arithmetic and control units, such as the accumulator.   It can also display the contents of any word of memory if the address of that word is supplied on appropriate buttons or switches.   (3) It is used to enter information into the arithmetic and control units.   This is usually done by entering one computer word into a set of *keys* or switches whose setting is then placed in memory.   (4) It contains *indicators* that exhibit certain conditions in the machine: error situations on reading of tapes, improper arithmetic operation, etc.*

The purpose of these controls and indicators is to allow the operator (who is not necessarily the programmer) to monitor the running of the computer.   If the computer stops without apparent cause, he may be able to detect the reason; often he can at least note information on the console that offers a clue to the trouble.   He can run the computer slowly, manually "executing" the instructions so that he can see what happens when a small number of successive instructions are executed.   The role of the computer operator in helping to detect errors in programming is discussed in Chapter 19.

3.2 COMPUTER OPERATION

Programs in Memory

A computer program is defined in Section 1.1 as a list of instructions whose execution performs a sequence of calculations.   In Chapter 2, problems to be

---

*One improper arithmetic operation is an attempted division by zero, detected by most computers.

solved on computers are analyzed as flowcharts. In this section we examine the manner in which such analyses are translated into programs and placed in memory. The discussion here is informal, and it cannot be said to cover the techniques of coding. That topic is discussed in the chapters of Part II.

Consider the flowchart drawn in Fig. 2.2 (page 28) to indicate the summation of n numbers. For the present we assume a computer with instructions that perform the operations indicated there. The analysis, given in Section 2.2 and slightly revised, follows.

1. $0 \to S$.
2. $1 \to i$.
3. $S + a_i \to S$.
4. $i + 1 \to i$.
5. If $i \leqslant n$, continue at step 3; if $i > n$, continue at step 6.
6. Stop.

Here we assume these instructions: (1) set a quantity equal to a particular value; (2) add a given number to a particular quantity; (3) test a quantity and continue at one of two steps, depending on the sign on that quantity; and (4) stop. (Comparing two numbers is equivalent to checking the sign of their difference.)

One significant way in which a computer program differs from a list of steps of the type just given is that with *all* instructions an indication of the next instruction to be performed must be given or be implied. If this is done to the list we have made, the result is:

1. $0 \to S$; continue at step 2.
2. $1 \to i$; continue at step 3.
3. $S + a_i \to S$; continue at step 4.
4. $i + 1 \to i$; continue at step 5.
5. If $i \leqslant n$, continue at step 3; if $i > n$, continue at step 6.
6. Stop.

Most programs consist of instructions that will be executed one at a time without interruption of the sequence, as will steps 1 through 5 given. Hence it is sensible to establish this rule in program execution: "Unless given an order to do otherwise, after executing one instruction, execute the *next* one." To define "next" it is necessary to number the instructions, as we have done here. Then the "next" instruction is the one whose number is one greater than the current one. In random-access computers this rule is built into the circuitry, so that the extra information does not need to be added.* In the following discussion the rule applies.

---

* Computers with magnetic-drum memories require the "next" address to be included in the instruction. Words are numbered sequentially around the drum. During one instruction execution, several words pass under the drum reading station. To minimize the total running time instructions that occur in sequence are spaced around the drum, and it is necessary to indicate the location of the next instruction.

Programs can be so placed in memory that their instructions are numbered by means of the addresses in memory. If, for example, we place the summation program starting in location 658, the complete program is located as follows:*

location 658: $0 \to S$.
location 659: $1 \to i$.
location 660: $S + a_i \to S$.
location 661: $i + 1 \to i$.
location 662:   If $i \leqslant n$, continue at 660; if $i > n$, continue at 663.
location 663:   Stop.

The instruction at location 662 bears further attention. It corresponds to the decision box in the flowchart and provides the means for terminating the loop at the proper time. An instruction of this type is called a *conditional-jump* instruction because, under a stated condition (if $i \leqslant n$), a jump is made out of the normal sequence of proceeding to the next instruction. Under a different stated condition (if $i > n$), the next instruction is executed.

The operation boxes of flowcharts have been translated here into computer instructions of the "normal-sequence" type. The decision box has been translated into a jump instruction that may break this sequence. Although it is incidental to this program, we may note that the statement "Stop" has been translated into an instruction also.

Control

To understand the manner in which a sequence of instructions in a program in memory is executed, the concept of *control* is important. Before considering it we examine more closely the execution of instructions.

At a given instant exactly one instruction is being either interpreted or executed. "Being interpreted" means that the nature of the instruction is being determined by the control unit and the operands are being identified. For example, suppose that the instruction at location 660 is being interpreted:

$$660: \quad S + a_i \to S.$$

The control unit must identify these parts of this instruction: "add" (corresponding to the plus sign), S, and a_i. It then sends signals to the arithmetic unit, which performs the addition.†

When an instruction is both interpreted and executed, its address (here 660)

---

* The instructions here are placed one to a word, so that a distinct address is associated with each instruction. Many new computers, which have large word capacities, have two instructions stored in each word.

† A detailed analysis of the cycle of instruction interpretation and execution is considered later in this section.

is located in the *address register* (AR).*   Control is said to be "with" or "at" that instruction. After each instruction is executed, the C(AR) is normally increased by 1. Then the next instruction to be executed is the one located at the next address in memory. If the instruction is a jump instruction, there may be a change in the normal sequencing of control. The address in the AR may be changed by any amount, that is, to the value stated in the instruction. Consider the instruction at location 662:

662:   If $i \leqslant n$, continue at 660; if $i > n$, continue at 663.

Just before this instruction is executed, the C(AR) = 662. After it is executed, provided $i \leqslant n$, the C(AR) = 660. Thus the next instruction executed is the one at 660.

We see from this example that the C(AR) actually determines which instruction is to be executed. Either that address is increased by 1, or it changes as directed by the instruction.   This sequencing of control is called *flow of control.* If the C(AR) is changed by other than 1, there is a *change of control.* This is a "jump," as defined earlier.† In computers that do not obey the rule of proceeding normally through sequential addresses the concept of flow of control also applies.   "Normal" flow of control, however, has little meaning then.

The Machine Cycle

The *machine cycle* is the period that elapses from the time an address is placed in the AR to the time the following address is placed in it. This period, as seen above, consists of two parts or cycles: (1) the *interpretation cycle* and (2) the *execution cycle.*

Let us assume that an address is placed in the AR. This may be done either by normal sequencing or by a jump instruction, and it may be done manually by an entry on the console. During the interpretation cycle the following actions take place.

1. The contents of the word whose address is in the AR is placed in another special register, the *instruction register* (IR). This word contains an instruction.

2. The instruction consists of an operation and associated operands, all represented internally as numbers. These numbers are decoded by the circuitry of the control unit.

During the execution cycle the following actions take place:

3. Signals are sent to the arithmetic unit if the instruction is arithmetic. Other signals are sent to the memory unit for the removal of information to the arithmetic unit.

---

* This register is also known as the *location counter, instruction counter,* and *program address counter.* As with many words we use, the terminology varies from one computer to another.

† Other names for a jump are *transfer* and *branch.*

4. The arithmetic is performed if there is any to be done. If the instruction is a conditional jump, the appropriate test is made.

5. If any information is to be placed in memory, this is done.

6. The C(AR) is changed in accordance with the nature of the instruction: it is either increased by 1 or set to a new value by a jump instruction.

After these steps are all performed step 1 follows, and the whole process is repeated. In this manner instructions are executed in their proper sequence, as determined by the programmer, and the program is *run*.

The Stored Program

A concept that has been implicit in the explanation of the program execution process is that the program is located in the memory with the data and constants it processes. Results of the calculations are also placed in memory. All these items, instructions, data, constants, and results, are stored in memory in identical form. All appear as numbers internally. A program stored in memory in this way is called a *stored program*. Most computers currently in use have stored programs.

The word whose address is located in the AR is placed in the IR. Regardless of its significance, this word is interpreted as an instruction and executed. If for some reason the word is not an instruction, a number of things may happen, depending on the computer circuitry. The computer may stop. It may execute some instruction. It may make a spurious action. In any case, a mistake is almost certainly the result. The question of how the computer distinguishes between instructions and data or constants is almost academic; when the address of a location is placed in the AR the contents of that location is interpreted as an instruction.

Despite the possibility of errors there are two sound reasons for this method of program storage. First and most importantly, it permits the instructions themselves to be treated as data and modified by arithmetic. This is very useful in coding, as we see in Chapter 7. Second, it provides for greater flexibility in the use of the computer memory. If portions of the memory were designated permanently for programs, and others were designated for data and results, the ambiguity would not exist. Programs vary considerably in their structure, however. One program may fill 90% of memory with its data; another may fill only 40%. A boundary designation of the type mentioned would work an undue hardship on some programs.

The Running of Programs

For a computer to solve a problem these steps must be taken: (1) the program must be placed in memory, (2) it must be executed, and (3) the answers must be supplied. The details of these operations are discussed in several later chapters. Here we look briefly at the manner in which they are normally performed at a computer installation.

On-line and off-line operations were mentioned in Section 3.1; the concepts can be generalized. *On-line operation* refers to a mode of operation wherein a program and its data, located in a deck of punched cards, are placed directly into the computer memory by an on-line card reader.* This machine converts the information on the cards to a form internally usable by the computer and places it in memory. The output phase of on-line operation is accomplished by an *on-line printer,* a printer connected directly to the computer. This machine converts information in memory to printed information. To summarize, on-line running of programs consists of these steps:

1. The problem deck (the program and its data) is placed in the on-line card reader, and the information in the deck is placed in memory.

2. The program is executed.

3. Answers are printed by the on-line printer directly from the memory.

Off-line operation differs from on-line operation in one important respect. Magnetic tapes are used as intermediate storage between punched cards and memory (on input) and memory and printed paper (on output). Tapes are used because both tape-reading and tape-writing operations are much faster than card reading and paper printing. Information punched on cards can be read at about $\frac{1}{100}$ to $\frac{1}{500}$ the rate that information on tape can be read. Similarly, information can be printed on paper at about $\frac{1}{25}$ to $\frac{1}{100}$ the rate that it can be written on tape.† These comparisons indicate why off-line operation is preferable. Off-line equipment similar to on-line equipment is used.

Off-line operation consists of these steps:

1. The problem deck is placed in the off-line card reader, and the information in this deck is placed on magnetic tape.

2. At a later time the program is placed in computer memory, going from tape directly into memory.

3. The program is executed.

4. Answers are written on magnetic tape from memory.

5. At a later time the answers are printed on paper by an off-line printer from the tape.

Computers are expensive; they may cost as much as $1000 an hour to operate. For this reason a computer installation attempts to increase the efficiency of its

---

* As noted in Section 3.1, information for computers may exist in various forms. Punched cards are used most frequently because instructions in a deck can easily be inserted, deleted, or changed. We speak here of a "deck of punched cards" but actually refer to several media. Similarly, we use a printer as a typical output medium.

† These are approximations at best, since computer equipment varies among manufacturers and generally is steadily improved over a period of time. Currently tapes can be read at a rate of about half a million characters per second.

operations as much as possible. Off-line equipment is essential for efficiency, because it offers such great speed advantages. Placing several programs on one tape in sequence and later running these one after another can further increase efficiency.

An *input tape* is filled with perhaps 25 to 100 programs, read off-line from decks with their data. Later the programs are read into memory one at a time and then executed. Results, also in sequence, are placed on an *output tape* for subsequent printing.

In order to control the on-line processing operations of reading from tape, execution of programs, and writing on tape, an *input-output monitor program* is used. Among its several functions is the job of reading in each program and writing answers on tape. The coding for input-output operations is usually fairly complex. By using the monitor program for input-output purposes, the programmer is saved the associated coding efforts.

3.3 COMPUTER LANGUAGES

The Language Barrier

The instructions that comprise a computer program are stored in memory as a sequence of integers. The language of the computer (the machine language) is embodied in these integers, which indicate the operations to be performed and the operands involved. The language of the programmer's problem, on the other hand, is English or mathematics, or perhaps a combination of the two. There is a great discrepancy between the language of the problem and that of the computer. The term *language barrier* is frequently used to describe this situation.

Despite the discrepancy, man and machine manage to communicate with one another satisfactorily. This is accomplished in several stages, some of which have already been examined. In Chapter 2 a few problems were transformed from their statements in English to more concise mathematical forms: sequences of steps and flowcharts. For example, the problem

"Determine the square root of A to the following accuracy . . ."

was written as a sequence of four operations and as a flowchart with four boxes.

The next stage in the communication process is coding, where the operations are translated into a special language that bears some resemblance to mathematics and some resemblance to computer instructions.

Following the coding is a further translation from the special coding language to pure machine language. This is done by a translation program, which, in effect, is an extension of the computer. The special language becomes, for the programmer, the language of the machine. Chapter 6 contains a detailed explanation of one such language. Other coding languages are considered in Part III.

Lists into Programs

The problem of summing n numbers was written as a program in Section 3.2. We noted that one characteristic of a computer program is that accompanying each instruction is a real or implied indication of the next instruction. Computer programs have other characteristics that are best illustrated by an example of an arithmetic problem.

Equation 9 of Section 2.1 (page 18) requires the evaluation of the radical*

$$R_1 = \sqrt{b^2/4 + a^3/27}$$

This problem can be analyzed as follows, where the T_i are intermediate results:

$$T_1 = b^2$$
$$T_2 = T_1/4$$
$$T_3 = a^3$$
$$T_4 = T_3/27$$
$$T_5 = T_2 + T_4$$
$$R_1 = \sqrt{T_5}$$

This list can be rewritten, with the operations placed first and written out:

$$T_1 = \text{square: } b$$
$$T_2 = \text{divide: } T_1, 4$$
$$T_3 = \text{cube: } a$$
$$T_4 = \text{divide: } T_3, 27$$
$$T_5 = \text{add: } T_2, T_4$$
$$R_1 = \text{square root: } T_5$$

This second list is only slightly different from the first; the operations are simply placed before the operands. We write it because some coding languages have this alternate structure in their instructions.†

Consider the first operation in the list:

$$T_1 = \text{square: } b$$

If interpreted in terms of a computer operation, this means

"Compute the square of b and store the result T_1."

The quantity b is located in a word in memory, say, location 429. The result is to be placed in another location, say, 555. This statement can thus be rewritten in terms of the addresses of the words involved:

"Compute the square of *the contents of* location 429 and store the result in location 555."

---

* The radicand is assumed positive.
† The language described in Chapter 6 has this structure.

This form of the statement of the operation is significant because it points out another characteristic of computer programs. Computer instructions generally refer indirectly to operands; contained within the instructions are the *addresses* of the operands.

The distinction between the contents of a word and the address of a word must always be kept clearly in mind. In our notation

$$C(429) = b \quad \text{and} \quad L(b) = 429$$

If, for example, it is true that

$$b = 1,567,000$$

then the number 1,567,000 is stored in location 429.

Our list can be written as a computer program. Let the locations be assigned as follows:

$$L(T_i) = 554 + i, \quad i = 1, 2, \ldots, 6$$
$$L(a) = 428$$
$$L(b) = 429$$
$$L(4) = 500$$
$$L(27) = 501$$

In the program that follows, arrows are used in a way similar to their earlier usage. Now they indicate the physical placement of information into the locations named in the second column. The program is placed in memory, starting at location 200.

Location of Instruction	Location of Result	Operation and Addresses	Remarks
200	555 ←	square: 429	square b
201	556 ←	divide: 555, 500	form $b^2/4$
202	557 ←	cube: 428	cube a
203	558 ←	divide: 557, 501	form $a^3/27$
204	559 ←	add: 556, 558	$b^2/4 + a^3/27$
205	560 ←	square root: 559	square sum

At the conclusion of this program the result R_1 is stored in location 560.

The role of each of the many addresses associated with this program must be clearly understood. The program, consisting of six instructions, is stored in locations 200 through 205 in memory. The constants of the program (the numbers 4 and 27) are stored in locations 500 and 501. The data (the variables a and b) are stored in locations 428 and 429. Finally, locations 555 through 560 are used for results.

Note that it is not necessary to use six locations for the results. The result of the first division could have been placed back in location 555, where b^2 had been stored:

$$555 \leftarrow \text{divide: } 555, 500$$

In our program only two locations are needed for results.

To be useful a computer program must be general; that is, it must apply to many different sets of data. By making references to operand addresses, a program achieves this end. As different sets of data are supplied to a program, its structure need not change. For example, regardless of the numbers stored in locations 428 and 429, the program we have given evaluates the radical. It has been written to perform the evaluation for all values of a and b, provided they fit within single computer words.

We saw in the last section that when instructions are placed in memory they have the form of numbers. Consider again the divide instruction:

$$556 \leftarrow \text{divide: } 556, 500$$

The word in memory that contains this instruction, location 201, must contain the following parts or *fields:* three addresses and one operation (divide). A numeric code must be used for the operation; this is termed the *operation code.* If the operation code for division is 42, the contents of location 201 might appear as follows:

$$42 \ 556 \ 500 \ 556$$

The spaces between fields are inserted for clarity.

The Format of Instructions

Every instruction on a computer has associated with it an *operator* (often called an *operation*) and one or more operands.* For example, in the program just written, the squaring, cubing, and square-rooting instructions each have one operand. The addition and division instructions each have two operands. Moreover, all the instructions have one address for the result.

Computers are often characterized by the number of operands contained within their instructions. On a given machine the number of operands varies among the instructions, as we have just observed, and the maximum number of operands in an instruction on the given computer typifies it. For example, the imaginary computer we have assumed is a *three-address* computer; the three addresses are the two operand addresses and the address for the result. This structure is typical of three-address computers. If an instruction requires only one operand, one address field is not used.†

Four-address computers use the extra address field to indicate the location of

---

* A confusion of concepts may occur here. The word *operation* has been previously used in its usual sense, to designate "anything that is done," such as the addition of two numbers or the evaluation of a radical. The word as used here refers to a single action performed by a computer instruction. Context must be relied on for the meaning.

† Ambiguity also exists about the word *address,* since it is commonly used three ways. The convention here is as follows: *address* means *location address,* the numerical designation or name of a memory location; *operand address* means the address of an operand of an instruction; the *address field(s)* of an instruction is the portion(s) of the instruction word containing an operand address(es).

the following instruction. As noted in Section 3.2, drum-memory computers require such information.

Two-address computers use their address fields in two ways. In one use the two fields contain operand addresses, and the results of operations are stored either in the accumulator or in one of the locations of the operands. Examples are the following:

"Add the C(3005) to the C(2223) and place the sum in the accumulator."
"Add the C(3005) to the C(2223) and place the sum in location 3005."

In the second two-address use, for a drum memory computer, one address field is used for an operand address and the other is used for the address of the next instruction.

One-address computers use the accumulator to hold one operand and the result. The single address field contains an operand address. As an illustration of a one-address program, the problem of evaluating the radical R_1 is recoded. Location assignments are as previously stated.

Location of Instruction	Operation and Operand Address	Remarks
200	load AC: 429	b to AC
201	square AC	b^2 in AC
202	divide: 500	$b^2/4$ in AC
203	store AC: 555	$b^2/4$ to 555
204	load AC: 428	a to AC
205	cube AC	a^3 in AC
206	divide: 501	$a^3/27$ in AC
207	add: 555	$b^2/4 + a^3/27$
208	square root	R_1 in AC
209	store AC: 560	R_1 to 560

If we compare the three-address and one-address programs for the evaluation of R_1, we note two things: the latter program is longer (ten instructions against six instructions), and new instructions ("load AC" and "store AC") are required for moving data between the accumulator and memory. These are general trends. As the number of addresses per instruction decreases, both the program length (in number of instructions) and the number of distinct instructions required increases.

The squaring, cubing, and square-rooting operations of our imaginary computer rarely exist on real digital computers. Formation of the quantities b^2 and a^3 is accomplished by successive multiplication. If the R_1-evaluation program were rewritten with such operations, it would be somewhat longer than the one-address program here.

Some computers have a *variable*-address structure. When instructions require fewer than three address fields, less space is assigned to them in memory than if all three fields are required. In this way space is conserved.

About half of all modern computers use one-address instructions. Programs are then longer than they would be on two- or three-address computers, but one-address instructions require less memory space. The savings are sufficient to compensate for the longer programs. The use of one-address instructions offers no loss in coding flexibility.

Types of Instruction

The set of instructions associated with a computer can be classified by the nature of the operations performed. Five types can be identified: (1) arithmetic, (2) data-moving, (3) decision, (4) indexing, and (5) input-output instructions.*

Arithmetic instructions are already familiar. They perform the operations of addition, subtraction, multiplication, and division.

Data-moving instructions move numbers between registers in the arithmetic unit (such as the accumulator) and memory. The "store AC" instruction is an example. Moving a word from memory to the accumulator is accomplished by "load AC."

Decision instructions cause a change of control if certain conditions are met. The program written in Section 3.2 to sum n numbers contains a decision instruction at location 662:

"If $i \leqslant n$, continue at [location] 660; if $i > n$, continue at [location] 663."

The condition to be met for a change of control at location 660 is that i be less than or equal to n when this instruction is executed. In one-address computers the action of most decision instructions depends on conditions in the accumulator: whether it is negative, positive, zero, etc. Since only one address is present, a typical instruction would be

"If $i \leqslant n$, continue at 660; if $i > n$, continue at the next instruction."

In this instruction only one address is given. "Next" refers, as usual, to the next sequential location.

Indexing instructions were mentioned in Section 2.2, where the importance of indexing techniques was indicated. Most computers contain index registers for automatically indexing problem variables. Instructions are available for performing operations on these registers.

Input-output instructions move information between the input-output equipment and the computer memory.

---

* Some computer instructions cannot readily be classified into one of these five types, so that this classification is crude. The *logical* instructions described in Chapters 12 and 15 are such instructions. Nonetheless, for our present purposes the categories given are significant.

Languages for Coding

We have seen how the language barrier problem is partially solved through stages of problem statement translations. The last of the stages of human translation is coding: the writing of programs in special coding languages later translated into machine language.

The main difference between programs written in these coding languages and the programs written here is that *symbols* are used to refer to memory locations in the former. Symbols are alphabetic names for addresses. It is necessary to refer to memory addresses in a program; in doing this in the programs coded here, we caused instructions to lose their algebraic form. The statement

$$T_1 = b^2$$

is easier to write and understand than its program equivalent

$$555 \leftarrow \text{square: } 429$$

Symbolic coding combines the algebraic appearance of the former statement with the structure of the latter by permitting the use of symbols with mnemonic significance. For example, the address of the word containing b (location 429) may be called B; the location of b^2 may be addressed as BSQUARE; the result of a summation may be placed in SUM.

Let the following symbols be used in the problem of evaluating R_1:

$$L(a) = A$$
$$L(b) = B$$
$$L(4) = FOUR$$
$$L(27) = TWSEVEN$$

TEMP will be used to name a temporary storage location. The value of R_1 is stored in ANSWER.

The one-address program, coded symbolically, is shown in the accompanying table.

Location of Instruction	Operation and Operand Address	Remarks
200	load AC: B	b to AC
201	square AC	b^2 in AC
202	divide: FOUR	$b^2/4$ in AC
203	store AC: TEMP	$b^2/4$ to TEMP
204	load AC: A	a to AC
205	cube AC	a^3 in AC
206	divide: TWSEVEN	$a^3/27$ in AC
207	add: TEMP	$b^2/4 + a^3/27$
208	square root	R_1 in AC
209	store AC: ANSWER	R_1 to ANSWER

A second type of coding language is available. It permits us to write instructions that resemble algebraic formulas. The problem just coded evaluates R_1:

$$R_1 = \sqrt{b^2/4 + a^3/27}$$

In a formula-like language, the instruction might be written as follows:*

$$\texttt{R1 = SQRTF(B**2/4. + A**3/27.)}$$

In this expression the double asterisk indicates exponentiation. In addition to the two types of coding language illustrated here, others are available. Some of these are studied briefly in Part III.

The examples of programs given in this section are clearly no more than *possible* solutions to the coding problems presented. There are other, equally valid programs for the problems. For example, the quantity $a^3/27$ could have been evaluated *before* the quantity $b^2/4$, instead of afterward. In more complex problems there are more alternatives, and it is not unusual for hundreds of different programs to exist for the correct solution of a particular problem. None is more valid than any other, if the only criterion is correctness of results.

3.4 PROBLEM ANALYSIS FOR COMPUTERS

Restrictions of a Computer

When problems were analyzed in Chapter 2, no consideration was given to the nature of a computer. In theory, any analysis that leads ultimately to a correct answer is valid. In practice, the characteristics of a digital computer impose restrictions both on the methods of analysis and solution and on the nature of the numbers of the computation.

Each memory word in a computer is of finite length, holding typically a number with 8 to 12 decimal digits. Calculations that assume infinite precision are at best approximated in a computer. Although errors in individual words are small, large errors can accumulate that may eventually lead to serious deviations from correct values. It is possible for one number to be stored in two words, with half of its significant digits in each word. This method, called *double-precision arithmetic,* yields much greater accuracy, but computation is much slower.

The numbers stored in memory words are signed, real numbers, and arithmetic operations performed on them are real operations. Many problems, among them the solution of a cubic equation, must deal with complex numbers. In order to represent complex numbers in memory, two words per number are usually used: one each for the real and imaginary parts. Complex arithmetic must be realized by a sequence of real arithmetic operations.

*The language is FORTRAN, described in Chapter 14.

Computer memories are finite in size. Although several magnetic tapes may be attached to a computer, thereby increasing storage capacity to a very large degree, the size of high-speed memory space is often a limiting factor. The relatively high access times of tapes often limit their value. As a result it is frequently necessary to conserve space and not use it carelessly.

These computer restrictions—finite word size, absence of complex arithmetic, and finite high-speed memory space—are not serious. Each can be largely circumvented, but special effort is necessary.

Computer Flowcharts

After a flowchart has been drawn for a problem analysis, it is often a help to redraw the chart in terms of the structure and operation of a computer. Some of the modifications made to flowcharts in this process are described now.

Since all data and computed results must be assigned space in memory, it is helpful if these assignments are indicated on the flowchart. For this purpose the *memory box* is used.[5] Each entry in the box consists of a problem variable or constant and the address or symbol of the location in memory. The memory box in Fig. 3.4 indicates that

x is in location NUMBER
r is in location R
y_i is in location LIST $+$ i, that is, i locations after LIST.

The memory box can be used to eliminate from the operation and decision boxes all references to specific locations. If the assignment of locations is changed, the memory boxes alone need be changed.

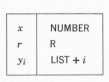

Fig. 3.4. A memory box.

The operation of moving data, including input-output, is not considered in a problem analysis. Data moving is, however, an important process in machine computation. Data read from tape may be so extensive that it cannot be placed in memory at one time. It is possible to read in one portion of the data, process it, then read in another portion, etc. An operation box might indicate the manner of reading in the data. Similar considerations apply to the output. During a calculation a set of data may have to be moved from one memory area to another. An operation box may be drawn for this purpose. None of these operations had to be considered when a flowchart that merely indicated the problem was drawn, but a flowchart for computer processing offers a somewhat different point of view.[6]

The distinction was made in Section 2.2 between two basically different types of problem repetition. In one, illustrated in Fig. 2.2 (page 28), a set of numbers a_i was summed. Each a_i is a distinct number in this set. In the other, illustrated in Fig. 2.8 (page 36), a sequence of estimates x_i was calculated. Each x_i is a new estimate for a desired number ($\sqrt{A}$). Flowcharts drawn for a computer should indicate this distinction. Figure 3.5 is a redrawing of Fig. 2.8; the symbol e is used to represent the newest estimate for $\sqrt{A}$. The statement

$$\frac{1}{2} \left(e + \frac{A}{e} \right) \rightarrow e$$

indicates the calculation of a new value of e that replaces the old value. By writing this statement instead of the corresponding one in Fig. 2.8, the implication is that only one word of memory is needed for the estimates. This is the case, however, since only the latest estimate need be saved. We might note that an iterative problem of this type needs no index. The problem terminates when the estimate has achieved a desired accuracy.

Section 5.3 contains three examples of flowcharts that are modified when computer characteristics are considered. Among the reasons for the changes are: (1) multiple branches at a decision box are not generally realizable with a single instruction; instead, a sequence of binary (two-way) decisions must be made;* (2) a number, as the result of a calculation, may be left in the accumulator, so that what appears on the flowchart as a "store" instruction is redundant.

Other situations may also lead to the re-analyzing of a problem: (1) numbers in memory are not necessarily stored in sequence in increasing memory addresses;

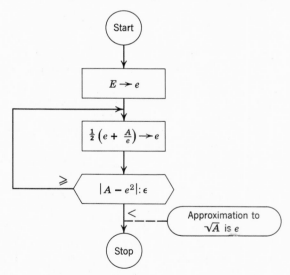

Fig. 3.5.   Computer flowchart for square-root computation.

* There is one exception; a three-way branch that depends on the relative values of two numbers is frequently possible with a "compare" instruction. See Section 9.1.

(2) double-precision arithmetic or complex arithmetic requires two words per number; and (3) complicated operations may have to be further detailed to incorporate specific available instructions.   There are many other conditions that will involve flowchart modifications.

Summary

A digital computer is organized as an integrated group of functional units. The arithmetic, control, memory, and input-output units all operate under the

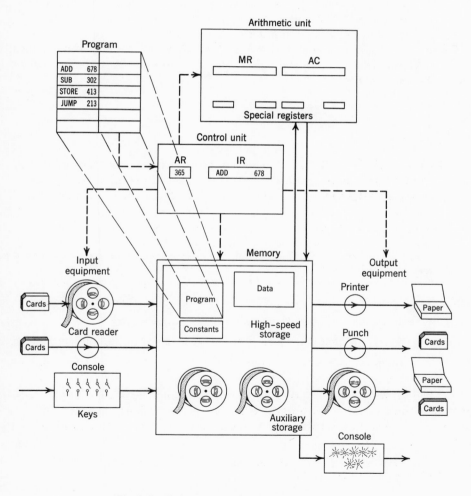

Fig. 3.6.   Computer organization (with some details).

guidance of the program stored in memory. Data are read into memory by the input unit and processed by the arithmetic unit. Results are read out by the output equipment.

During the execution of the program the control unit interprets instructions and sends control signals to the other units. The address register contains at all times the address of the instruction currently being executed. Unless a jump instruction sets this register to a specific address, its contents increase uniformly by one at each instruction. In this way control passes through a sequence of instructions, and the program is executed.

Communication with the computer is a requisite to coding it. The differences between mathematical language and computer language are overcome in several stages. These include analysis and flowcharting using a consistent and concise notation, translation to a computer program written in a special coding language, and finally translation by the computer itself to machine language.

The structure of a computer is shown in Fig. 3.6, which supplies some details to the block diagram given in Fig. 3.1. Figure 3.6 also summarizes some of the material of this chapter.

Notes

1–4. Each of the following books contains further information on the arithmetic unit, the control unit, the memory unit, and the input-output equipment. They also describe the design of computers and the mathematics used in it.

C. V. L. Smith, *Electronic Digital Computers*, McGraw-Hill, 1959.

P. Siegel, *Understanding Digital Computers*, Wiley, 1961.

E. M. Grabbe, S. Ramo, and D. E. Wooldridge, *Handbook of Automation, Computation, and Control*, Vol. 2, Wiley, 1959.

I. Flores, *Computer Logic—the Functional Design of Digital Computers*, Prentice-Hall, 1960.

The following book devotes two chapters to the use of punched cards.

E. W. Martin, Jr., *Electronic Data Processing*, Irwin, 1961, Chapters 3 and 4.

5. The material on memory boxes is based on material in the following book:

H. D. Leeds and G. M. Weinberg, *Computer Programming Fundamentals*, McGraw-Hill, 1961, pages 86–87.

6. The following book describes the nature of computer flowcharts (flow diagrams) in some detail. The authors consider such flowcharts to be analyzed to the point of having each two- or three-address instruction indicated in its own box.

G. W. Evans II and C. L. Perry, *Programming and Coding for Automatic Digital Computers*, McGraw-Hill, 1961, pages 65–78.

PROBLEMS

Section 3.1

3.1. Draw an "organization chart" of the use of a desk calculator, paralleling the chart drawn in Fig. 3.1 for a computor. Discuss the analogies between corresponding boxes in the two charts.

3.2. The chart of Fig. 3.1 indicates nothing about the time sequencing of the several units. Consider a particular problem, such as the summation of five numbers that are punched on a card, and describe the manner in which the units interact (and in what sequence) to solve the problem and supply the answer.

3.3. Memory words may each be used to store two or three numbers, if the numbers are small enough. What are the advantages and disadvantages of this method of storage?

Section 3.2

3.4. Consider again the problem of summing five numbers. Assume that the summation program is stored starting at memory location 658 (as in the text) and that the numbers are stored starting at location 777. Trace all steps executed during the solution of the problem, assuming that control starts at location 658. Consider the actions of the instruction register, the address register, and the control, arithmetic, and memory units of the computer.

3.5. The use of a stored program permits the modification of a program during its execution. Discuss the reasons for so modifying a program.

3.6. The course or flow of control of a program may be modified during its execution. Discuss this feature in the light of the manner in which control passes through a program.

3.7. Discuss the reasons for using both on-line and off-line equipment and performing both on-line and off-line operations.

Section 3.3

3.8. The evaluation of the radical R_1 is coded in the text on an assumed three-address computer capable of extracting square roots. Code this problem on the same three-address computer without using the square-root instruction; use the iterative approach described in Section 2.2.

3.9. Using the structure of the one-address program in the text, write programs to evaluate the following formulas.

(a) $F_1 = a^2/b^3$ (b) $F_2 = (x + y)/(x^2 - y^2)$

(c) $F_3 = (a + b)(c + d)(e + f)$ (d) $F_4 = \sqrt[3]{\sqrt{a^2 + b^2} - \sqrt{a^2 - b^2}}$

Locate each program and its constants in memory and make appropriate memory references.

3.10. What characteristics should a coding language have to be useful in solving a particular class of problems? Consider problems other than those having formulas to be evaluated; consider, for example, alphabetizing words or sorting numbers.

Section 3.4

3.11. A set of 100,000 complex numbers is written on a magnetic tape and is to be read into a 32,000-word computer for processing. Draw flowcharts for determining (a) the sum of these numbers and (b) the number whose magnitude is the largest. Each complex number is to be stored in memory in two words, the real part in one word and the imaginary part in another word. Clearly the numbers have to be read into memory in batches; assume an operation of the form "read n words into memory from tape."

3.12. Computers offer restrictions on problems other than those listed in the text. What are some of these? Explain how each would affect the flowcharts for the operations in Problem 3.11.

4

COMPUTER ARITHMETIC

All computer operations are performed on numbers stored within the computer memory. These numbers are not necessarily in the decimal system. In this chapter we study the decimal, binary, and octal number systems to provide an understanding of the differences (when they exist) between internal and external arithmetic. Of particular interest are the means for performing arithmetic in each system and for converting numbers between systems.

Among the operations of interest in arithmetic are manipulations with signed numbers, scaling of numbers, and floating-point operations. Numbers in floating-point form are expressed as integers multiplied by powers of a number, such as 10; in this form arithmetic operations are readily performed within a computer even when wide ranges of magnitudes are present. These several operations are also studied here.

4.1 NUMBER SYSTEMS

Positional Notation

Consider the measurement of a period of time. Such a measurement is made in units: seconds, minutes, hours, days, and so on. We shall use two rules to express the measurement: (1) the number of each unit is given as a pure number, and the set of numbers is ordered with smaller units at the right; and (2) all quantities are "reduced" so that the number of times each unit is present does not equal the next higher unit. As an example, the measurement of 90 minutes and 35 seconds is written as

$$1, 30, 35$$

This stands for "1 hour, 30 minutes, and 35 seconds." Because the units are given in a specified order, they need not be identified; they are understood. For consistency, some number of each unit must be listed, even if it is zero.

This is precisely the method used for the representation of numbers. The units of "measurement" are powers of a *base* or *radix*. The understood order of units proceeds to the left and right of a *radix point,* written as a "period." If the radix is r, a number N can be written as the sum of powers of r:

$$N = \sum_i a_i r^i$$

where $0 \leqslant a_i < r$. The limits of the sum vary; they may be infinite. Whenever the number has a finite number of digits, the limits are finite.

In the *decimal* system, the one in common use, $r = 10$. As an example, the number 6504.38 can be written as

$$6 \times 10^3 + 5 \times 10^2 + 0 \times 10^1 + 4 \times 10^0 + 3 \times 10^{-1} + 8 \times 10^{-2}$$

The *positional notation* of the number 6504.38 indicates that digits to the left of the decimal point represent the nonnegative powers of 10, starting with the zero power, increasing to the left. Similarly, the digits to the right of the decimal point represent the negative powers of 10, starting with the (-1)th power, decreasing to the right.

The positional notation is the same in all number systems. The number r is then expressed as "10," read "one, zero" (with the radix point understood to the right), for any radix r, since

$$r = 1 \times r^1 + 0 \times r^0$$

for all r. For this reason, only positive digits *less than r* are used as multipliers of the powers of r. A larger digit would be more easily expressed in two- or higher-digit form. Thus the integers $0, 1, 2, \ldots, r - 1$ are used as digits in the system with radix r.

Positional notation is very convenient for arithmetic operations, since it is necessary to know only the $2r$ sums $a_i + a_j$ and the $2r$ products $a_i \times a_j$ in order to perform the arithmetic.

Computer Numbers

The numbers stored in computer memories and operated upon by arithmetic units are usually *binary* numbers, numbers with radix 2. Only two different digits, 0 and 1, are required in the binary system. Representation within the machine is correspondingly simple. A spot on a magnetic tape or the material in a magnetic core is polarized in one direction or another. The voltage at a circuit terminal is either high or low. A vacuum tube is either conducting or not. A switch is either open or closed. Each of these devices can represent one binary digit or *bit*. A collection of them can represent a binary number.

A parallel and related consideration is the arithmetic circuitry required for binary arithmetic. Since $r = 2$ in the binary system, only four addition and four multiplication operations need be performed. The circuitry needed to realize these operations is relatively simple. The decimal system is used in some computers; however, its physical representation and rules of arithmetic are more complex.

It is necessary to provide for the storage of alphabetic information. For example, it is desirable to be able to print a title on the printed matter produced by a computer. Letters of the alphabet are coded as numbers, usually six bits in size in a binary computer, permitting sixty-four distinct combinations.

The Binary System

A number in the binary system is written as a sequence of 1's and 0's. For example, 1011100.11 is the following number, expressed in decimal terms:

$$1 \times 2^6 + 0 \times 2^5 + 1 \times 2^4 + 1 \times 2^3 + 1 \times 2^2 + 0 \times 2^1 + 0 \times 2^0$$
$$+ 1 \times 2^{-1} + 1 \times 2^{-2}$$

In the decimal system this is

$$64 + 16 + 8 + 4 + \tfrac{1}{2} + \tfrac{1}{4} = 92.75$$

Arithmetic in the binary system is simple.[1] The rules may be expressed in addition and multiplication tables, as in Table 4.1.

TABLE 4.1 BINARY ARITHMETIC TABLES

+	0	1
0	0	1
1	1	10

×	0	1
0	0	0
1	0	1

Examples of binary arithmetic are:

```
  1001110101                    101101001
+ 1110110010                 ×      11010
  11000100111                  1011010010
                               1011010010
                              101101001
                              10010010101010
```

The Octal System

The radix in the *octal* system is 8. Digits are 0, 1, 2, 3, 4, 5, 6, and 7. As an example, consider the octal number 5406.7:

$$5 \times 8^3 + 4 \times 8^2 + 0 \times 8^1 + 6 \times 8^0 + 7 \times 8^{-1}$$

This is 2822.875 in the decimal system. To distinguish among numbers written with different radices subscripts are used:

$$10111.01_2 = 27.2_8 = 23.25_{10}$$

Frequently numbers in the decimal system are written without subscripts. This convention is used in this book.

Octal arithmetic rules are embodied in Tables 4.2 and 4.3.

TABLE 4.2 OCTAL ADDITION TABLE

+	0	1	2	3	4	5	6	7
0	0	1	2	3	4	5	6	7
1	1	2	3	4	5	6	7	10
2	2	3	4	5	6	7	10	11
3	3	4	5	6	7	10	11	12
4	4	5	6	7	10	11	12	13
5	5	6	7	10	11	12	13	14
6	6	7	10	11	12	13	14	15
7	7	10	11	12	13	14	15	16

TABLE 4.3 OCTAL MULTIPLICATION TABLE

×	0	1	2	3	4	5	6	7
0	0	0	0	0	0	0	0	0
1	0	1	2	3	4	5	6	7
2	0	2	4	6	10	12	14	16
3	0	3	6	11	14	17	22	25
4	0	4	10	14	20	24	30	34
5	0	5	12	17	24	31	36	43
6	0	6	14	22	30	36	44	52
7	0	7	16	25	34	43	52	61

Examples of octal arithmetic are:

```
  674034510              4563
+ 345620075           ×   42
 1241654605            11346
                       22714
                      240506
```

Conversions between Systems

Table 4.4 compares the decimal, octal, and binary systems. The first thirty-six integers in each system are tabulated. The first seven entries in the octal and binary columns are of special interest because they indicate the conversion of octal digits to binary numbers. Using these entries the conversion of any octal number to its binary equivalent is easily done. Consider again the num-

TABLE 4.4 COMPARISON OF INTEGERS

Decimal Numbers	Octal Numbers	Binary Numbers
0	0	0
1	1	1
2	2	10
3	3	11
4	4	100
5	5	101
6	6	110
7	7	111
8	10	1000
9	11	1001
10	12	1010
11	13	1011
12	14	1100
13	15	1101
14	16	1110
15	17	1111
16	20	10000
17	21	10001
18	22	10010
19	23	10011
20	24	10100
21	25	10101
22	26	10110
23	27	10111
24	30	11000
25	31	11001
26	32	11010
27	33	11011
28	34	11100
29	35	11101
30	36	11110
31	37	11111
32	40	100000
33	41	100001
34	42	100010
35	43	100011
. . .	. . .	. . .

ber 5406.7_8. It may be written as follows, using small binary numbers as coefficients:

$$101_2 \times 8^3 + 100_2 \times 8^2 + 000_2 \times 8^1 + 110_2 \times 8^0 + 111_2 \times 8^{-1}$$

Making the substitution $8 = 2^3$, we obtain

$$101_2 \times 2^9 + 100_2 \times 2^6 + 000_2 \times 2^3 + 110_2 \times 2^0 + 111_2 \times 2^{-3}$$

But this number can be written as the following binary number:

$$101\ 100\ 000\ 110.111$$

Clearly this could have been obtained directly by a simple substitution of a three-bit number for each octal number, using the equivalences in the first seven rows of Table 4.4. Other octal-binary equivalences appear in subsequent rows; the use of the conversion rule we have given can be observed in these rows.

Because binary numbers, as stored in computers, are lengthy and clumsy to read, they are usually written in their octal equivalents. For example, consider the number

$$100010110010001111000101111010100011$$

Its octal equivalent is easier to read and write:

$$426217057243$$

Generally we shall use the octal equivalent of all binary numbers.

The conversion of a number in one system to its form in another is most readily accomplished as follows. Suppose an integer N must be expressed in terms of a new radix r, given in another system. The integer can be written

$$N = a_n r^n + a_{n-1} r^{n-1} + \cdots + a_2 r^2 + a_1 r + a_0$$

The digits a_i must be determined in the desired form of N. Dividing through by r yields the quotient q and remainder s:

$$q = \frac{N}{r} = a_n r^{n-1} + a_{n-1} r^{n-2} + \cdots + a_2 r + a_1$$

$$s = a_0$$

This remainder a_0 is the first digit to the left of the radix point in the desired system. Dividing again by r yields a remainder of a_1, the second digit. Successive division yields all the digits of the number N expressed in the radix-r system.

As an example consider the conversion of 5501 to the octal system. Arithmetic is carried out in the decimal system.

$$
\begin{array}{ccccc}
\begin{array}{r} 687 \\ \overline{8)5501} \\ 48 \\ \overline{70} \\ 64 \\ \overline{61} \\ 56 \\ \overline{5} \end{array}
&
\begin{array}{r} 85 \\ \overline{8)687} \\ 64 \\ \overline{47} \\ 40 \\ \overline{7} \end{array}
&
\begin{array}{r} 10 \\ \overline{8)85} \\ 8 \\ \overline{5} \\ 0 \\ \overline{5} \end{array}
&
\begin{array}{r} 1 \\ \overline{8)10} \\ 8 \\ \overline{2} \end{array}
&
\begin{array}{r} 0 \\ \overline{8)1} \\ 0 \\ \overline{1} \end{array}
\end{array}
$$

Writing the remainders in the reverse order yields the number: 12575_8.
    Convert the number 103 to the binary system.

51	25	12	6	3	1	0
2)$\overline{103}$	2)$\overline{51}$	2)$\overline{25}$	2)$\overline{12}$	2)$\overline{6}$	2)$\overline{3}$	2)$\overline{1}$
10	2	2	12	6	2	0
3	11	5	0	0	1	1
2	10	4				
1	1	1				

The number in binary form is 1100111_2. Division by 2 can be carried out mentally, so that decimal-binary conversion is simple.
    Conversion to the decimal system requires arithmetic to be done in the system of the original number, if this division method is used. Since it is clumsy to do arithmetic in the octal and binary systems, a more convenient approach is to use the multiplication method embodied in the positional notation of numbers. In the latter approach, arithmetic is decimal throughout. Consider reconversion of 12575_8:

$$1 \times 8^4 + 2 \times 8^3 + 5 \times 8^2 + 7 \times 8^1 + 5 \times 8^0$$
$$4096 + 1024 + 320 + 56 + 5 = 5501$$

Conversion from binary to decimal is performed in a similar manner.

    The conversion of a fraction less than 1 is considered next. Let it be required that the fraction be written in this form, where r is the new radix:

$$F = a_{-1}r^{-1} + a_{-2}r^{-2} + \cdots + a_{-m+1}r^{-m+1} + a_{-m}r^{-m}$$

Now we must multiply through by r repeatedly to determine the digits a_i in the fractional form desired.

$$rF = a_{-1} + a_{-2}r^{-1} + \cdots + a_{-m+1}r^{-m+2} + a_{-m}r^{-m+1}$$

The integral part of this number is a_{-1}, the first digit to the right of the radix point in the desired form. Multiplying by r again yields a_{-2}, the second digit. Successive multiplication thus yields all the a_i of the fraction F expressed in the radix-r system.
    The next example shows a conversion of the fraction 0.789 to the octal system. To do this it is necessary to multiply successively by 8, carrying out arithmetic in the decimal system. At each step the digit to the left of the decimal point takes no part in following multiplications.

0.789	0.312	0.496	0.968	0.744	0.952	
8	8	8	8	8	8	$\cdots$
6.312	2.496	3.968	7.744	5.952	7.616	

The fraction is $0.623757\cdots_8$. Fractions expressable as terminating decimal fractions are not necessarily terminating in other systems.

Convert the fraction 0.1 to the binary system.

0.1	0.2	0.4	0.8	0.6	0.2	0.4	0.8	
2	2	2	2	2	2	2	2	$\cdots$
0.2	0.4	0.8	1.6	1.2	0.4	0.8	1.6	

The fraction is $0.000110011\cdots_2$, a repeating fraction in the binary system.

If a mixed fraction is to be converted, the integral and fractional portions should be converted separately and added. For example,

$$5501.789 = 5501 + .789$$
$$= 12575_8 + .623757\cdots_8$$
$$= 12575.623757\cdots_8$$

4.2 ARITHMETIC OPERATIONS

Modulo Arithmetic

There are many physical systems in which integers are used as designators. Some of these require only a finite set of integers used repeatedly in a cyclic manner. The hour designation on a clock is an example. Hours are indicated by the integers 1, 2, 3, . . . , 11, and 12. After 12, the set repeats.

In such a closed system of integers, the number of distinct integers is called the *modulus*.* In the clock system the modulus is 12. Two integers are said to be *congruent* with respect to a modulus k if their difference is a multiple of k. Thus, 8 and 32 are congruent with respect to the modulus 12, since their difference (24) is a multiple of 12. This fact is written

$$8 \equiv 32 \ (\text{mod } 12)$$

In a k-modulus system of integers all numbers are expressed as integers less than or equal to the modulus. Numbers are reduced by successive subtractions of the modulus until one of the integers in the set is attained. Thus, the hour 103 hours from midnight is considered to be the hour 5 (that is, 5 o'clock), since

$$103 - 8(12) = 5$$

Sometimes it is more convenient to replace the integer equal to the modulus itself by zero. In the clock system, this would mean that 0 replaces 12.

Modulo arithmetic is arithmetic performed in a closed set of integers of the type described. All the results of arithmetic operations are reduced to congruent numbers in the set of k integers. Some examples of modulo arithmetic in the 12-modulus system are

---

* These concepts apply equally well to numbers that are not integers. However, we restrict ourselves to integers here.

$$9 + 6 + 12 + 7 = 34 \equiv 10$$
$$8 - 10 = -2 \equiv 10$$
$$9 \times 9 = 81 \equiv 9$$

Addressing within a computer memory usually employs modulo arithmetic. If, for example, a memory has 10,000 locations addressed from 0000 to 9999, the following arithmetic applies:

$$4291 + 8431 \equiv 2722$$
$$6944 - 7725 \equiv 9219$$

In words, we might say, "the address 8431 locations beyond location 4291 is 2722" and "the address 7725 locations before location 6944 is 9219." In other words, memory can be considered as a closed cyclic system, just like time on a clock. There is one slight difference; 0000 is used as an address, whereas 0:00 is not used as a time. The location "following" location 9999 is location 0000.

Scaling

The range of numbers that can be stored in each memory word of a fixed-word-length computer is limited because the number of stored digits is limited. Consider a computer capable of storing signed 10-decimal-digit numbers, one to a word. (We use the decimal system for illustration because of its familiarity.) Although 10 significant digits can then be stored for each number, the implied accuracy is deceiving. In one problem, for example, the numbers 0.0000345, 67.8, and 7895671 may all be present. We may place the decimal point anywhere within a memory word, but regardless of its position, the three numbers cannot all be stored with full accuracy.

To process these numbers correctly the decimal points must be aligned, as in manual arithmetic:

$$0.0000345$$
$$67.8$$
$$7895671.$$

Fourteen places for decimal digits are required to hold all three numbers in the manner shown. The difficulty can be bypassed by *scaling,* that is, by applying a *scale factor,* a power of 10, to each number:

$$0.0000000345 \times 10^3$$
$$0.0000000678 \times 10^9$$
$$0.0007895671 \times 10^{10}$$

In this form the decimal points are aligned but 10 places are sufficient for all the numbers. It is necessary, however, to provide for storage of the power of 10. Since the base of the exponent is always 10, that information need not be stored.

More commonly, numbers are stored in *normalized* form, with fractions having a nonzero digit immediately to the right of the point:

$$0.3450000000 \times 10^{-4}$$
$$0.6780000000 \times 10^{2}$$
$$0.7895671000 \times 10^{7}$$

As an example of a more complex scaling analysis, consider this problem:

$$S = \frac{2.41 + 36.1}{0.763 \times 2.44}$$

If these numbers are all to be stored in memory in normalized form, each one must be scaled by an appropriate scale factor. If the result is to be interpreted correctly, it is also necessary to determine the scale factor that applies to it. The value of S is 20.7 (to three digits), but the answer will not appear in this form.

Scaling a complicated expression can be very tedious. The ranges of all the numbers involved must be known fairly accurately if all intermediate and final calculations are to produce numbers in the proper range. Unless precautions are taken to store products in two words when necessary, some digits can be lost. For example, in this product

$$.0000034500 \times .0067800000 = .0000000233|9100000000$$

the digits 9 and 1 would be lost if only 10 digits were retained. Although all numbers may be initially normalized by scaling, the results of calculations are not necessarily normalized.

If rescaling is done during the calculations, it is possible to minimize the loss of significant digits. Most modern computers are built to provide rescaling automatically during computation. For this purpose numbers may be stored in a special format, similar to the normalized form described.

Floating-Point Arithmetic

A *floating-point number* contains two parts: the digits of a number and the exponent of the number. Assuming once more that a computer word contains 10 decimal digits, let us allow 8 digits for the fraction and 2 digits for the exponent. If the number can be represented as

$$0.xxxxxxxx \times 10^{yy}$$

then the computer word can be structured as follows:

$$zzxxxxxxxx$$

The number zz is equal to 50 more than the number yy; it is referred to as the *characteristic* of the number. By adding this constant to all exponents, the two digits can represent the range -50 to $+49$, and a sign for the exponent need not be stored. The actual number (zz) lies in the range 00 to 99. Note that the symbols 0, ., $\times$, and 10 of the original form of the number are extraneous and excluded from the computer word. If the leftmost x digit is nonzero, the number is in *normalized* floating-point form. Examples of such numbers are:

Usual Notation	Normalized Floating-Point Form
$+ 1$	$+5110000000$
$- 67852.1$	-5567852100
$- 0.00078911$	-4778911000
$- 6.78 \times 10^{-13}$	-3867800000

In a computer that performs floating-point arithmetic, all numbers in memory are treated as normalized floating-point numbers, and the results of each operation are normalized.* Rescaling is thus done automatically at each step and digits are not lost by the presence of leading zeros. Note that fewer significant digits can be stored in a word than when integers (fixed-point numbers) are used. The gain in ease of programming, however, far outweighs this loss of significance. Some modern large-scale computers have 48- or 60-bit words. The former can hold more than 10 decimal digits and a characteristic.

Following are some examples of floating-point arithmetic. In addition and subtraction it is necessary to modify the form of the numbers so that exponents (or characteristics) are equal. This can be accomplished by shifting the digits left or right (keeping the decimal point fixed) an amount equal to the required change in the exponent. For example, a shift left two places multiplies the number by 10^2; this must be accompanied by a decrease of 2 in the exponent.

1. *Addition*

$$
\begin{array}{lcl}
.43560000 \times 10^{-4} & & .00435600 \times 10^{-2} \\
.53160000 \times 10^{-3} & \rightarrow & .05316000 \times 10^{-2} \\
\underline{.96431000 \times 10^{-2}} & & \underline{.96431000 \times 10^{-2}} \\
& & 1.02182600 \times 10^{-2}
\end{array}
$$

The answer, normalized and rounded to four digits, is $.1022 \times 10^{-1}$.

2. *Subtraction*

$$
\begin{array}{lcl}
.46373900 \times 10^{6} & & .46373900 \times 10^{6} \\
\underline{-.16436100 \times 10^{3}} & \rightarrow & \underline{-.00016436 \times 10^{6}} \\
& & .46357464 \times 10^{6}
\end{array}
$$

3. *Subtraction*

$$
\begin{array}{l}
.38764000 \times 10^{7} \\
\underline{-.38512000 \times 10^{7}} \\
.00252000 \times 10^{7}
\end{array}
$$

---

* In some computers unnormalized results can be produced optionally.

The answer, normalized, is $.25200000 \times 10^5$.

4. *Multiplication*

$$
\begin{array}{r}
.23410000 \times 10^8 \\
\times .13070000 \times 10^{-6} \\
\hline
.03059687 \times 10^2
\end{array}
$$

The answer, normalized, is $.30596870 \times 10^1$.

Since many digital computers are binary in word structure, floating-point representation in binary format should be examined. A 36-bit binary word (with 1 bit used for the sign) holds slightly more information than a 10-decimal-digit word with a sign. Of the 35 bits used to hold the number, 8 are used for the characteristic and 27 are used for the fraction.* With 8 bits, integers from 0 to 255 can be stored. A characteristic is formed from an exponent by adding 128, so that exponents from -128 to $+127$ can be represented. In a binary number, the exponent refers to a base of 2, so that scale factors range from 2^{-128} to 2^{127}, or approximately 10^{-38} to 10^{38}. A normalized floating-point number is one having a 1 in the leftmost bit of the fraction.

Examples of the conversion of decimal numbers to normalized floating-point binary numbers follow.

Convert the number 1.0:

> Binary form: 1.0
> Normalized binary form: $.1 \times 2^1$
> Normalized octal form (fraction only): .4
> Characteristic: $128 + 1 = 129 = 201_8$
> Number in memory (in octal): 201400000000

Convert the number 3697:

> Binary form: 111001110011
> Normalized binary form: $.111001110011 \times 2^{12}$
> Normalized octal form (fraction): .7163
> Characteristic: $128 + 12 = 140 = 214_8$
> Number in memory (in octal): 214716300000

The reverse, conversion from floating-point binary to decimal form, is accomplished by performing these steps in reverse order.

These conversion processes are not automatic on most computers; a few computers have instructions for this purpose. A conversion program is usually necessary, since data are usually presented to a computer in decimal form. One is also needed at the output so that numbers can be printed in readily readable form.

---

* This is the form of the IBM 7090 computer floating-point number.

In performing the floating-point operations in the four examples we gave, it was necessary to (1) shift numbers for addition and subtraction, (2) normalize the result, and (3) round the result (drop insignificant digits). A computer does the first two of these things automatically, but it does not necessarily drop all insignificant digits. All the digit positions of the fractional part of a floating-point number word are used. Even if some of the digits are insignificant, they will not be dropped. It is the responsibility of the programmer to interpret final results correctly.

The situation present in example 3 is one that the programmer usually cannot be aware of in a particular subtraction. It arises when two numbers that are nearly equal are subtracted. Here the difference has only 3 significant digits, whereas the minuend and subtrahend have 5 each. Unfortunately there is no simple way to detect this situation.

Erroneous calculations may result because of the finite size of fixed-word-length computers. Since the number of stored significant digits is finite, there may be a *roundoff* error. As calculations proceed, errors can accumulate to the point of invalidating results. The problem is further considered in Section 13.3.

Summary

The binary system is widely used in computer word structure. Operations in the binary system are performed in the same manner as in the decimal system. Because the binary arithmetic rules are simpler, the circuits used to perform arithmetic are also simpler. Binary numbers require, however, both manual and computer effort for the conversion process from decimal form.

Within a computer memory, numbers are stored and operated on in formats that differ from common usage. Floating-point numbers are used because of their flexible structure; a wide range of numbers can be stored and processed. Scaling is done automatically and at every step by floating-point computer operations. Because word size is finite in most computers, roundoff errors may accumulate and invalidate results. Care must be taken both in noting such errors and in interpreting answers. Insignificant digits, not so identified by the computer, must be dropped.

Notes

1. The topic of binary arithmetic operations is examined in great detail in

R. K. Richards, *Arithmetic Operations in Digital Computers,* Van Nostrand, 1955, Chapters 4 and 5.

Descriptions of computer circuits used to realize binary operations are also given.

PROBLEMS

Section 4.1

4.1. Perform the following arithmetic in the octal system.

(a)   340776   (b)   3204.1304   (c)   32147501
       +224114   +2277.6062   −14320642

(d)   3200.1765   (e)   220.10   (f)   .002276
       −3330.0224   × 55.22   ×   57.04

(g) 34012 ÷ 2201 (to 3 octal places)

(h) 22.135 ÷ .00243 (to 5 significant figures)

4.2. Perform the following arithmetic in the binary system.

(a)   110101110.10   (b)   1010111.10001   (c)   1011011   (d)   11.001101
       +100100101.11   −1111000.01101   × 110110   ×   11.11

(e) 1100.1101 ÷ 110.111 (to 3 binary places)

(f) .0100011 ÷ 1.10011 (to 5 significant figures)

4.3. Convert the following decimal numbers to octal form and binary form.

(a) 34522   (b) 880132   (c) 231.678   (d) 2278.002342

4.4. Convert the following binary numbers to decimal form.

(a) 110101   (b)110010101.101   (c) 1010101110101.0001101

Section 4.2

4.5. Perform the indicated arithmetic with respect to the indicated moduli.

(a) 24 + 36 (mod 40)   (b) 12 + 8 + 14 − 10 (mod 20)

(c) 6 × 8 (mod 10)   (d) 14 × 12 × 4 (mod 19)

4.6. Write the following numbers in normalized form, using the structure in the text consisting of an 8-digit decimal fraction and a 2-digit power of 10.

(a) 0.000222   (b) 2417.0 × 10^{−6}   (c) 435.8967 × 10^4

4.7. Write the following numbers in the normalized floating-point format described in the text for 36-bit binary computers.

(a) 4   (b) 0.004   (c) 3.14 × 10^3   (d) 0.413 × 10^{−2}   (e) 367.2222

PART TWO

CODING FUNDAMENTALS

IF A COMPUTER is to solve a problem, the problem must be coded in a language that is suitable for use on that computer. The language may be specifically designed for the computer, or it may be more general, so that it can be used on a number of computers. These two basically different types of computer languages were discussed in Chapter 3.

In Part II a hypothetical computer is introduced. In order that it can be coded, a specific language is introduced for it. If coding is to be learned and understood, it is desirable that a specific language be used for examples and for problems. The fundamental aspects of coding are introduced here. Once these are learned, any simple problem can be coded and solved. The topics covered are the set of instructions on the hypothetical computer, a symbolic coding language, program loops, automatic indexing using index registers, realizing decision points of a flowchart, the use of programs for specific purposes, and input-output operations. All these topics were introduced in general terms in Part I; now, through the medium of the machine-coding language, they are studied in more detail and more specifically.

5

BASIC OPERATIONS

We have seen that computer instructions can be classified into five types, two of which are *arithmetic* and *decision* instructions. If the flowcharts of Chapter 2 are examined, it appears that these two types of instruction suffice for all simple problems. Indeed, this is the case if we also add data-moving instructions (which have no place in problem flowcharts). Input-output instructions are necessary of course, if information is to be inserted in and removed from memory. Indexing instructions make the coding and program execution efforts less involved.

With this chapter we begin our study of instructions. The term *basic* refers here to the two classes of instructions listed above (supplemented by data-moving instructions), since these instructions comprise the simplest set of computer operations. They are basic to many programs, and serve as an introduction to coding. We consider programs that illustrate the use of these instructions.

A hypothetical computer is introduced to provide a means for the illustration of coding techniques. Some of its characteristics and instructions are introduced here; others are introduced in later chapters.

5.1 THE HYPOTHETICAL COMPUTER

The techniques of coding are best learned (1) by studying a number of examples of computer programs written to solve specific problems and (2) by coding other problems. A coding language must be available so that the examples can be written.   In this book the hypothetical DELTA 63 computer is described, and a coding language suitable for it is introduced.   In this chapter machine language coding is used to provide the reader with an understanding of the language in which the computer executes its programs.   In later chapters symbolic coding is used.   A few of the characteristics and instructions of the 63 are introduced here; many other features are described in later chapters as they are needed.

A description of the DELTA 63 as it concerns the programmer is given first; then come explanations of some of its instructions.   The 63 is typical of most large-scale digital computers; many of its characteristics are the same as those of other machines.   Therefore, in addition to studying this machine, we are in effect studying many.   This computer was chosen to be of the one-address type, since that is the most common type of computer.   It was chosen to be a binary machine because many concepts in coding are more easily illustrated in a binary system.

General Structure*

The DELTA 63 is a binary machine having a memory of 32768 (2^{15}) 36-bit words. These words are addressable either in decimal form (00000 to 32767) or octal form (00000 to 77777); the latter method is more useful, and we shall use it exclusively.   Bits in memory words are labeled S, 1, 2, . . . , 35.   The S-bit holds the sign, so that a signed 35-bit number can be stored in each word.   A positive sign is stored as 0.†

Magnetic tape units are connected to the 63 for input-output purposes.   Information may be read from tape or punched cards and may be written on tape, punched on cards, or printed on paper.   Off-line equipment permits information to be read from cards to tape and from tape to punched cards or paper.

Each instruction is placed in one 36-bit word in memory, the format of which is shown in Fig. 5.1.   Bits 3–8 are used for the operation code, a 6-bit number representing the operation of the instruction.   Bits 21–35 comprise the address field, and they are employed to hold the operand address of the instruction.   The other bits have functions that will be described in later chapters.

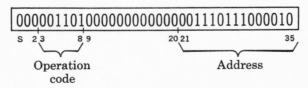

Fig. 5.1.   Format of DELTA 63 instruction word.

---

* As mentioned in the preface, the small type is used to describe and illustrate the DELTA 63. Any information in full-sized type can be assumed to be of a general nature, applicable to most computers, unless otherwise identified.

† The memory capacity and word size described here are the same as those in the IBM 704–709–7090 series of computers.

The octal representation of the instruction in Fig. 5.1 is 015000016702. The operation code is 15_8, and the operand address is 16702_8.

Integers and fixed-point numbers each may occupy up to 35 bits, filling bits 1–35; the S-bit is used for the sign. Floating-point numbers each also occupy one word; one number is pictured in Fig. 5.2. Bits 1–8 hold the characteristic, and bits 9–35 hold the fraction. The binary point is assumed to be immediately to the left of the fraction. Numbers are stored exactly as described in Section 4.2 on floating-point arithmetic (page 78). The octal form of the number in Fig. 5.2 is -20622050400, which is the number -18.07904.*

The *accumulator register* (AC) has 36 bits and is used for addition and subtraction, sums and differences being accumulated there. Its contents may be tested for certain conditions, and jumps then occur if these conditions are met. The *multiply register* (MR) is an adjunct to the AC. It also has 36 bits and is used with the AC for multiplication and division. Then the two registers sometimes act as a single 72-bit register.

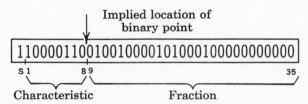

Fig. 5.2. Format of DELTA 63 floating-point number.

5.2 BASIC ARITHMETIC OPERATIONS

Addition and Subtraction

The main emphasis in the problems that have thus far been considered has been on arithmetic. The operations in arithmetic are familiar, so they readily provide a starting point for the study of coding. Instructions to perform addition and subtraction are described next. Other instructions are required in arithmetic programs. A flowchart of an arithmetic problem includes little, if anything, about the job of moving data between memory and the arithmetic unit. Nevertheless this process is essential in a computer, and coding must take it into account. Therefore data-moving instructions are also described. Finally, an instruction to stop the computer is required.

In all instruction descriptions, the following sequence of information is given: the instruction name in full, an abbreviated form for the instruction, the numerical operation code, and the description. The Y that is mentioned in the description refers to a memory

* The "octal" number here is not precisely octal, since the leftmost "2" is quartal, representing two bits (1 and 2). It is customary, however, not to include the sign in the leftmost digit, for the sake of clarity. As a true octal number, the form is 406220504000.

word and represents the operand address. All registers affected by the instruction are mentioned.

LOAD ACCUMULATOR (LOAD Y) (01). The C(Y) replaces the C(AC). The C(Y) is unchanged.

STORE ACCUMULATOR (STORE Y) (02). The C(AC) replaces the C(Y). The C(AC) is unchanged.

ADD (ADD Y) (04). The C(Y) is added algebraically to the C(AC), and the sum is placed in the AC. The C(Y) is unchanged.

SUBTRACT (SUBT Y) (05). The C(Y) is subtracted algebraically from the C(AC), and the difference is placed in the AC. The C(Y) is unchanged.

HALT (HALT) (00). The computer stops on executing this instruction.

As the result of an addition or subtraction, if the C(AC) is zero, the sign of the AC is unchanged. Thus if the C(AC) = −60 and the C(Y) = +60, then after the addition of the C(Y) the C(AC) = −0. This is a common convention on computers.

The means are now available for coding simple arithmetic problems; two examples follow. Before these are studied, however, comments on these and future programs are appropriate.

In the examples, problems are stated, analyzed, and coded; they are accompanied by flowcharts where appropriate. In some programs location addresses and word contents are given numerically; the form is always octal, written without an 8 subscript. Addresses are frequently referred to as 5-digit octal numbers: 00500. In the lists of the contents of instruction words, spaces are left around the fields of instructions for clarity, as in

$$\text{0 04 0000 00676}$$

The 04 and 00676 fields contain the operation code and operand address.

Programmers structure their programs in various ways. In these examples instructions are placed first and are followed by data, constants, and space for results. The indicated starting addresses of the several portions of a program are not significant (since these examples are not being placed in a computer for execution).

Example 5.1   Find the sum of 56, −45, 23, and −39. These numbers are located in sequence, beginning at location 00300. Place the sum in location 00304.

Since addition is performed in the AC, the first number must be loaded into the AC, and all other numbers must then be added to the first. Finally, the sum must be stored in 00304. The program is written to begin at location 00100 and end at location 00105. Location 00304 is set aside for the sum.*

Location	Contents	Remarks
00100	0 01 0000 00300	LØAD 56 INTØ AC
00101	0 04 0000 00301	ADD −45 TØ AC, YIELDING 11

(Continued)

---

* Some computer printers use the symbol Ø for the letter O and the symbol O for zero. These symbols are used in this way here. Printers do not have small letters available; they can supply only capital letters, digits, and some punctuation marks.

```
00102      0  04  0000  00302     ADD 23, YIELDING 34
00103      0  04  0000  00303     ADD -39, YIELDING -5
00104      0  02  0000  00304     STØRE SUM IN 00304
00105      0  00  0000  00000     HALT

00300      +000000000070          56        (NUMBERS APPEAR
00301      -000000000055          -45         IN ØCTAL AT LEFT)
00302      +000000000027          23
00303      -000000000047          -39
00304      +000000000000          FØR  SUM
```

Two points mentioned in Section 3.1 should be reiterated here. (1) If the contents of a word or register is moved to another location, the original contents is unaffected. (2) If a quantity is stored in a word or register, the old contents is destroyed. Therefore after the completion of the program in Example 5.1 the four original numbers are still located in locations 00300 to 00303, and 00304 contains the sum, -5.

Example 5.2   Find the value of m, where

$$m = a + b - c + d$$

The quantities a, b, c, and d are stored in sequence, starting at location 00675. Place the sum in location 00674.

The structure of this program is similar to the one in Example 5.1, except that one quantity (c) is subtracted from the C(AC). The program is written to start at location 00020. Location 00674 is set aside for the sum.

Location	Contents	Remarks
00020	0 01 0000 00675	LØAD A INTØ AC
00021	0 04 0000 00676	ADD B, FØRMING A + B
00022	0 05 0000 00677	SUBTRACT C, FØRMING A + B - C
00023	0 04 0000 00700	ADD D ... A + B - C + D
00024	0 02 0000 00674	STØRE SUM
00025	0 00 0000 00000	HALT
00674	+000000000000	FØR RESULT
00675	+XXXXXXXXXXXX	A
00676	+XXXXXXXXXXXX	B
00677	+XXXXXXXXXXXX	C
00700	+XXXXXXXXXXXX	D

The contents of the four words containing a, b, c, and d are shown as X's with plus signs. The X's stand for any digits, and the signs may be negative.

When summation is performed it is possible for the accumulator to overflow. This happens when the sum exceeds the capacity of the accumulator. Many computers have an *overflow indicator* which is turned on in that event and instructions that can test the status of the indicator. In these programs we assume that overflow never occurs.

These two examples and their programs differ in one important respect. The first program sums four specific numbers, whereas the second evaluates a formula for any set of values for the four quantities a, b, c, and d. The second program is therefore more general, just as the problem stated in Example 5.2 is more general. Nothing has been said about the manner in which the numbers of the problems are placed in memory. If the second program is indeed to be general, it must be possible to load *any* four numbers into locations 00675 through 00700, provided the word capacities are not exceeded. This problem is one of input-output and is dealt with in Chapters 7 and 11.

Multiplication and Division

The arithmetic operations of multiplication and division are considered next. After descriptions of instructions for these and related operations are given, three simple problems in arithmetic are coded.

MULTIPLY (MULT Y) (06). The C(Y) is multiplied algebraically by the C(AC), and the product is placed in the AC and the multiply register (MR). The less significant half of the product is placed in the AC, and the more significant half is placed in the MR. The sign of the product is placed in the signs of both registers.*

To illustrate the multiplication process, let us assume that the AC, the MR, and location Y have 4 bits and a sign for simplicity. Let

$$C(AC) = -1011_2$$
$$C(Y) = +0111_2$$

The product of these numbers is -01001101; it appears in the AC and MR as follows:

$$MR: -0100_2 \qquad AC: -1101_2$$

Note that if the product is small enough (4 bits here, or 35 bits in the case of the true accumulator), all significant bits are located in the AC.

DIVIDE (DIV Y) (07). The C(AC) is divided algebraically by the C(Y), and the quotient is placed in the AC. The remainder is placed in the MR.

To illustrate the division process, assume again that registers and words have 4 bits and a sign each. Let the AC contain the number -15 (-17_8); the C(MR) is irrelevant. Let the C(Y) = 4. The quotient is -3, and the remainder is 3. The answer appears as

$$MR: +0011 \qquad AC: -0011$$

Instructions to load and store the multiply register are required to perform these operations.

LOAD MULTIPLY REGISTER (LOADM Y) (10). The C(Y) replaces the C(MR). The C(Y) is unchanged.

---

* The MR corresponds to the M-, Q-, and MQ-registers mentioned in Section 3.1. In some computers this register holds the less significant half of the product; in others, it holds the more significant half. The term *multiply register* is used in this book both to refer to the DELTA 63 register and in a general sense to refer to the equivalent register on a computer. The usage will be clear by context.

STORE MULTIPLY REGISTER (STOREM Y) (11). The C(MR) replaces the
C(Y). The C(MR) is unchanged.

In the next example the problem of what to do with decimal points presents
itself. Generally, if the numbers in a problem are not integers, floating-point
arithmetic is used. Floating-point instructions, described in Chapter 13, are
available for this purpose. Programs so written are similar to those discussed
here, except for the use of floating-point operations. For the present we use the
fixed-point arithmetic instructions already described; the principles are the same
either way. Sometimes in the use of fixed-point arithmetic it is necessary to
scale the numbers so that all significant digits are retained. Implicitly, the
decimal point is regarded as lying at the extreme right of a fixed-point number,
unless scaling has occurred.

Special attention must be paid to fixed-point division, because the remainder
may be discarded. If, for example, 50 is divided by 4 and both numbers appear
in memory words at the right (the usual situation), the quotient will be 12. If
all significant digits are required, it is necessary to scale the dividend. This may
be done, for example, by multiplying by a power of 10 or 2; the latter is preferable in a binary machine.

Example 5.3   Determine the value of the expression

$$f = (a + b)(c + d)/ac$$

The quantities a, b, c, and d, having the values 1.5, -3.5, 12.1, and 14, respectively, are
stored in sequence, starting at location 01000. Place the value of f in location 00777. Scale
all numbers upward by a factor of 10.

The numbers in this problem are small enough so that the AC alone suffices for all calculations; the MR is not needed. It is necessary here to store an intermediate result, the
quantity $(a + b)$, temporarily. This is stored in the location set aside for the value of f,
location 00777.

(In this listing of the program, the C(AC) is shown with each instruction; the contents
after execution is given.)

Location	Contents	C(AC)	Remarks
00100	0 01 0000 01000	+000000000017	LØAD A
00101	0 04 0000 01001	−000000000024	ADD B ... A + B
00102	0 02 0000 00777	−000000000024	STØRE TEMPØRARILY
00103	0 01 0000 01002	+000000000171	LØAD C
00104	0 04 0000 01003	+000000000405	ADD D ... C + D
00105	0 06 0000 00777	−000000012144	MULT ... (A + B)(C + D)
00106	0 07 0000 01000	−000000000534	DIVIDE BY A
00107	0 07 0000 01002	−000000000002	DIVIDE BY C
00110	0 02 0000 00777	−000000000002	STØRE F
00111	0 00 0000 00000	−000000000002	HALT
00777	+000000000000	FØR RESULT (F)	
01000	+000000000017	A	(NUMBERS HERE ARE
01001	−000000000043	B	SCALED UP BY 10)
01002	+000000000171	C	
01003	+000000000214	D	

After the multiplication operation, the $C(AC) = 12144_8$ (5220). Division by 17_8 (15) gives 534_8 (348) with no remainder. Division of this number by 171_8 (121) gives 2 with a remainder of 106_8 (70). The value of f that is stored is 2; a more accurate value is 2.9, but the 9 digit is lost unless precautions are taken. Scaling all four original quantities does not improve accuracy, as examination of the expression for f reveals. To avoid the loss of accuracy in division, it is necessary to scale the dividend up, leaving the divisor alone. This problem is characteristic of fixed-point division in any computer and provides a good argument for floating-point arithmetic.

Example 5.4   Evaluate p^4; $p = -13$ and is stored in location 00160. Place the answer in the AC.

Location	Contents	C(AC)	Remarks
00200	0 01 0000 00160	−000000000015	LØAD P
00201	0 06 0000 00160	+000000000251	MULT ... P−SQUARE
00202	0 06 0000 00160	−000000004225	MULT ... P−CUBE
00203	0 06 0000 00160	+000000067621	MULT ... P−FØURTH
00204	0 00 0000 00000	+000000067621	MULT ... ANS. IN AC
00160	−000000000015	P	

Example 5.5   Evaluate the polynomial

$$F = 8x^5 + 4x^3 - x^2$$

x is stored in location 01000; F is to be left in the AC.

If the program is written in the manner of earlier programs—evaluating each term separately and then storing it temporarily—sixteen instructions are required. If we note, however, that terms have common factors, some coding (and program execution time) can be saved. For example, all three terms share the factor x^2. The function may be regrouped as follows:

$$F = x^2[x(4 + 8x^2) - 1]$$

The program can be written by starting within the inner parentheses and performing all operations in sequence, ending the program outside the brackets. The program follows.*

Location	Contents	Remarks
00100	0 01 0000 01000	LØAD X
00101	0 06 0000 01000	MULTIPLY BY X ... X(2
00102	0 06 0000 00201	MULTIPLY BY 8 ... 8X(2
00103	0 04 0000 00200	ADD 4 ... 4 + 8X(2
00104	0 06 0000 01000	MULTIPLY BY X
00105	0 05 0000 00202	SUBTRACT 1
00106	0 06 0000 01000	MULTIPLY BY X
00107	0 06 0000 01000	MULTIPLY BY X
00110	0 00 0000 00000	HALT

(Continued)

---

* Because of computer printer restrictions, the form X(2 is used to represent x^2 in the "remarks" column.

```
      00200      +000000000004            4
      00201      +000000000010            8
      00202      +000000000001            1

      01000      +XXXXXXXXXXXX            X
```

In all the problems examined we have assumed that all the numbers were small enough so that no calculations put significant bits into the MR at the left. In general, of course, allowance must be made for "overflow" into the MR. If this is not done and significant bits are placed in the MR, they will be lost and an error will result. The problem is not pursued here because the use of floating-point instructions obviates any concern over it.

Division may also cause difficulties. Since an attempted division by zero can lead to trouble, computers generally have a division-checking procedure to test the divisor. If the divisor is zero, some appropriate action occurs. We assume that the situation does not arise.

Analysis for Coding

The need for problem analysis was emphasized in Chapter 2. In Example 5.5 an analysis of the structure of an expression resulted in a relatively short program. In general it is not possible to write a list of rules to obey in coding a variety of problems. Each class of problems, or perhaps each individual problem, must be analyzed by itself. In a formula evaluation, however, it can be noted that the number of instructions executed can be minimized if the number of operations indicated in the formula is minimized.

Computer programs are usually written for general rather than specific use. It is often more of a coding job to so write them, but the efforts are almost always justified. A more general program can be used in a larger number of situations, so that "usage per instruction coded" is larger. Let us re-analyze the polynomial-evaluation problem (Example 5.5) to confirm this concept.

The evaluation of

$$F = 8x^5 + 4x^3 - x^2$$

is obviously not of use to many people, whereas the evaluation of

$$G = ax^5 + bx^4 + cx^3 + dx^2 + ex + f$$

where $a, b, \ldots, f$ are real numbers, probably would be of wide interest. For this reason we now examine a method that is general and also yields a minimal number of operations.

The polynomial can be written

$$G = ([\{(ax + b)x + c\}x + d]x + e)x + f$$

There are only 10 operations here, and 11 instructions are required. Evaluating
G term by term requires 24 instructions.*

Example 5.6 Write a program to evaluate a general fifth-order polynomial, leaving the
result in the AC. The coefficients a, b, c, d, e, and f are located in sequence starting at
location 01000; x is in location 00700.

The coding for this problem follows directly from the last form for G given. The program starts within the inner parentheses and proceeds outward.

Location	Contents	Remarks
00100	0 01 0000 01000	LØAD A
00101	0 06 0000 00700	MULTIPLY ... AX
00102	0 04 0000 01001	ADD B ... AX + B
00103	0 06 0000 00700	MULTIPLY ... (AX + B)X
00104	0 04 0000 01002	ADD C ... (AX + B)X + C
00105	0 06 0000 00700	MULTIPLY
00106	0 04 0000 01003	ADD D
00107	0 06 0000 00700	MULTIPLY
00110	0 04 0000 01004	ADD E
00111	0 06 0000 00700	MULTIPLY
00112	0 04 0000 01005	ADD F, FØRMING G
00113	0 00 0000 00000	HALT
00700	+XXXXXXXXXXXX	X
01000	+XXXXXXXXXXXX	A
...	.....	..
01005	+XXXXXXXXXXXX	F

This general program is approximately as long as the program in Example
5.5, but this one, if supplied the values of the polynomial coefficients and the
value of x, will evaluate any fifth-order polynomial over a wide range of coefficient values. Another benefit of the approach given here is more subtle. The
program in the last example is easier to code because its coding is highly
repetitive. Since the program in Example 5.5 lacks this structure, it requires
more careful planning and more care for the avoidance of errors.

There are techniques available that reduce or eliminate the need for repetitive
coding in the same way that the use of loops eliminates the need for repetitive
analysis. In Chapter 7 the problem of the polynomial is coded using a program
loop.

---

* Although it does not concern us here, the time for execution of instructions should be considered if a serious attempt is made to avoid wasting execution time. Fixed-point multiplication takes about three to five times as long as fixed-point addition on a computer. The revised
form of the polynomial evaluation has a speed advantage also, because it has only five multiplication operations.

5.3 BASIC DECISION OPERATIONS

Jump Instructions

Decision instructions are exemplified by the *conditional jump* instructions. In their execution a stated condition is checked, and if it is met, control passes as indicated.   The accumulator is usually checked for the condition in question; the form of the instruction is "If the condition P is true of the accumulator, transfer control to location Q."   Another required instruction is the *unconditional jump* instruction, "Transfer control to Q (unconditionally)."

JUMP (JUMP Y) (20).   The computer takes its next instruction from location Y and proceeds in sequence from there.*

JUMP IF PLUS (JUMPPL Y) (21).   If the sign of the AC is positive, the computer takes its next instruction from location Y and proceeds from there.   If the sign is negative, the next instruction in sequence is taken.

JUMP IF MINUS (JUMPMI Y) (22).   If the sign of the AC is negative, the computer takes its next instruction from location Y and proceeds from there.   If the sign is positive, the next instruction in sequence is taken.

JUMP IF ZERO (JUMPZE Y) (23).   If the magnitude of the C(AC) is zero (regardless of sign), the computer takes its next instruction from location Y and proceeds from there.   If the magnitude of the C(AC) is nonzero, the next instruction in sequence is taken.

JUMP IF NONZERO (JUMPNZ Y) (24).   If the magnitude of the C(AC) is nonzero, the computer takes its next instruction from location Y and proceeds from there. If the magnitude of the C(AC) is zero, the next instruction in sequence is taken.

Some thought indicates that the four conditional jump instructions are not all necessary.   For example, if a jump to location 00500 is to occur if the C(AC) is minus and to continue in sequence otherwise, either of the following serves.

```
(1)
00400        0 22 0000 00500     JUMP IF AC IS MINUS

(2)
00400        0 21 0000 00402     JUMP TØ 00402 IF AC IS PLUS
00401        0 20 0000 00500     JUMP IF AC IS MINUS
```

Thus, the JUMPMI instruction is not required.   The JUMPNZ instruction can be eliminated similarly.   If these two (or two others) are eliminated, then the same conditional jumps can be accomplished, but the programs will be somewhat longer.

* The phrase "in sequence" in these descriptions means "in numerical sequence"; that is, the contents of the address register is increased by 1 successively—until another "jump" is encountered.

Symbolic Operations

The reader realizes by this time that coding is easier if the abbreviated instruction name is used rather than the numerical operation code. For example, JUMPPL is easier to remember and is more recognizable than 21. In all future coding examples, the abbreviation or *symbolic* form is used. Special coding languages were described and illustrated in Section 3.3. The usage of symbolic operations is the first step towards the use of one of these languages. The next step is described in Chapter 6.

The following technique is used in writing symbolic operations. The seven leftmost octal digits (bits S, 1–20) of the instructions are replaced by the symbolic form. Thus where formerly we wrote

$$0 \quad 01 \quad 0000 \quad 00742$$

now we write

$$\text{L\O AD} \quad 00742$$

The location address and operand address are still written as octal numbers.

Coding Some Decisions

We consider several examples that require jump instructions. First we turn again to the summation problem, programmed in Section 3.2, to borrow and restate an "instruction."

Example 5.7   Code the following operation: if $i \leqslant n$, continue at location 00150; if $i > n$, continue in sequence. The flowchart in Fig. 5.3a pictures this decision.

The two conditions can be rewritten as "if $i - n \leqslant 0$" and "if $i - n > 0$." Since a test against n is not available, this revision is necessary. Conditional jump instructions are used to check for the first condition, which is really two conditions as far as the computer is concerned: "if $i - n < 0$" or "if $i - n = 0$." If neither condition holds, the program continues in sequence. The flowchart in Fig. 5.3b pictures the revised decision.

Location	Contents		Remarks
00170	L\O AD	00500	L\O AD I, L\O CATED IN 00500
00171	SUBT	00501	F\O RM I – N ... N IS IN 00501
00172	JUMPMI	00150	JUMP IF (I – N) IS NEGATIVE
00173	JUMPZE	00150	JUMP IF (I – N) IS ZER\O

Control will go to 00174 if $i - n > 0$, as required.

In the next examples three-way and four-way decisions must be made. Since all jump instructions can make only two-way decisions, it is necessary to place jump instructions in sequence to accomplish these multiple decisions.

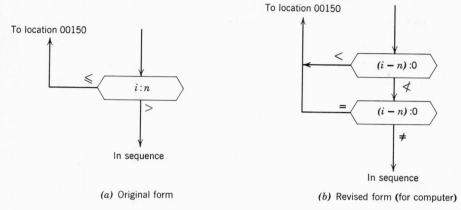

(a) Original form   (b) Revised form (for computer)

Fig. 5.3.   Flowcharts for Example 5.7.

Example 5.8   If the C(00500) is (1) negative or zero, (2) positive but less than 20, or (3) 20 or greater, send control, respectively, to locations (1) 00600, (2) 00700, or (3) 01000.   This decision is drawn in Fig. 5.4a.

Let the C(00500) $= x$.   The conditions are

1.   If $x \leqslant 0$, go to 00600;
2.   if $0 < x < 20$, go to 00700;
3.   if $20 \leqslant x$, go to 01000.

The steps in the coding process can be listed as follows.

1.   Place x in the AC; jump to 00600 if negative.
2.   Jump to 00600 if zero.
3.   Having taken care of x nonpositive, form $x - 20$ because condition 2 now becomes "if $x - 20 < 0$, go to 00700."   Jump as indicated.
4.   Having taken care of $x < 20$, simply jump to 01000 (if $x \geqslant 20$).

A modified flowchart is drawn in Fig. 5.4b.

Location	Contents		Remarks
00100	LØAD	00500	LØAD X
00101	JUMPMI	00600	JUMP IF X IS NEGATIVE
00102	JUMPZE	00600	JUMP IF X IS ZERØ
00103	SUBT	00200	FØRM X − 20
00104	JUMPMI	00700	JUMP IF (X − 20) IS NEGATIVE
00105	JUMP	01000	JUMP IF (X − 20) IS NØN−NEG.
00200	+000000000024		20

The instructions at 00600, 00700, and 01000 and the subsequent locations are not listed.

Example 5.9   Either the quantity a (located in 00400) or the quantity b (located in 00402) is to be stored in location 00000, depending on these conditions:

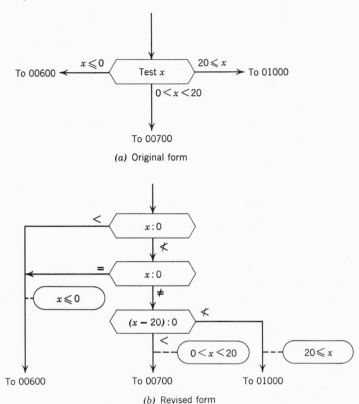

Fig. 5.4. Flowcharts for Example 5.8.

If a is positive and b is zero, store a;
if a is positive and b is nonzero, store b;
if a is negative and b is zero, store b;
if a is negative and b is nonzero, store a.

To simplify the coding, assume that a is not zero. The flowchart for this problem is drawn in Fig. 5.5a. The coding follows directly from the flowchart, which is labeled with addresses to match the program that follows. As the result of the two tests (on a and on b), a four-way branch occurs. The four paths merge, however, into two paths, because there are only two actions to be taken. A modification of part of the flowchart is shown in Fig. 5.5b.

Location	Contents		Remarks
00120	LØAD	00400	LØAD A
00121	JUMPPL	00125	GØ TØ 00125 IF A IS +
00122	LØAD	00402	LØAD B
00123	JUMPZE	00130	GØ TØ 00130 IF B IS 0

(Continued)

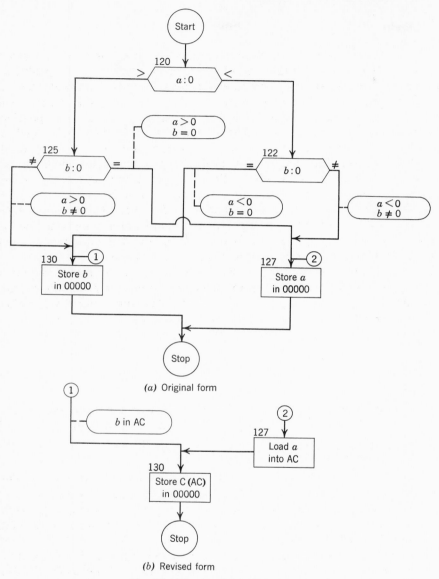

(a) Original form

(b) Revised form

Fig. 5.5.   Flowcharts for Example 5.9.

```
00124      JUMP      00127      GØ TØ 00127 IF B IS NØT 0
00125      LØAD      00402      LØAD B
00126      JUMPNZ    00130      GØ TØ 00130 IF B IS NØT 0
00127      LØAD      00400      LØAD A AGAIN
00130      STØRE     00000      STØRE AC (A ØR B) IN 00000
00131      HALT
```

Summary

The first four chapters of this book covered a variety of topics, all of a general nature, applying to all digital computers. Here we turned to the problem of coding, for which a particular computer was hypothesized to illustrate the process. Three types of instructions—arithmetic, data moving, and decision—were introduced and used in the coding of elementary arithmetic and testing problems.

The manner in which a computer program is established and coded was described. Portions are set aside for instructions and for data and results. Flowcharts are useful in analyzing the problem; from these the coding may proceed directly. Sometimes the original flowchart drawn to represent the problem must be redrawn to reflect the nature of the computer being used.

Programs are more useful if they are written for general situations. A program that evaluates any fifth-order polynomial is more useful than one that evaluates a specific fifth-order polynomial. A program that evaluates *any* polynomial (up to a particular finite order) is more useful still.

The groundwork for all programs has been laid down. In future chapters we improve the coding language, establish coding loops for problems requiring them, and utilize a flexible indexing system. The fundamentals introduced here, however, remain applicable throughout the study.

PROBLEMS

Section 5.2

5.1. Write programs to evaluate each of the following algebraic expressions.

(a) $f = ab + cd$
(b) $g = (a + b)(c - d)$
(c) $2a^3b^2 - 3a^{-2}b^{-3}$
(d) $x = a(b - c)/d(b + c)$
(e) $y = a^3b^3 + 4a^2b^4 - 6ac^3 + 8c^2d^2$

Assume that the parameters in these expressions are located in memory as follows:

$$L(a) = 00360, \ L(b) = 00361, \ L(c) = 00370, \ L(d) = 00400$$

The required constants are located in 00500, 00501, ... All quantities may be considered to be integers. In these programs an attempt should be made to minimize the number of instructions.

5.2. More useful than the program that evaluates a fifth-order polynomial (Example 5.6) would be one that evaluates an nth-order polynomial for variable n. Consider such a program and the way in which it might be written. Is a loop of value here? If so, why?

5.3. Consider the possibility of accumulator overflow in the programs in the text. In what way will the programs have to be modified if overflow is to be taken into account? An overflow indicator may be assumed to exist.

5.4. In the programs in the text remainders after division operations were discarded. How might this loss of significance be taken into account or reduced?

5.5. In the programs in the text "overflow" of products into the MR has also been ignored. How would the programs have to be modified to allow for such overflow?

Section 5.3

5.6. Write programs to evaluate the quantities x_i as given by the expressions or conditions below. The parameters a, b, c, and d are to be assumed located as in Problem 5.1. *Hint:* checking for the sign of a quantity may be done to establish its absolute value.

(a) $x_1 = a + |b| - |c|$

(b) $x_2 = $ the largest of a, b, c, and d

(c) $x_3 = $ sum of the positive numbers in the set a, b, c, and d

(d) $x_4 = \begin{cases} ab + cd & \text{if } a \text{ and } b \text{ are of the same sign} \\ ac - bd & \text{if } a \text{ and } b \text{ are of different signs} \end{cases}$

5.7. Code the following operations.

(a) If a is zero and either b or c is not zero, store d in location 00300; otherwise, store a in 00300.

(b) If a and b are both positive or if c and d are both of the same sign, store the larger of a and b in location 00400; otherwise, store the larger of c and d in that location.

(c) Sort the numbers a, b, c, and d into the 4-word block starting at 00440, putting the largest in location 00440.

5.8. Rewrite the programs in Problems 5.6 and 5.7 without using the JUMPMI and JUMPNZ instructions.

5.9. Write a program to reduce a quantity modulo 5, that is, to reduce it to a number in the range 1 to 5 inclusively.

5.10. Write a program to evaluate the expression

$$q = \frac{a}{b} + \frac{c}{d}$$

provided both b and d are nonzero. If either b or d is zero, set q equal to 1000.

6

SYMBOLIC CODING

We were introduced to symbolic languages in Chapter 3. These languages have a structure that resembles both the mathematics of problems and the nature of instruction words in memory. Here a particular symbolic language is introduced, and its characteristics and use are illustrated by examples.

A step-by-step description of the translation from symbolic coding to machine language is given.

6.1 THE PURPOSE OF SYMBOLIC CODING

Symbolic Language and Machine Language

The instructions that are located in the memory of a digital computer are binary or decimal numbers. Writing a program using instructions in this form is an extremely tedious process, and special, symbolic coding languages have been written to ease the coding effort.

An example indicates the disparity inherent in the languages of mathematics and the computer. If we wish to evaluate

$$a = b + c$$

and our computer is binary, the proper instructions are of the form*

* These are DELTA 63 instructions.

000000001000000000000000000010000000000

000000100000000000000000000010000000001

000000010000000000000000000010000000010

These binary numbers are images of the computer memory words. The numbers would more commonly be written in octal form:

001000001000

004000001001

002000001002

where the L(b) = 01000, the L(c) = 01001, and the L(a) = 01002.

The use of symbolic abbreviations for operations, introduced in Section 5.3, yields a language that is easier to use and understand.

LØAD   01000

ADD   01001

STØRE   01002

In a similar manner symbols may be used for addresses. Before this use described, however, let us consider the problems arising from the use of numerical or *absolute* addressing, the kind used in the examples of Chapter 5.

Disadvantages of Absolute Addressing

The most difficult aspect of numerical (or *absolute*) coding is the fact that we do not know, as we write an instruction, exactly where in memory a particular operand will be located. For example, if it is necessary to jump to a later instruction, as in Example 5.9 (page 96), the operand address must be left blank at first and filled in later. In that example the first two instructions can be written initially as

Oper.   Address

LØAD   00400   LØAD A
JUMPPL   .....   GØ TØ ..... IF A IS +

It is known at the start that A is located at 00400, but the operand address of the JUMPPL instruction is not known initially. In this simple program its address can be readily determined, but in complicated programs the address may not be known at this point. If an instruction refers to data, as does the LOAD instruction here, the address can be assigned and the data can be placed in the designated location. This approach, however, may waste space between the instructions and the data.   Refer to Example 5.5 (page 90); the constants, the variable x, and the temporary storage were placed in high addresses "to get them out of the way" of the instructions.   The ultimate length of the program was not known as it was being written.

After a program has been completed and checked unused locations can be removed, and the entire program can be compressed to use locations in sequence. In Example 5.5, locations 00111 to 00114 can be used for constants and data, but if the program will be changed in any way, the quantities will probably have to be moved.   Modification of a computer program is very common, since new ideas and methods develop and new information is sought.

Computer programs are frequently used in conjunction with one another; some are specifically written for this purpose.*   It is necessary for such programs to be compatible; no two programs should occupy the same portions of memory.   Programs written with absolute addresses are moved to new locations in memory only with great difficulty, since all the operand addresses will require modification.   Unfortunately, the desired locations in memory cannot always be anticipated, so that such modifications are inevitable.

A Symbolic Program

In using a symbolic language a programmer refers to the locations of instructions, data, and constants by symbolic names.   Symbols may be assigned in an arbitrary manner; when reference is to be made to the locations having these names, the symbols are used.   Mnemonic symbology is convenient.   For example, a word containing the number 3 might be called THREE, a sum might be placed in SUM, and the start of a program might be START.

As an example we code the program in Example 5.5 symbolically.

Example 6.1   Evaluate the polynomial

$$F = 8x^5 + 4x^3 - x^2$$

x is stored in location X; F is to be left in the accumulator.

In this program, written in symbolic language, ØNE, FØUR, and EIGHT are used for the addresses of the constants 1, 4, and 8, respectively.

Location	Oper.	Address	Remarks
START	LØAD	X	LØAD X
	MULT	X	FØRM X↑2
	MULT	EIGHT	FØRM 8X↑2
	ADD	FØUR	... 8X↑2 + 4
	MULT	X	
	SUBT	ØNE	
	MULT	X	
	MULT	X	
	HALT		

---

* *Subroutines,* discussed in Chapter 10, are written for use with other programs.

Location	Contents
ØNE	+000000000001
FØUR	+000000000004
EIGHT	+000000000010
X	+XXXXXXXXXXXX

Several items can be noted about a symbolic program by reference to this example.

1. Operand addresses can be supplied at the time each instruction is written, since the symbolic address, written later, can be placed anywhere without affecting the instruction.

2. Space is not wasted between instructions and data, since locations are set aside in sequence for all listed items. The insertion of further coding does not usually necessitate the modification of instructions.

3. The location in memory of a program is irrelevant to the coding, since the program can be placed anywhere, provided it does not conflict with other programs.

4. The use of mnemonic symbols brings the coding language closer to English and results in a more easily understood program. Remarks, used liberally in the examples of Chapter 5, are needed less often.

The Assembler

The task of converting symbolic operations and addresses is completely straightforward. For operations the only required process is that of looking in a table for each symbol and replacing it with the numerical operation code. For addresses the process is somewhat more complicated, since the choice of symbols is up to the programmer, but it is still essentially a replacement problem.

It occurred to computer people very early in the development of computers that the computer itself could be programmed to do the translation. A program that does this job is called an *assembler* or *assembly program*.

6.2 THE ASSEMBLER LANGUAGE

Special programs are available to translate coding languages into machine language. The term *assembler* is usually reserved for a program that translates a language consisting of symbolic instructions into machine language. This is generally a one-to-one conversion, the correspondence being between symbolic instructions and machine instructions. In Section 3.3 a second coding language, wherein algebraic formulas constituted the instructions, was mentioned. A translating program that converts these formulas to machine language is usually called a *compiler*. Two such languages are studied in Chapter 14. The term *translator* is used to apply to any program that translates coding into machine language.*

The program written by the programmer is called the *source program,* and its language is the *source language.* The program that the computer executes is the *object program,* and its language is the *object language.*

A hypothetical assembler is used to illustrate assembly languages. It is called HAP (Hypothetical Assembly Program) and is similar in structure to most assemblers currently available. The characteristics of assemblers for various machines are more similar than the computers for which they are written. Therefore, as with the hypothetical DELTA 63, a study of HAP is to a large extent a study of all assemblers.† Every concept introduced here is of general applicability, although the specific symbology varies somewhat from actual assembly languages.

The characteristics of HAP are described in the following paragraphs.‡

Symbols

A *symbol* is a sequence of from one to six nonblank characters, each of which is a letter, a digit, or a period, and at least one of which is not a digit. Examples are: ABC, THREE, X12345, NUMBER, and ..222. The requirement of at least one nonnumerical character is necessary to distinguish a symbol from an absolute address. For example, "350" is interpreted by the assembler as location address 350. If an integer is used, it is interpreted as a *decimal* number, so that "350" would be treated as location 00536_8.

Symbols are used as names for locations in memory and may be referred to in that sense. The nature of the symbols used has a significance only to the program containing them. All symbols used are independent, there being no numerical or other relation among them unless the programmer so chooses.§ Mnemonic symbols are commonly used and are suggested, since they convey meaning to the programmer as well as having significance as address names.

A symbol is said to be *defined* when it is used to name a location. All references to that location may therefore be made using that symbol. If the programmer refers to a symbol he has not defined, the symbol is said to be *undefined.* If the programmer uses a symbol to name two locations, the symbol is

---

* The terms "assembler," "compiler," and "translator" are not used universally as used here. There is, unfortunately, no standard terminology for these programs.

† HAP is based on BE-FAP, the assembler at the Bell Telephone Laboratories used with the IBM 7090 computer. BE-FAP is a modification of SAP, an assembler written by United Aircraft for the IBM 704 computer.

‡ The material in this section appears in full-sized type because of its general applicability, although it is described in terms of HAP.

§ This is not universally true. Some assemblers assume a specified relationship between such symbols as A0024, A0376, and A2214.

said to be *multiply defined*. The assembler will detect these two errors and report them to the programmer with his *program listing*.*

The symbolic abbreviations used in Section 5.3 for operation codes are not under consideration here. They refer to operations only and *must* be used as indicated. There is no choice or arbitrariness involved.

Addressing

Addressing refers to the process of using an address, symbolic or other, to refer to a memory location. A location N addresses beyond one that is symbolically named WØRD may be referred to as

$$WØRD+N$$

Here N is a decimal integer. If successive words in memory are to be referred to, it is convenient to generate addresses naming them symbolically in this manner. This is more convenient than naming each location. For example, if all the words in a sequence of words are to be referenced, it is more convenient to name the first word, say GRØUP, and refer to successive words as GRØUP + 1, GRØUP + 2, etc. Backward references may also be made, as GRØUP − 5.

The technique of using addition or subtraction to modify an address in this manner is called *relative addressing*. Although the method is convenient, it must be used with caution. Since relative addressing is a combination of symbolic and absolute addressing, it has one of the disadvantages of the latter. If the instruction

$$JUMP \qquad WØRD+6$$

is used, the programmer introduces an error if he inserts instructions between the instruction at WØRD and the sixth following instruction. For example, if he inserts three instructions, he must change the jump instruction to

$$JUMP \qquad WØRD+9$$

if he wishes to cause a jump to the same instruction as previously.

Relative addressing refers to the numerical sequence of memory locations, not to the sequence of instructions in a program, which may be different. If WØRD is defined at location 00100, then WØRD + 6 refers to location 00106. The reader is cautioned here to remember that the operand of an instruction with the address WØRD + 6 is the C(WØRD + 6), not the C(WØRD) + 6.

Although binary machines are addressed with octal addresses, the integers appearing in addresses are treated by the assembler as decimal numbers, because it is more convenient to code in decimal terms. We may have a block of 1000 numbers to process. If we can address them in memory decimally, we are

---

* The listing is described later in this section.

spared the need for conversion; the assembler will do it for us. This offers the disadvantage, however, of having to convert the numbers in memory from octal to decimal in the attempt to read the program listing.

Sometimes it is necessary to make an address reference relative to the "current instruction." For example, "Jump to the instruction three locations beyond this instruction." If "this instruction" is located at 00544, this means "jump to location 00547." Symbolically this is accomplished through the use of the character $*$. The jump instruction described is written as

JUMP   *+3

In Section 4.2 it was pointed out that addressing in a computer is done with modulo arithmetic, the modulus being the number of memory words in the computer. For this reason the arithmetic indicated in a symbolic address is performed with modulo arithmetic. Since the DELTA 63 has 32768 words, the summation in an expression such as

LIST+2000

is done modulo 32768, then (as always) converted to octal. For example, suppose LIST is assigned to location 76000. Then the value of this expression is

$$76000_8 + 2000_{10} = 76000_8 + 3720_8 = 101720_8$$

This is reduced by $100000_8(32768)$ and assembled into the instruction as the operand address 01720_8.

Instruction Format

Since punched cards constitute the most common medium for the input to a computer, the format of symbolic instructions is described for cards. As indicated in Example 6.1, an instruction may contain three items of information: a symbol (as a name for the location of the instruction), an operation, and an address. For these items, three *fields* or groups of adjacent columns are delineated on a card.

The use of the columns on each HAP symbolic instruction card and the fields they comprise are:

Columns	Field	Contents
1– 6	Location field	Symbol (definition)
8–14	Operation field	Symbolic operation
16–72	Address field	Address
73–80	(Not used)	

The location field of a symbolic instruction may be left blank; several instructions in Example 6.1 have no symbols in their location fields. A symbol is defined by being placed in the location field of an instrument. A HAP symbolic instruction is shown in Fig. 6.1.

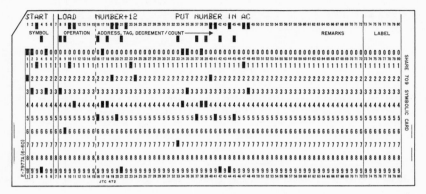

Fig. 6.1.   A symbolic instruction card (HAP).

Pseudo-operations

The assembly program translates symbolic instructions into machine instructions. It is sometimes necessary to provide the assembler with information on the manner in which the assembly of a program is to proceed. A *pseudo-operation* is an operation that is not translated into a machine instruction but which directs the assembler in some way. Its operation symbol is placed in the operation field as with other operations.

Pseudo-operations are used for a number of purposes; among them are the following: (1) to indicate the start and end of a program, (2) to generate constants, and (3) to reserve space for data or a set of results. A group of consecutive memory locations, used for a set of results, is called a *block*. In the following paragraphs five of the HAP pseudo-operations are described and illustrated.

ØRIGIN. The address field of this pseudo-operation indicates the address to be assigned to the next instruction. This pseudo-operation is used to set the initial location for a sequence of instructions; it is the first card of a symbolic deck. The assembler then automatically assigns successive instructions to successive memory locations until directed otherwise, as by this pseudo-operation. The following pair of cards

Oper.	Address
ØRIGIN	100
LØAD	WØRD

directs the assembler to assign the location 100 (144_8) to the next instruction, thereby assembling the LØAD instruction at 00144_8.

END. The use of this pseudo-operation signals the end of the symbolic program; it must be the last card in the deck. The address of this pseudo-operation is the location at which the program starts, that is, the address of the first executable instruction. When the program is run later, this address must be given to the computer so that it can start executing the program properly. The following card states that the first instruction to be executed is located at 00100_8:

Oper.	Address
END	64

Alternately, a symbolic address may be given on the END card. For example, if the starting instruction is called BEGIN, this card may be used:

Oper.	Address
END	BEGIN

Very often the starting instruction is the first instruction in the deck, but it is not necessarily so.

ØCTAL. The octal numbers in the address field of this pseudo-operation are assigned to successive locations in memory at the point in the program at which this card occurs. It is used to generate one or more octal constants in the program. Numbers are separated by commas with no intervening blank spaces. Assume that an instruction was assembled at location 00567. If the next card is

Location	Oper.	Address
NAME	ØCTAL	70,0,−235,+1000,,60

then the following generation of octal numbers would result at the addresses indicated:

Location	Contents
00570	+000000000070
00571	+000000000000
00572	−000000000235
00573	+000000001000
00574	+000000000000
00575	+000000000060

The symbol NAME is assigned to the first of these locations, 00570. Note that (1) minus signs must be given, but plus signs may be omitted; (2) "null" numbers, that is, adjacent commas, generate 0; (3) one word is generated for each number listed (including nulls).

DECML. The decimal numbers in the address field of this pseudo-operation are assigned to successive locations in memory at the point in the program at which this card occurs. The format of this card and the resultant assembler action is similar to that of the ØCTAL pseudo-operation. The card

Oper.	Address
DECML	80,−10,1,0,3000

used at the same point in a program as the ØCTAL card directs the assembler to generate these words, given as octal numbers:

Location	Contents
00570	+000000000120
00571	−000000000012
00572	+000000000001
00573	+000000000000
00574	+000000005670

BLØCK. A block of words of the size indicated in the address field of this pseudo-operation is set aside for later use at the point in the program at which this card occurs. This pseudo-operation is used to create blocks of words for data and the storage of results. Assume again that an instruction was assembled at 00567, and that the next card is

Location	Oper.	Address
NUMBRS	BLØCK	1000

The symbol NUMBRS is assigned to location 00570, and 1000 locations are set aside; the block starts at location 00570 and ends 999 locations later at location 02537. The next instruction would then be assembled at location 02540.

Sometimes it is necessary to name a location without putting anything into it when the program is written. For instance, a location called XSQUAR in a program might have nothing in it initially, although the value of x^2 is placed there when the program is run. In other words, a memory word containing 0 is desired. This may be done by writing the operation

Location	Oper.	Address
XSQUAR	DECML	0

The same thing may be accomplished by leaving the operation and address fields blank:

Location	Oper.	Address
XSQUAR		

HAP will then assemble a full word of 0-bits. If the operation field alone is blank, 0-bits will fill bits 3–8, the operation field of the instruction. If the address field alone is blank, 0-bits will fill bits 21–35, the address field of the instruction.

Qualifiers

Normally, an integer that appears in the address field of a card is treated as a decimal number. If it is desirable to write an octal number, a *qualifier* may be used. A qualifier is a special indicator that identifies an octal number. In mathematics this may be done with a subscript: 100_8. Subscripts are not used on computer equipment, so another convention is required. The characters /Ø/ precede any numbers intended to be octal. The following card directs the assembler to assign location 00100 to the next instruction:

Oper.	Address
ØRIGIN	/Ø/100

The qualifier must appear immediately before each octal number.

The Assembly Listing

The assembler, after producing the object program, prepares a listing with object and source programs side by side. The program in Example 6.1 serves to illustrate this.

Example 6.2   Following is a listing of the program to evaluate the polynomial

$$F = 8x^5 + 4x^3 - x^2$$

Object Program (octal)		Source Program (symbolic)		
Location	Contents	Location	Oper.	Address
00100			ØRIGIN	/ Ø / 100
00100	0 01 0000 00114	START	LØAD	X
00101	0 06 0000 00114		MULT	X
00102	0 06 0000 00113		MULT	EIGHT
00103	0 04 0000 00112		ADD	FØUR
00104	0 06 0000 00114		MULT	X
00105	0 05 0000 00111		SUBT	ØNE
00106	0 06 0000 00114		MULT	X
00107	0 06 0000 00114		MULT	X
00110	0 00 0000 00000		HALT	
00111	+000000000001	ØNE	DECML	1
00112	+000000000004	FØUR	DECML	4
00113	+000000000010	EIGHT	DECML	8
00114	+000000000000	X		
	00100		END	START

Advantages of Symbolic Coding

We have already noted in Section 6.1 the advantages of using symbolic coding, but they should be reiterated. Operand addresses can be supplied immediately; the address X in the first instruction in Example 6.2 can be written initially, since its actual location is irrelevant. Instructions and data follow one another without wasted space, and instructions can readily be inserted. Simply by changing the address on the ØRIGIN card the entire program can be moved to a new portion of memory; a reassembly of the program is required, however. The use of mnemonic symbols yields a program that is easier to write and to understand.

6.3 THE ASSEMBLY PROCESS*

The following sequence of steps occurs prior to and during the process of program assembly.

---

* This section may be skipped without any loss of continuity. Section 6.4, however, should not be skipped.

1. The program is coded in symbolic language. This is entirely a manual process, performed by the programmer.

2. The assembly program is placed in the computer.

3. The symbolic source program is assembled, one instruction at a time, by the assembler. As far as the assembler is concerned, the symbolic deck is a set of data to be processed. The result of this processing is an object program listing and an object program deck.

4. The assembled object program is loaded into the computer and executed. This last step may occur either immediately after step 3 or at a later time.

The purpose of this section is to describe step 3 in some detail by illustration; a simple symbolic program is assumed to be assembled by HAP, and each stage of the process is examined.

Steps in Program Assembly

A simple problem will be coded. A study of its assembly into a binary object program serves to illustrate the assembly process.

Example 6.3 Compare the quantities p and q, stored in P and Q, respectively. If $p < q$, place the number 1 in NUMBER; if $p = q$, place the number 2 in NUMBER; if $p > q$, place the number 3 in NUMBER.

These conditions can be rewritten:

1. If $p - q < 0$, store 1;
2. if $p - q = 0$, store 2;
3. if $p - q > 0$, store 3.

Case 2 must be checked first, because -0 and $+0$ are treated differently; the zero case should be disposed of initially. The flowchart is drawn in Fig. 6.2. Note that control is sent to one of three places so that the proper number (1, 2, or 3) can be obtained for storage in NUMBER. The three possible store operations are performed at one location, STØRE.

Location	Oper.	Address	Remarks
	ØRIGIN	/0/200	
START	LØAD	P	FØRM P − Q
	SUBT	Q	
	JUMPZE	GET2	JUMP IF ZERØ
	JUMPMI	GET1	JUMP IF MINUS
GET3	LØAD	THREE	HERE IF PLUS .... 3 TØ AC
	JUMP	STØRE	
GET1	LØAD	ØNE	1 TØ AC
	JUMP	STØRE	
GET2	LØAD	TWØ	2 TØ AC
STØRE	STØRE	NUMBER	

(Continued)

```
            HALT
P
Q
ØNE       DECML    1
TWØ       DECML    2
THREE     DECML    3
          END      START
```

Each card of the symbolic deck is processed individually. The assembly is a *two-pass* process; a *pass* is the processing of the complete deck once. In the first pass (*pass* 1), all the symbols defined in the location fields are entered into a *symbol table* with the locations at which they are defined. In the second pass (*pass* 2) the instructions are assembled; the symbol table just created is used. Pseudo-operations receive special treatment, since they direct the assembly in some manner.*

1. Pass 1 is started; the ØRIGIN card is first. The address, which is 00200₈ in the example, is used to set a *pseudo-address-register* (p-AR) to that value. The p-AR has a function similar to the actual AR in the computer. Its contents, at any time, is the address to be assigned to the next instruction.

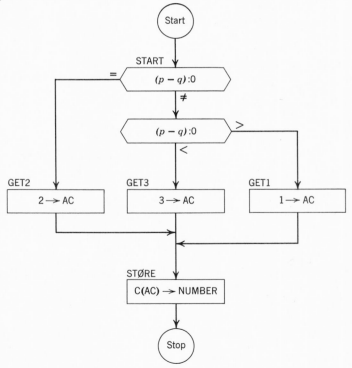

Fig. 6.2.   Flowchart for Example 6.3.

---

* Although two-pass assemblers are more common, one-pass assemblers are also used.

2. The next eleven cards all contain instructions. The only information extracted from them is the set of symbols defined in the location fields. For example, the symbol START appears on the first card. A double entry is made into the symbol table: (1) the symbol and (2) the address to be assigned to that instruction. The address is 00200 because that is the contents of the p-AR when that instruction is encountered by the assembler. This process repeats, the number 1 being added to the C(p-AR) after each instruction is processed. In this way successive memory locations are assigned to successive instructions. After the HALT instruction has been processed, the symbol table looks like this:

Symbol	Location
START	00200
GET3	00204
GET1	00206
GET2	00210
STØRE	00211

3. Pass 1 continues with the processing of the remaining cards. All of these are pseudo-operations (cards with blank operation fields are considered to be pseudo-operations), and each is a word-generating type. Therefore one word is to be assigned for each, and the p-AR is stepped by 1 each time as before. Symbols continue to be added to the symbol table.

4. Pass 1 is terminated when the assembler encounters the END card. The symbol on that card, START, is the name of the location where the program is to start being executed; this is location 00200, as noted in the symbol table. This information, stored for later use, is of no direct consequence during the assembly process. At the end of pass 1, the symbol table is sorted so that symbols may be found readily in pass 2. A sorted table follows; note that short symbols are listed before long ones:

Symbol	Location
P	00213
Q	00214
ØNE	00215
TWØ	00216
GET1	00206
GET2	00210
GET3	00204
START	00200
STØRE	00211
THREE	00217

5. If a BLØCK pseudo-operation were present in the deck, special action would have to be taken. Since the address on that card indicates the size of a block of words to be set aside, all that needs to be done here is to modify the C(p-AR). For example, the card

BLØCK   1000

states that 1000 locations are to be set aside. If, on encountering this card, the C(p-AR) was 00570, then locations 00570 through 02537 are to be used for the block. This is accomplished by adding 1000 to the C(p-AR), setting it to 02540_8. The next instruction is then assigned to that location.

6. If an ØCTAL or DECML card with more than one integer in the address field were present, the C(p-AR) would have to be increased by the number of integers on the card. For example, if 5 integers were given, 5 words would have to be used for them. By increasing the C(p-AR) by 5, these words are set aside for that purpose.

7. Pass 2 is then started. The information carried to it from pass 1 is the symbol table, as we have given it. The information in the symbolic program must now be fed to the assembler again. For this reason, it was temporarily stored on tape; it is now read into memory from that tape.

8. The ØRIGIN card resets the C(p-AR) as before.

9. The first instruction, a LØAD instruction, is read. The operation (LØAD) is compared to an *operation table*. This table, part of the assembly program, has a list of all symbolic operations with their corresponding numerical operation codes. It begins as follows:

Symbolic	Numeric
LØAD	01
STØRE	02
ADD	04
•••	••

The table is searched for the symbolic operation of the instruction; when it is found in the table, the numerical code is obtained and is stored in a memory word of the assembler. The word will become the assembled machine instruction. At this point the contents of it is

$$001000000000$$

It contains the operation code in the proper position.

10. The same instruction is examined again. The symbolic address in the address field (P) is now looked up in the symbol table formed in pass 1. The result of this search is the address at which the symbol was defined: 00213. This number is added to the partially formed machine instruction to produce the complete instruction:

$$001000000213$$

11. The newly assembled instruction is read onto a different tape along with its location address, 00200. This instruction is in machine language.

12. The remaining ten instructions are treated in the same manner. Processing each results in an assembled machine instruction. All are read onto tape with the first one.

13. The pseudo-operations are similarly processed. Since no further symbolic addresses are present in the address fields, no further searching in the symbol table is needed. The blank operation fields must, however, be processed to produce 0-bits in bits 3–8 of the corresponding machine words. Furthermore, the DECML pseudo-operations must be processed to produce words containing the decimal numbers in the address fields.

14. When the assembly is completed, the assembler provides a listing. Its appearance is similar to the listing in Example 6.2.

15. The assembler also punches an object program deck. The assembled program, stored temporarily on tape, is transferred to this deck. For a computer with 36 bits in each word, 36 hole positions on each card are used for each word. For a computer with

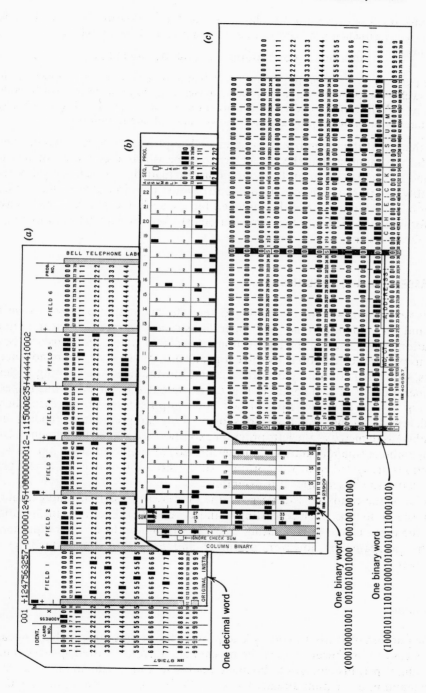

Fig. 6.3. Object program cards. (a) Decimal card. (b) Column binary card. (c) Row binary card.

10 decimal digits in each word, 10 columns are used for each word. For example, the first machine instruction word contains the bit pattern (in a binary machine)

0000000010000000000000000000010001011

This is punched on an object program card. Other information that must appear in the object deck includes (1) indications of the addresses assigned to the binary words on the cards and (2) the starting address of the program (saved in step 4). Figure 6.3 illustrates three types of object program card; individual words are identified.

At this point the assembly is complete. The programmer has two options. (1) He may request that the object program be run immediately; for this to be done, the object program from tape must be loaded into memory (after the assembly program is removed) and control must pass initially to the starting location. (2) He may take the punched binary deck and at a later time have its information loaded into the computer (most likely by way of an off-line tape unit) for execution.

6.4 ASSEMBLY AND EXECUTION

It is very important for the reader to keep the distinction between *assembly time* and *execution time* (*run time*) operations clearly in mind. Assembly time operations were listed in the last section. Execution time operations are those used to perform calculations to solve a problem. As we study more advanced topics, this distinction may become fuzzier, but the need for keeping it clear becomes greater. The diagram in Fig. 6.4 is presented as an aid in this respect.

In Fig. 6.4 the operations performed, the equipment used to perform them, and the results of the operations are shown. Program preparation (coding and assembly) is depicted at the left; program execution is depicted at the right. Off-line operations (manual and machine performed) are depicted at the top; on-line operations are depicted at the bottom. In the situation drawn the object program is run some time after it is assembled.

As far as the computer is concerned, the processes of assembly and execution are of the same type, each consisting of these steps: (1) reading in information from the input tape, (2) computing, and (3) writing results on the output tape. To the programmer, however, assembly and execution are quite different processes.

Summary

The purpose of symbolic coding is to provide the programmer with a language that is easy to use because it can be mnemonic, it avoids wasted space within a program, it permits changes to be made readily in a program, and it is easier to understand in a program already written. With symbolic coding the language

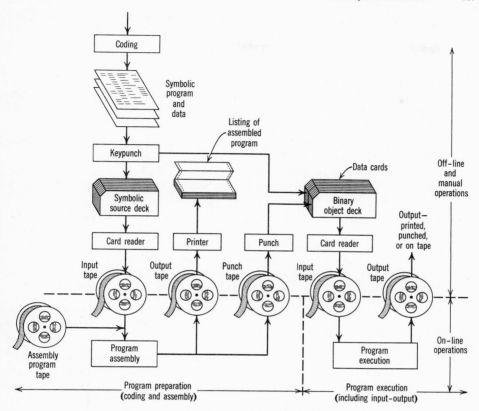

Fig. 6.4.   Diagram of assembly and run procedure.

barrier existing between mathematics and the language of a computer is largely overcome.   The symbolic language becomes a compromise between them.

An assembly program effects the translation between symbolic instructions (in the source program) and machine instructions (in the object program). Symbolic operations and symbolic names for memory locations used by the programmer in coding are translated into numerical machine words.   To direct the assembly process a number of pseudo-operations are used.   Operations that occur during this process are said to occur at "assembly time."   Operations that occur when the program is run are said to occur at "execution time."

PROBLEMS

Section 6.2

6.1.   What pseudo-operations, in addition to those described in the text, might be useful in an assembly language?

6.2. Consider the disadvantages of absolute coding and the advantages of symbolic coding, as listed in the text. In what way do the several features of the HAP assembly language provide the stated advantages and avoid the stated disadvantages?

Section 6.3

6.3. Some assemblers use only one pass in the assembly process. Describe the procedure such an assembler might use to assemble a program. Compare the procedure with a two-pass procedure.

6.4. What kinds of operations does an assembler have to perform to carry out its function of assembly?

6.5. Can the DELTA 63 computer assemble programs for other computers? If not, state why not. If so, describe the differences between that process and the normal assembly process.

6.6. If a symbolic language is to be used for coding, it must be used properly; certain conventions must be obeyed, as with any language. What types of programming and coding errors is it possible for an assembly program to detect? Consider errors both in analysis and in writing instructions. Which would be readily detectable and which would be difficult to detect?

7

PROGRAM LOOPS

Problems that are programmed for computer solution have some repetitious aspects. When a flowchart for a repetitious process is drawn, a loop is the result. A flowchart may have several loops, and loops may be nested within one another. In this chapter the job of coding loops is examined, and the significance of the stored-program approach—that instructions may be treated as data and may be modified arithmetically—is demonstrated.

A short *loading program* is introduced both to provide an introduction to input-output operations and to serve as an example of a looping program. The specific jobs of loading a program and its data and writing results are described, as are several tape characteristics and operations.

7.1 ADDRESS MODIFICATION

Why Use Loops?

The flowcharts containing loops that we have studied represented problems having repetitious processes. To avoid drawing a sequence of almost identical operation boxes, we instead indicated a return to an earlier operation. In so returning the computation then involves either a new item of data or a new estimate of a computed quantity, and thus repetitions of the operation can be effected. It is necessary to check for the end of the loop computation in order that the computation be terminated properly.

This technique of returning to an earlier step in the computation is incorporated in the coding of the problem.   Before examples are given to illustrate the method, the difficulties embodied in a nonloop approach are examined.*

Example 7.1   Compute the value of x^{10}.   The value of x is small enough so that the number x^{10} does not exceed the capacity of a computer word.

From Example 5.4 (page 90) we note that a sequence of MULT instructions suffices.

Location	Oper.	Address
	LØAD	X
	MULT	X
	MULT	X
	MULT	X
	MULT	X
	MULT	X
	MULT	X
	MULT	X
	MULT	X
	MULT	X
	STØRE	RESULT
X		
RESULT		

The main difficulties with this approach are that the coding is tedious and lengthy and a great deal of memory space is required if the exponent is large. Furthermore, the exponent might be a variable of the problem; a more useful program is one that computes x^n for a variety of values of both x and n.   The program in Example 7.1 was written for a particular value of n, 10.   To provide for variable n would require testing at every point to see if the nth power were already computed.   The conclusion to be reached is that a loop approach is preferable.

A Simple Loop

The last problem is recoded now using a *program loop,* the coding counterpart of a flowchart loop.   The problem is generalized to allow any power of x to be computed, provided x^n fits in a computer word.

Example 7.2   Compute the value of x^n.

A flowchart for this problem appears in Fig. 7.1.   The quantity p is the current value of the product; its initial value is 1.   Counting is done with index i; its initial value is also 1.   The important step is the multiplication of the accumulated product by x, producing one more power of x:

$$p \times x \to p$$

*ØRIGIN and END cards are omitted from examples.

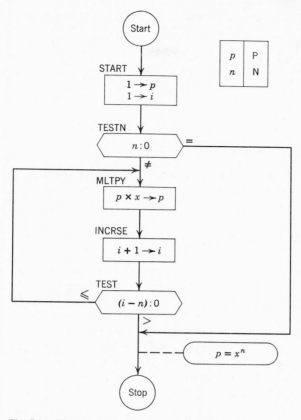

Fig. 7.1. Flowchart of computation of x^n (Example 7.2.).

To allow for the case $n = 0$ a test is made; in that event, p is set equal to 1. The symbolic names used to label flowchart boxes correspond to the symbols in the following program. The test for loop termination is accomplished by checking $(i - n)$ against zero.*

Location	Oper.	Address	
START	LØAD	ØNE	1 TØ P AND I
	STØRE	P	
	STØRE	I	
TESTN	LØAD	N	
	JUMPZE	DØNE	TEST FØR ZERØ N
MLTPY	LØAD	P	P*X TØ P
	MULT	X	
	STØRE	P	
INCRSE	LØAD	I	I+1 TØ I

(Continued)

---

* In the program remarks, the asterisk is used for the multiplication operator.

```
          ADD      ØNE
          STØRE    I
TEST      SUBT     N              TEST FØR END
          JUMPMI   MLTPY          BACK IF NØT DØNE
          JUMPZE   MLTPY
DØNE      HALT

N
X
P
I
ØNE       DECML    1
```

Note that through the use of a program loop it is a simple matter to include *n* as a variable of the problem.

A Loop with Address Modification

The problem in the last example lacks a feature common to most repetitious problems: the performance of an operation on a *sequence* of data. Instead, this problem is concerned with multiplication of a quantity by the same number (x) each loop cycle. Consider now the problem of summing *n* numbers, a problem analyzed in Section 2.2.

In the summation the addition operation must be performed on a sequence of numbers. Assume that these numbers are located in the block of words whose first address is NUMBRS. The coding might begin as follows, where the C(SUM) is initially zero:

Oper.	Address
LØAD	SUM
ADD	NUMBRS
ADD	NUMBRS+1
ADD	NUMBRS+2
ADD	NUMBRS+3
ADD	NUMBRS+4
• • •	• • • • •

This approach, as we saw, is undesirable. A loop of the type given in Example 7.2 is satisfactory, except that the ADD instruction must be modified in some way each time control passes to it. This is necessary because the operand address changes as different numbers are added.

Words in memory all have the same structure, whether they contain instructions or data. Therefore instructions can be operated on arithmetically in the same manner as data. A DELTA 63 instruction that reads

ADD   NUMBRS

looks like this in memory:

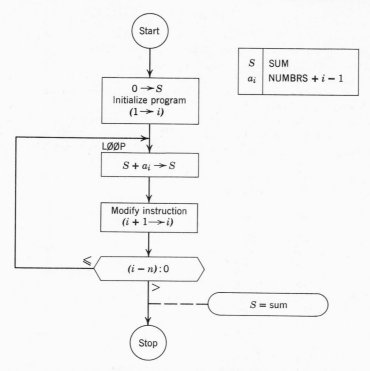

Fig. 7.2.   Flowchart of summation of n numbers (Example 7.3).

004000001050

If it is modified by the addition of 1, it corresponds to the symbolic instruction

ADD   NUMBRS+1

By successively adding 1 to this instruction we can effectively produce the symbolic instructions desired, those that add the sequence of numbers to form the sum. This technique is called *address modification*. It is illustrated with an example, after a new instruction is introduced.

CLEAR STORAGE (CLEARS Y) (13). The C(Y) is set to zero and its sign is set plus.

Example 7.3 Determine the sum of a given set of n numbers. The numbers are stored in the block beginning at NUMBRS; their sum is to be placed in SUM.

The flowchart for this problem is drawn in Fig. 2.2 (page 28). The test for the case $n = 0$ is omitted.

That flowchart is modified to include the operation of address modification; it is re-drawn in Fig. 7.2. The memory box indicates that a_i is stored in location NUMBRS+i−1. Thus, initially, the program sums the C(NUMBRS); to sum a_i, the program sums the C(NUMBRS+i−1). After the last number is summed, the operand address of the ADD instruction is NUMBRS $+ n - 1$.   The flowchart shows, however, that the test for the end of the problem *follows* the modification of the index, so that the operand address at the time of the test is NUMBRS $+ n$.   Thus, the loop must terminate when the ADD instruction has been modified exactly n times.

In the following program, the ADD instruction is modified after each number is summed.   A *data instruction,* or instruction that is used as a constant, can be established initially to check for the final value of the ADD instruction.   When this constant matches the ADD instruction, the loop terminates; a JUMPNZ instruction does the matching. In addition, another data instruction (at SETWD) is used to "initialize" the ADD instruction to its initial value.   The flowchart statement "initialize program" refers to these operations.

It is necessary to set aside a block of words for the n numbers.   Here 1000 words are reserved.   A word is also set aside for n.

Location	Oper.	Address	
	CLEARS	SUM	O TØ SUM
	LØAD	SETWD	INITIALIZE INSTRUCTIØN
	STØRE	ADDNUM	
	ADD	N	SET TEST WØRD
	STØRE	CØMPAR	
LØØP	LØAD	SUM	ADD A NUMBER
ADDNUM	ADD	NUMBRS	
	STØRE	SUM	
	LØAD	ADDNUM	MØDIFY INSTRUCTIØN
	ADD	ØNE	
	STØRE	ADDNUM	
	SUBT	CØMPAR	TEST FØR END
	JUMPNZ	LØØP	BACK IF NØT DØNE
DØNE	HALT		
SUM			
SETWD	ADD	NUMBRS	
CØMPAR			(ADD NUMBRS+N)
N			
NUMBRS	BLØCK	1000	

A note of caution is necessary on the use of address modification.   A number of computers include the signs of instruction words in the operation code.   For example, -050 and $+050$ may mean different operations.   If address modification is used carelessly, the result may be subtraction instead of addition when a word is modified by adding 1 to it.

Polynomial Evaluation

The problem of evaluating a fifth-order polynomial, given its coefficients, was coded in a nonloop manner in Example 5.6 (page 92).   Because the problem is repetitious a loop is called for.   Furthermore, if the problem is generalized to allow a polynomial of any order to be evaluated, a loop is almost demanded.

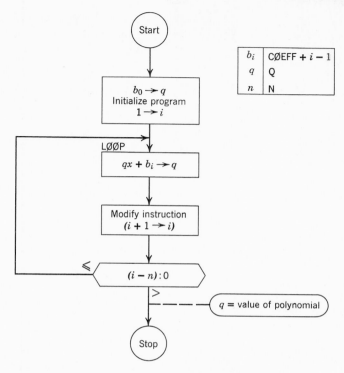

Fig. 7.3.   Flowchart of polynomial evaluation (Example 7.4).

Example 7.4   Write a program to evaluate a polynomial of order n, for n as large as 100. The number n, the $n + 1$ coefficients, and the variable x are all given.   These are located, respectively, in N, the block starting at CØEFF, and X.   The coefficients are b_0, $b_1, \ldots, b_n$:

$$F = b_0 x^n + b_1 x^{n-1} + \cdots + b_n$$

The flowchart appears in Fig. 7.3.   The program has a structure similar to the one in Example 7.3 as regards its address modification and initialization.   The significant operation is the calculation of q, a quantity whose value is the accumulated partial polynomial. The calculation is

$$qx + b_i \to q$$

Reference to Example 5.6 indicates why this operation repeated for successive coefficients b_i yields the value of F.*

Location	Oper.	Address		
	LØAD	CØEFF	B(0) TØ Q	
	STØRE	Q		
		(Continued)		

---

* The symbol B(X) as used in the remarks in this program means b_x.

```
           LØAD     SETWD          INITIALIZE
           STØRE    MØD
           ADD      N              SET TEST WØRD
           STØRE    CØMPAR
   LØØP    LØAD     Q              Q*X + B(I) TØ Q
           MULT     X
   MØD     ADD      CØEFF+1
           STØRE    Q
           LØAD     MØD            MØDIFY INSTRUCTIØN
           ADD      ØNE
           STØRE    MØD
           SUBT     CØMPAR
           JUMPNZ   LØØP           BACK IF NØT DØNE
   DØNE    HALT

   Q
   SETWD   ADD      CØEFF+1
   CØMPAR                          (ADD CØEFF+1+N)
   N
   X
   CØEFF   BLØCK    101
```

Modified Computer Organization

Having studied the concept of address modification, we should reexamine Fig. 3.1 (page 42), which shows the organization of a computer. A necessary addition to that diagram results in Fig. 7.4. Arithmetic can be performed on the program, and solid lines have been drawn between the arithmetic unit and the program, since information flows between these two units. We might argue that a separate box for the program is redundant, since the program actually is located in the memory unit. This is a valid argument, but the program box is

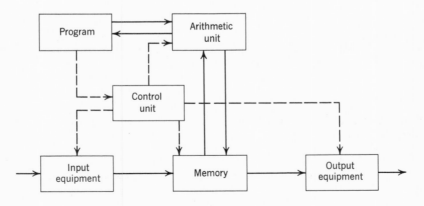

Fig. 7.4. Modified computer organization.

drawn separately to indicate that it exercises control over the control unit by virtue of its set of instructions.

Address modification, an important process, is made possible by having the program stored in the memory of the computer. Most computers have automatic address modification, a very useful feature when a great deal of indexing has to be done.

7.2 INTRODUCTION TO INPUT-OUTPUT

Completing the Program

The basic coding picture is nearing completion. Through Chapter 5 we studied arithmetic, data-moving, and decision instructions. Although indexing instructions are not described until the next chapter, it is possible to simulate their task by address modification. The fifth type is now introduced: the input-output instructions.

For computer programs to be useful they must provide answers to the programmer in readable form. For this purpose computers have instructions for such operations as writing on tape, punching cards, and writing on a printer. Because off-line printing is so common with high-speed computers, only tape-writing instructions are of immediate interest here. The DELTA 63 has one such instruction.

In the same way a program and its data must be loaded into the computer. For this purpose the 63 has a tape-reading instruction. Prior to tape reading, of course, the information in a deck must have been written on tape. Finally, in order to start the program at the first executable instruction, a means is available for supplying the information about starting.

For a computer program to be of general use, it must be written for data not specified at the time of coding. For example, a program to evaluate a polynomial must be written in terms of parameters for which space is left in the program. This was done in Example 7.4, where a block of 101 words was set aside for the coefficients, and 1 word was made available each for the variable x and the polynomial order n. The same was done in most of the other programs coded so far.

When a program is placed on the computer, the procedure is to load the program and follow it with its data. The program then reads in the data, stores it in proper locations, performs the calculations, and produces answers. In the remainder of this section only the execution phase of a program is considered.

Normally, a sequence of programs is run in succession, as explained in Section 3.2, for reasons of economy. As an introduction to input-output operations, however, the problem of loading a single program into a computer and executing it is considered.

Information on Tape

Information on magnetic tape is always in binary form, whether the computer is binary or not. Bits are represented by magnetized spots on the tape; the spots are polarized "to the left" and "to the right" for 0- and 1-bits.

Across the width of the tape is space for 7 bits.* Six of these carry meaningful information, and the seventh is a *check* (or *parity*) bit. Its value is such that the total number of 1-bits across the tape is odd. If, in reading or writing, any bit is reversed, the number of 1's in its line will be even and an error will be indicated. We are not concerned further with the check bit, so let us consider the other 6.

Assuming that a computer word has 36 bits, the contents of each word are placed in 6 lines of 6 bits each. For example, the two binary words

$$\textbf{000110001101000011010111011010010011}$$

$$\textbf{111011101000000101111111011101110101}$$

would appear on tape as shown in Fig. 7.5. The upper row on the tape is the check bit row. The 36 bits are located, in sequence, top to bottom and left to right in the figure. Bit positions are shown as subscripts.

Information is written on tape by the tape unit *writing head,* under which the tape moves continuously and uniformly during writing. As it writes, 6 bits at a time are placed on tape, and no spaces are left between words, provided there is no stoppage of the tape. A group of words stored consecutively on tape constitutes a *record*. Records are separated by blank spaces called *record gaps,* which are formed when the head stops writing. During the small amount of time required for the tape to stop, the head moves through part of the record gap; as the tape starts and increases its speed, it moves through the other part. When the tape is still, the head is positioned over the center of the gap. Words are read by the *reading head* from an entire record without any tape stoppage. Usually one head serves the purposes of both reading and writing.

First word						Second word						
1	0	1	1	0	0	0	1	1	1	1	1	← Check bits
0_S	0_6	0_{12}	0_{18}	0_{24}	0_{30}	1_S	1	0	1	0	1	
0	0	0	1	1	1	1	0	0	1	1	1	
0	1	0	0	1	0	1	1	0	1	1	0	
1	1	0	1	0	0	0	0	1	1	1	1	Data bits
1	0	1	1	1	1	1	0	0	1	0	0	
0_5	1	1	1	0	1_{35}	1	0	1	1	1	1_{35}	

Fig. 7.5.   Two words on magnetic tape.

---

* The format of information on magnetic tape varies among tape unit models. The format described here is typical, however.

A group of records constitutes a *file*. Files are terminated by end-of-file marks. The information constituting a file varies; frequently a complete program with its data is placed on tape as a file. The number of words in a record, the number of records in a file, and the number of files on a tape are all variable and are determined by the program that causes the writing on tape.

Tape Reading and Writing

The off-line card reader reads either machine words, binary or decimal, or symbolic information. The information on one card is placed into one record on tape. Later the information can be read into memory by an on-line operation. On output the reverse is true. Information in memory can be placed on tape for later, off-line printing. When records on tape are formed from words in memory, the records may be large, perhaps on the order of 50 or 100 words in size. When records on tape are formed from cards, the records are smaller because fewer words can be placed on a card.

The DELTA 63 off-line card reader reads 72 columns of card information. If the information is binary, as in an assembled object deck, 24 words are read. Since each binary word occupies 3 columns (36 hole positions), 24 binary words fit on 1 card. The reading of symbolic cards is not presently of interest; the general reading problem is considered in Chapter 11.

The DELTA 63 has 8 tape units associated with it. These units are designated A, B, C, . . . , and H. Internally they are referred to by digits: 0, 1, 2, . . . , and 7, respectively. This digit appears in bits 6–8 of the operation code of the tape instructions. There are two tape instructions and one card-reading instruction.

WRITE TAPE X (WRITEX Y)* (70–77). A single record of information is written on tape X from the block of words starting at location Y. If a nonzero integer m appears in bits 9–14 of this instruction word, the m words from locations Y through $Y+m-1$ form a record on tape. The number m cannot exceed 63. If $m = 0$, it is interpreted as though it were 64.

READ TAPE X (READTX Y)* (60–67). A single record of information is read from tape X into the block of words starting at location Y. If a nonzero integer m appears in bits 9–14 of this instruction word, the first m words of the record are read into the m words from locations Y through $Y+m-1$, provided at least m words are present. If n is the number of words present, and $m > n$, then n words are read into locations Y through $Y+n-1$. If bits 9–14 contain 0, the entire record is read into locations Y through $Y+n-1$. If the tape reading head is positioned at an end-of-file mark, the computer continues in sequence to the next instruction; otherwise, the next instruction is skipped.

The skip feature of the READTX instruction permits this decision to be made:

"Read a record unless the program or data is at an end, that is, unless the end-of-file mark is encountered; if the data is at an end, send control out of the reading loop."

This feature is illustrated later in this section.

* The X in the symbolic instruction abbreviations represents the tape involved.

READ CARD (READC Y) (57). The contents of a binary card (24 words) are read into locations Y through Y + 23, unless a nonzero integer m appears in bits 9–14 of this instruction word. If the integer m appears, the first m words on the card are read into locations Y through Y + m − 1; if $m > 24$, only 24 words are read. If no further cards are present in the on-line card reader, the computer continues in sequence to the next instruction; otherwise, the next instruction is skipped.

Before we examine a few examples of writing and reading instructions a few remarks on *skip* instructions should be made. Skip instructions are instructions making a decision of the form

If condition p exists, continue in sequence; otherwise, skip one instruction.

By following the skip instruction with a jump instruction, a programmer creates a conditional jump operation. Skip and jump instructions are both decision instructions, and both permit alternative transfers of control. Skip instructions usually require a reference to a memory location and hence their operand addresses are used to refer to that location, rather than to a location for transfer of control (in a one-address computer). The reading instructions are a variation on the usual structure of skip instructions, however. Their reference to memory is associated with an additional operation, that of reading information into memory. Normally references to memory are made for the purpose of checking the stated condition.

The integer m, which is part of the reading and writing instructions, is coded for assembly by being written as a decimal integer in the symbolic instruction. The integer is written after two successive commas without intervening blank spaces.* Following is the assembly of three input-output instructions: BLØCK is the location 04400.

	Machine Words	Symbolic Instructions Oper.	Address
1.	0 70 07 00 04400	WRITEA	BLØCK,,7
2.	0 75 20 00 04400	WRITEF	BLØCK,,16
3.	0 62 12 00 04400	READTC	BLØCK,,10

Note that m is placed in the fourth and fifth octal digits (bits 9–14). The spaces in the machine words are used for clarity.

The three instructions listed cause the following operations to be performed:

1. A 7-word record containing the contents of locations BLØCK through BLØCK + 6 is written on tape A.

2. A 16-word record containing the contents of locations BLØCK through BLØCK + 15 is written on tape F.

3. If the record read from tape C contains no more than 10 words, all words are read

* The reason for the double-comma convention is explained in Chapter 8.

into memory starting at location BLØCK. If the record contains more than 10 words, the first 10 are read into locations BLØCK through BLØCK +9.

Loading a Program

For a program to be executed it must be loaded into the memory of the computer. The following procedure accomplishes this task. We assume that the entire memory is *cleared,* that is, that all its registers and words contain +0.*

To load a program into the DELTA 63 memory the *keys* on the console are used. The keys are a set of 36 binary switches, each one of which can be independently set (1-position) or reset (0-position). There is also a *load keys button* on the console; when it is pushed, the binary number stored in the keys is placed into location 00000 and control passes to that location. For example, if the keys are set as

$$0, 0, 1, 1, 0, 0, 1, 1, 0, 0, 1, 1, 0, \ldots$$

then the binary number 0011001100110··· is placed in location 00000.

The word usually placed in the keys for program-loading purposes is a READ instruction, either READTX or READC. This instruction is then executed, since control goes to location 00000 after the instruction in the keys is placed there. The instruction then loads the computer with a *loading program* which, in turn, loads an object program for execution.

The loading program that precedes the object program must contain the loading point of the latter program (where the first word of the program will be stored) and the starting point of the latter program (the address of the first executable instruction). Following is an example of a loading program; though written here in symbolic language, it would be punched in binary form on a card for use.

Example 7.5   Write a loading program to load from tape A.

The instruction to be placed in the keys reads one record of 7 words from tape A. The instructions in this record must be placed starting in location 00001, so that they are executed following the instruction in 00000. The keys' instruction word is

Machine Word	Symbolic Instruction
0 60 10 00 00001	READTA 1, ,8

A simple reading loop, using the skip feature of the READTX instruction to terminate the loop, can be established. A flowchart is drawn in Fig. 7.6. After a record of 24 words is read in, the reading instruction is address modified so that the next record is read into memory at a location 24 addresses later. This process repeats until the file is exhausted.

---

* The following description of the loading procedure is similar to the procedure used on most computers. Console switches and buttons of the type described are present, though the details are different.

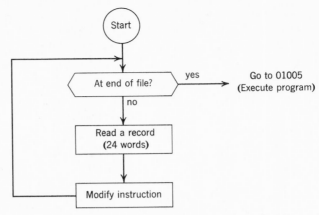

Fig. 7.6.   Flowchart of loading program (Example 7.5).

In the following loading program, the loading point is location 01000, and the starting point is location 01005.

Location	Oper.	Address	
READIN	READTA	/0/1000	LØADING PØINT
	JUMP	/0/1005	STARTING PØINT
	LØAD	READIN	MØDIFY INSTRUCTIØN
	ADD	N24	
	STØRE	READIN	
	JUMP	READIN	
N24	DECML	24	

This program has 7 words and comprises the first record on tape, read in by the keys instruction. As soon as the object program is loaded, control goes to location 01005 and the program is executed.

Loading Data

After a program is loaded into the computer memory its data must also be loaded. Data loading is usually accomplished by the program being executed, however, not by the loading program. For complete generality it is necessary to permit the programmer to place data wherever in memory he wishes. If data were loaded by the loading program in the same manner that the object program were, the former would immediately follow the latter in memory.

To signal the loading program to stop loading when the object program is in memory but before the data are in, an *end-of-program* card may be used. Reading instructions within the object program then read in data—a method for reading data that has this advantage: there may be so many data that they cannot all be placed in memory at the same time. The data can be read in and processed in batches, enough being read at a time to fill the available space. If the loading program read the data, all would have to be read at once.

Before the next example is given another instruction is introduced. This instruction enables part of the contents of the accumulator to be stored in a memory word.

STORE ADDRESS (STØRAD Y) (03). The contents of the address field of the AC, that is, bits 21–35, replaces the contents of the address field of location Y. The C(AC) and the other bits of Y are unchanged.

Example 7.6 Write a card-loading program that stops loading on encountering an end-of-program card, which contains the octal number 777777777777 in the first word position.

This loading program is similar to the one coded in the last example, which reads information from tape. The only change (aside from the reading instruction) is that a test for the end-of-program card must be made after each card is read. As the first word of each card is read into a memory location, the contents of that location must be checked for "777777777777"; if that number is found, control goes to the object program for execution. If the end-of-program card is omitted, card reading would be attempted when no cards are present in the card reader, and the computer would stop. A flowchart appears in Fig. 7.7.

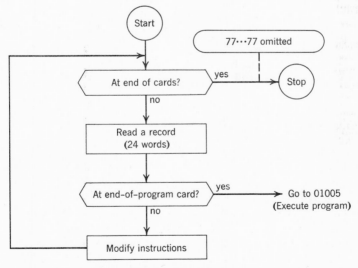

Fig. 7.7. Flowchart of modified loading program (Example 7.6).

Location	Oper.	Address	
READIN	READC	/Ø/1000	LØADING PØINT
	HALT		NØ "777777777777"
TEST	LØAD	/Ø/1000	TEST FIRST WØRD FØR
	SUBT	SEVENS	"777777777777"

(Continued)

```
        JUMPZE  /0/1005      GØ TØ PRØGRAM
        LØAD    READIN       MØDIFY INSTRUCTIØNS
        ADD     N24
        STØRE   READIN
        STØRAD  TEST
        JUMP    READIN

N24     DECML   24
SEVENS  ØCTAL   777777777777
```

As an example of a program that reads its data, consider the summation of n numbers; this problem was coded in Example 7.3 (page 123).

Example 7.7   Determine the sum of a given set of n numbers.   The numbers are stored in the block beginning at NUMBRS; their sum is to be placed in SUM.

The numbers are stored on data cards.   The number n is in the first word position of the first data card, and the n numbers are stored on the following cards, punched in binary, 24 to a card.   The last card is filled out with zeros.

The reading loop is similar to the loop in Example 7.5, where an object program is read in.

Location	Oper.	Address	
	READC	N,,1	READ IN N
LØØP	READC	NUMBRS	READ IN 24 NUMBERS
	JUMP	START	GØ TØ SUMMATIØN SEQUENCE
	LØAD	LØØP	
	ADD	N24	
	STØRE	LØØP	
	JUMP	LØØP	
START	CLEARS	SUM	
	• • •	• • • • •	

The program continues as in Example 7.3.

The placement of data on cards as in the last example is clumsy.   For example, if the number 595 is to be punched on a data card, it must be converted to binary form (1001010011) and then punched *down* three columns (with 26 leading zeros supplied to fill out the 36 bit positions allotted per binary word). It is far easier to punch the number 595 in three successive columns by a key-punch.   Since the binary form is essential in a binary machine, a conversion is necessary.   This problem is considered in Chapter 11.

Reading Out Results

The single remaining job to be considered in the process of elementary coding is the printing of results of a computation in usable form.   These results are usually printed on paper, but they may also be punched on cards or left on tape. Again we are only concerned here with tape writing, and for this purpose the

WRITEX instruction is used. We assume that the off-line printer prints the contents of one tape record on 1 or more lines, 10 words to a line, with 12 spaces allowed per word, in decimal form.

In the example that follows a complete program is written. Data are read in, computation is performed, and the results are written on tape.

Example 7.8 A deck of data cards contains n integers, one to a card, in the first word position, in binary form. Write a program that computes the sum of each set of three integers in succession and writes the $n/3$ sums on tape. The number n, a multiple of 3, appears on the first data card.

The program has two steps: (1) reading all the data and (2) computing the sums and writing them on tape.* A flowchart appears in Fig. 7.8.

In the first step the number n is read initially, into N. Then the n numbers are read in. The loop used for this purpose is similar to the reading loops in earlier examples in this section, except that it is not terminated by the end-of-file mark but is under the control of the number n. After n cycles, the loop terminates. In the event that the card reader detects a "no-cards" condition, control goes to ERRØR, the starting location of a coding sequence to deal with the situation. Hence if n is too large (that is, there are less than n numbers), the error will occur; if n is too small, some numbers will not be summed. After the numbers are read they are stored in successive locations starting at NMBRS. It is assumed that n never exceeds 3000.

In the second step three successive numbers at a time from the NMBRS block are summed, and the sum is written on tape B. In the loop it is necessary to modify three addresses, those that compute the sum. The first address is modified as usual, but the other two are set relative to the first, since they differ by 1 and 2 from that address. The STØRAD instruction must be used to set the second and third addresses because the AC will contain the LØAD operation code (01) during address modification of the first address. The operation code of the other instructions modified is that of the ADD instruction (04). The address of the comparison word CMPAR1 must be set to $NMBRS+2+n$, since that will be the address of the third modified instruction at the end; the comparison will be made against that instruction.

Location	Oper.	Address	
STEP1	READC	N,,1	READ N
	JUMP	ERRØR	JUMP IF END ØF FILE
	LØAD	SETWD1	INITIALIZE FIRST LØØP
	STØRE	LØØP1	
	ADD	N	
	STØRE	CMPAR1	
LØØP1	READC	NMBRS,,1	READ A NUMBER
	JUMP	ERRØR	
	LØAD	LØØP1	MØDIFY INSTRUCTIØN
	ADD	ØNE	
	STØRE	LØØP1	

(Continued)

---

* In both Examples 7.7 and 7.8, all the data are read into memory before any are processed. Most likely, this procedure would not be used in practice because of the space required. For example, in Example 7.8, three numbers would be summed as they were read in.

```
           SUBT      CMPAR1        TEST FØR N-TH NUMBER
           JUMPNZ    LØØP1

   STEP2   LØAD      SETWD2        INITIALIZE SECØND LØØP
           STØRE     LØØP2
           LØAD      SETWD3
           ADD       N
           STØRE     CMPAR2
   LØØP2   LØAD      NMBRS         ADD 3 NUMBERS
           ADD       NMBRS+1
           ADD       NMBRS+2
           STØRE     SUM
           WRITEB    SUM,,1        WRITE SUM ØN TAPE B
           LØAD      LØØP2         MØDIFY INSTRUCTIØNS
           ADD       THREE
           STØRE     LØØP2
           ADD       ØNE
           STØRAD    LØØP2+1
           ADD       ØNE
           STØRAD    LØØP2+2
           SUBT      CMPAR2        TEST FØR LAST SUM
           JUMPNZ    LØØP2
           HALT

   ØNE     DECML     1
   THREE   DECML     3
   N
   SUM
   SETWD1  READC     NMBRS,,1
   SETWD2  LØAD      NMBRS
   SETWD3  ADD       NMBRS+2
   CMPAR1                          (READC  NMBRS+N,,1)
   CMPAR2                          (ADD    NMBRS+2+N)
   NMBRS   BLØCK     3000
   ERRØR   ...       ....
```

Error Checking

Nothing has been said about input-output errors, aside from mention of the tape check bit. Tape-reading and tape-writing processes are far less reliable than data-moving operations within memory, so that special attention must be paid to input-output data transmission. The check bit is used in all cases to check for reversed bits. Sometimes an extra line of 7 bits appears at the end of each record; these are *longitudinal* check bits that perform the same function for channels of bits along the tape that the other check bits perform for lines of bits across the tape. Input-output checking may be accomplished either through coding or through circuitry; frequently, both techniques are used. We are not directly concerned with this problem; it is necessary, however, to be aware of the possibilities of errors.

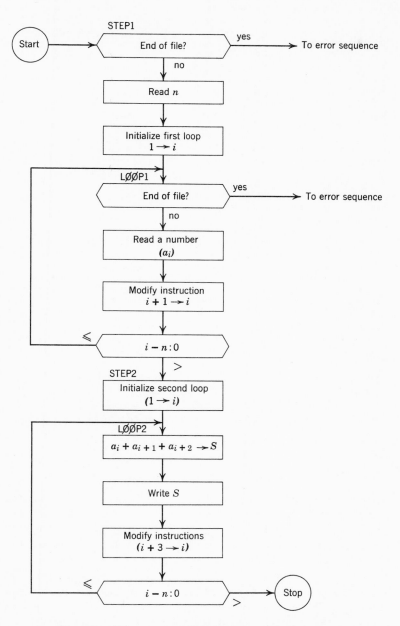

Fig. 7.8.   Flowchart for complete program (Example 7.8).

Summary

A loop that is present in the flowchart of a problem must be coded into a program loop. To process a sequence of data within the loop it is necessary to reference the sequence of memory locations in which the data are located. The technique of address modification is used to change the instructions in a manner that permits this sequential referencing. Instructions are operated on as though they were data, since the program is stored within memory.

A study of elementary input-output operations served two purposes in this chapter. First, several examples of the address modification technique were provided. Second, the processes of reading in a program and its data and writing out results were illustrated. With these operations and other operations studied in earlier chapters, the elementary coding picture has been completed.[1]

Notes

1. The following book has an introductory chapter on input-output coding techniques for the IBM 7090.

> H. D. Leeds and G. M. Weinberg, *Computer Program Fundamentals,* McGraw-Hill, 1961, Chapter 5.

PROBLEMS

Section 7.1

7.1. Write programs to evaluate the following expressions, where the $L(n)$ is N, the $L(x)$ is X, the a_i begin at NUMBRS, the b_i begin at DIGITS, i runs from 1 to n, and the result goes into ANSWER.

(a) $f_1 = \sum_{i=1}^{n} a_i^2$ (b) $f_2 = \sum_{i=1}^{n} a_i b_i$

(c) $f_3 = \sum_{i=1}^{n} \left(\frac{a_i + b_i}{a_i - b_i} \right)$ (d) $f_4 = \sum_{i=5}^{n-5} \left(\frac{a_i b_i}{a_i - b_i} \right)$

(e) $f_5 = \sum_{i=1}^{n/2} a_{2i}$ (n even)

7.2. What are the possible consequences of forgetting to reset addresses to their "initial values" when a program loop is begun?

7.3. Consider the recoding of the summation problem of Example 7.3 for a computer without a stored program. In such a computer constants in memory are available but the instructions that are executed are not.

7.4. In some computers the accumulator can be addressed. Discuss the advantages of this feature.

7.5. Operand addresses in a program can be modified to create addresses to which control is to be sent under various conditions. In some situations, the computed addresses depend on one parameter (i) or perhaps on a second (j) as well. Write coding sequences to execute the following transfers of control; i and j are integers in the range from 0 to 9 inclusively.

(a) If the $C(TEST) = i$, jump to $START + i$.

(b) If the $C(TEST) = i$, jump to $TABLE - 5i$.

(c) If the $C(TEST) = i$ and the $C(NEXT) = j$, jump to $LIST + ij$.

(d) If the $C(TEST) = i$, jump to $WØRD + i^2$.

(e) If the $C(TEST) = i$, jump to $START + C(WØRD + i)$.

7.6. In the following operations operand addresses are computed as a function of i and j to determine where quantities should be stored. Code these operations, where i and j are integers in the range from 0 through 6 inclusively.

(a) If the $C(TEST) = i$, add 1 to the $C(TABLE + i)$.

(b) If the $C(TEST) = i$, add 1 to the $C(LIST + 2i)$ and subtract 2 from the $C(LIST - 3i)$.

(c) If the $C(TEST) = i$ and the $C(NEXT) = j$, add the product $2ij$ to the $C(WØRD + ij)$.

Section 7.2

7.7. Recode the program in Example 7.8 so that 3 numbers are summed after they are read in. In this way it is not necessary to reserve space in memory for all n numbers.

7.8. Several sets of integers are punched on cards. Each set begins with a number punched on a card; this is the number of integers in the set of integers which follows. The integers are punched 5 to a card, except possibly for the last card in each set. Write a program that computes the sum of each set of integers and prints the result.

7.9. A set of $4n$ numbers is punched on cards, 4 to a card. The card following the last data card contains -0 in its first word position. Write a program that, for each card, reads in the numbers and prints the following information on one line: their sum, their product, the smallest of the 4, and the largest of the 4.

8

INDEX REGISTERS

Address modification was used in Chapter 7 to change memory references within a loop to process data located in sequence in memory. In this chapter we study the use of index registers, which modify instructions automatically and as a result, allow references to a sequence of memory locations to be made with little effort. Index registers provide indexing of the type described in Chapter 2. Computer instructions are available for setting, modifying, and testing the contents of index registers.

Index registers also find use in nonloop situations to permit rapid access to tables in memory. By this process, a number of operations can be executed rapidly.

8.1 THE USE OF INDEX REGISTERS

Indexing

In nearly all the problems that have been studied, a sequence of data was processed: the numbers of a set, stored in memory, were added, multiplied, or raised to a power. In analyzing the problems, we generally assigned a subscript to the variables, and the operations to be performed were indicated in terms of that subscript. For example, a_i represented the ith value of a series of numbers a_1, a_2, ... To indicate that, after a_i was processed, a_{i+1} was to be processed, an operation on the subscript was required:

$$i + 1 \rightarrow i$$

This means that 1 is to be added to the subscript, which generates the name of the next number.

To process the a_i as desired, it is necessary to modify the appropriate instructions. In Chapter 7 we saw that they can be modified by treating them as data, adding 1 to the operand addresses once each loop cycle. This characteristic of a problem, wherein an instruction must be periodically modified in order to process data stored in a sequence of memory locations, is extremely common. Most modern computers are built to permit the modification to be done simply and automatically.

Consider again the summation problem coded in Example 7.3 (page 123). Figure 7.2, which contains a flowchart for that problem, includes three operations on the index:

1. *Setting the index:*

$$1 \rightarrow i$$

2. *Increasing the index:*

$$i + 1 \rightarrow i$$

3. *Testing the value of the index*:

$$(i - n) : 0$$

It is desirable to have computer instructions available for performing these operations.

The Index Registers

All current large-scale and many small digital computers have facilities for performing indexing operations automatically. Special registers, called *index registers,* are used for this purpose. The contents of the index registers are used to modify automatically the operand addresses of computer instructions. Index registers are designated by number within the computer. If an instruction makes reference to an index register by its number, the contents of its operand address(es) are modified by the contents of that register.*

The DELTA 63 has 7 index registers, numbered 1, 2, ..., 7. Associated with most instructions is a *tag* which specifies one of these registers. Bits 18–20 in the instruction word comprise the *tag field,* pictured in Fig. 8.1. This 3-bit field may contain the integers 0, 1, ..., 7; 0 indicates that no index register is specified, whereas a nonzero integer designates a specific one. The symbol XR is used for "index register," and XR1, XR2, ..., XR7 refer to the 7 index registers.

* Recall that multi-address computer instructions may have two or more operand addresses.

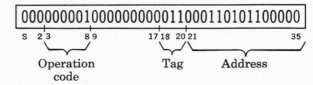

Fig. 8.1. Format of DELTA 63 instruction word showing the tag field (with a tag of 3).

A tag is indicated in HAP language by placing its numerical designator after a comma following the address, without an intervening blank space. The following instructions, shown both in symbolic and assembled form, indicate the use of XR1 and XR4, respectively:

Machine Word	Symbolic Instruction
0 01 0001 04500	LØAD LIST,1
0 04 0004 04500	ADD LIST,4

Each index register contains two 15-bit parts, the *modifier* and the *tally,* each containing an unsigned number. If XR*j* is indicated by a nonzero integer *j* in the tag field of an instruction, the effect on the instruction is that the operand address is temporarily increased by the contents of the XR*j* modifier.*

In an instruction with no tag (zero in the tag field), the address of the word that is processed is simply the operand address. In an instruction with a tag, however, the address of the processed word is given by the *sum* of the operand address and the contents of the XR modifier; the latter is written $C(XR)_m$. This address modification is automatic and temporary; the instruction does not change, but the effect is as though it were changed during the execution of the instruction. As an example, let the $C(XR1)_m = 100$; the instruction

ADD   WØRD,1

will cause the C(WØRD + 100) to be added to the accumulator.

The statements written in the operation boxes of a flowchart do not change, but if they contain subscripts their significance changes as the values of the subscripts change. Similarly, instructions in memory do not change if they have tags, but changing index register modifiers produce a sequence of effectively different instructions. This feature is reflected in the terminology applied to the operand address. The actual operand address in the instruction (for example, WØRD in the last instruction) is called the *direct address.* The sum of the direct address and the $C(XR)_m$ (for example, WØRD + 100) is called the *direct effective address,* or simply the *effective address.* The effective address is formed with respect to a modulus. In the DELTA 63, the addition is performed modulo 100000_8.†

* Some computers have operand addresses modified by subtraction of the XR modifier from the operand address; some have operand addresses modified by addition of the modifier.
† The symbol Y used in the descriptions of DELTA 63 instructions refers to the effective address.

Instructions

Index registers have their own set of instructions, referred to as *indexing instructions* in Section 3.3. Some of these are described here; others are described as needed.

SET INDEX REGISTER (SETXR Y) (31). The operand address of location Y replaces the contents of the tally of the specified index register, and the modifier of that index register is cleared. The C(Y) is unchanged.

SET INDEX REGISTER IMMEDIATE (SETXRI Y) (32). The operand address Y in this instruction word replaces the contents of the tally of the specified index register, and the modifier of that index register is cleared.

The following examples illustrate these instructions. (1) if the C(NUMBER) = 500, the instruction

$$\text{SETXR}\quad\text{NUMBER,1}$$

places the number 500 in the XR1 tally and sets the modifier to zero; (2) the instruction

$$\text{SETXRI}\quad\text{1000,1}$$

places the number 1000 in the XR1 tally and sets the modifier to zero.

INCREASE INDEX REGISTER MODIFIER (INCRXM Y) (33). The operand address Y in this instruction word is added to the contents of the modifier of the specified index register, and the sum is placed in the modifier.

As an example, to add 10 to the XR1 modifier, the following instruction is used.

$$\text{INCRXM}\quad\text{10,1}$$

The quantity Y may be negative. The instruction

$$\text{INCRXM}\quad -\text{10,1}$$

decreases the $C(XR1)_m$ by 10. Since index register modifiers hold unsigned numbers, negative numbers are stored as their complements with respect to 100000_8. Thus, -10 (-12_8) is stored in the modifier as 77766_8. Subtraction is treated as addition of a negative number, so if a modifier contains 20 (24_8), decreasing its contents by 10 is accomplished as follows:

decimal: $20 + (-10) = 10$
octal: $00024_8 + 77766_8 \equiv 00012_8 \ (\text{mod } 100000_8)$

INDEX JUMP (XJUMP Y) (34). If the modifier of the specified index register is less than the tally of that index register, the computer takes its next instruction from location Y and proceeds from there. If the modifier equals or exceeds the tally, the next instruction in sequence is taken.

Two of these indexing instructions have a feature different from all other instructions already studied. In the SETXRI and INCRXM instructions, the address field of the instruction does not contain the address of the operand but rather contains the operand itself. This addressing technique is called *im-*

mediate or *zero-level* addressing; the more common use of the address field is for direct or *first-level* addressing.

These four indexing instructions provide the means for performing the three indexing operations listed earlier in this section: setting, increasing, and testing indices. SETXR and SETXRI are used to set an index register; INCRXM is used to increase the contents of an index register; XJUMP is used to compare the contents of an index register with a predetermined number, thus providing a decision point in a program.

The term *indexable* refers to instructions whose operand addresses are modifiable by index registers. All the instructions introduced prior to this chapter are of this type, but the four indexing instructions just described are not. The operand addresses of the latter instructions are used for special purposes, as explained in the descriptions of the instructions, and cannot be index register modified.

The Variable Field

On a HAP symbolic card, the field composed of columns 16 through 72 was called the *address field* in Section 6.2. That field is renamed here as the *variable field*. This name is preferable because it more accurately reflects the nature of that field. Referring to the examples in recent chapters, we see that the contents of that field may vary in structure, as illustrated by the following instructions:

Oper.	Variable Field
LØAD	NUMBER
READC	DIGIT,,10
SETXR	WØRD,5

The variable field of a HAP symbolic card is considered to consist of three *subfields*, the *address, tag,* and *count.* These are supplied by using symbols or integers separated by commas without intervening blank spaces. The HAP assembler translates the symbols into numeric addresses and assigns the contents of the subfields to the following portions of a machine word:

Subfield	Machine Word Portion
Address	Bits 21–35
Tag	Bits 18–20
Count	Bits 9–14

The count is applicable only to input-output instructions.

A null subfield (delimited by two successive commas) causes a zero to be assembled in the corresponding portion of the machine word; the omitted tag of the READC instruction we have given is an example.

8.2 CODING WITH INDEX REGISTERS

In this section a number of problems are coded using index registers; input-output operations are omitted. Some of these problems were coded in earlier chapters and are recoded here so that index register coding may be compared with coding by other means.

Several comments must be made first, however, on an important difference that exists between index register values and indices. It is common practice to refer to a set of n numbers with the notation $a_1, a_2, \ldots, a_n$. If these numbers are placed in sequence in memory, they may be located in a block of n words starting at BLØCK. If that is done, then

$$C(\text{BLØCK} + i) = a_{i+1}$$

since a_1 is placed in BLØCK, a_2 is placed in BLØCK$+1$, etc. The address BLØCK$+i$ can be formed as an effective address if the modifier of an index register contains the index i, but there is a mismatch of one in that index and in the corresponding subscript.

This mismatch of one is unfortunate, but if the widely used conventions of subscripting and storage into memory blocks indicated here are used, the discrepancy must exist. The examples in this and later chapters reveal the discrepancy. The flowcharts that accompany the programs reflect the normal convention in mathematics. The rule that can be applied is: "The contents of the XR modifier is one number less than the corresponding subscript."

Example 8.1 Compute the value of x^n.
This problem was previously coded in Example 7.2 (page 120); a flowchart appears in Fig. 7.1.

In the program here, XR1 is used to represent the index i of Example 7.2; its modifier is initially set to 0 (for the reasons given earlier), and its tally is set to n. After each multiplication, the $C(\text{XR1})_m$ is increased by 1, and a test for the end of the problem is made by the XJUMP instruction. In executing that instruction, the computer compares the tally value n to the current value i in the XR modifier; when $i = n$, control no longer returns to the start of the loop but is sent to the next instruction (the end of the problem). Since an *index* i corresponds to a *subscript* $i + 1$, the condition of equality here corresponds to the condition under which a loop is terminated in Fig. 7.1: when subscript $i > n$.

The test for the case $n = 0$ is included. To allow for the possibility, the $C(P)$ is set equal to 1 initially; if $n \neq 0$, the $C(P)$ is later changed to x^n.

Location	Oper.	Var. Field	
START	SETXR	N,1	0 TØ XR—MØDIFIER
	LØAD	ØNE	1 TØ P (FØR CASE ØF ZERØ N)
	STØRE	P	
	LØAD	N	TEST N ... ØUT IF ZERØ

(Continued)

```
              JUMPZE   DØNE
              LØAD     ØNE              1 TØ AC
      MLTPY   MULT     X                AC*X TØ AC
              INCRXM   1,1              INCREASE INDEX BY 1
              XJUMP    MLTPY,1          TEST FØR END
              STØRE    P                STØRE RESULT
      DØNE    HALT

      N
      X
      P
      ØNE     DECML    1
```

This program is particularly simple; as can be seen, no address modification is needed, since the same operand, namely x, is used in each loop cycle. Only three instructions comprise the loop. A more general loop involves address modification, since operands usually occur in sequence in memory. The next example has such a loop.

Example 8.2   Determine the sum of a given set of n numbers. The numbers are stored in the block beginning at NUMBRS; their sum is to be placed in SUM.

This problem was previously coded in Example 7.3; a flowchart appears in Fig. 7.2.

The ADD instruction must refer to all n numbers in sequence, so that it is tagged; XR1 is used. Initially, the $C(XR1)_m = 0$, so that the instruction

$$\text{ADD} \qquad \text{NUMBRS,1}$$

makes the required reference to NUMBRS. The second time through the loop, the $C(XR1)_m = 1$, so that the effective address is NUMBRS + 1. This process continues, with successive numbers added each loop cycle until the loop is terminated. The ADD instruction is unchanged, but modification of the index register changes the effective address.

```
      Location    Oper.     Var. Field

                  CLEARS    SUM
                  SETXR     N,1
                  LØAD      SUM
      LØØP        ADD       NUMBRS,1        ADD A NUMBER
                  INCRXM    1,1             I+1 TØ I
                  XJUMP     LØØP,1          TEST FØR END
                  STØRE     SUM
                  HALT

      SUM
      N
      NUMBRS  BLØCK    100
```

Comparison of this program with the one coded in Example 7.3 indicates the usefulness of the index register. In Example 8.2, the accumulator is used for summation while the index register is used for counting. By performing these two arithmetic processes in different registers, it is not necessary to begin each loop cycle with an instruction that loads the current sum into the accumulator (as in Example 7.3). Instead, the loop can begin with the ADD instruction. It is not necessary to store the current sum each loop cycle; the sum can be stored once, at the end of the program. Similar comments can be made about Example 8.1. Furthermore, initialization of instructions is not necessary here, since they do not change as the program is run.

Example 8.3   Write a program to evaluate a polynomial of order n, for n as large as 100. The number n, the coefficients, and the variable x are located in N, the block starting at CØEFF, and X, respectively.

This program was previously coded in Example 7.4 (page 125); a flowchart appears in Fig. 7.3. Further analysis of the problem is not necessary; the principles embodied in the last two examples are used here.

Location	Oper.	Var. Field	
	SETXR	N,1	
	LØAD	CØEFF	B(0) TØ AC
LØØP	MULT	X	AC*X + B(I) TØ AC
	ADD	CØEFF+1,1	
	INCRXM	1,1	I+1 TØ I
	XJUMP	LØØP,1	TEST FØR END
	STØRE	Q	PØLYNØMIAL TØ Q
	HALT		
Q			
N			
X			
CØEFF	BLØCK	101	

The following two indexing instructions are used, respectively for (1) loading a specific quantity into each part of an index register and (2) for saving the contents of an index register for later use.

LOAD INDEX REGISTER (LØADXR Y) (35).   The leftmost 15 bits (bits S, 1–14) and the rightmost 15 bits (the address field) of the C(Y) replace the tally and modifier, respectively, of the specified index register. The C(Y) is unchanged.

The middle 6 bits of location Y do not transfer. Since Y has 36 bits and an index register has only 30, 6 must be left behind.

STORE INDEX REGISTER (STØRXR Y) (36).   The contents of the tally and the modifier of the specified index register replace the leftmost 15 bits and the rightmost 15 bits, respectively, of the C(Y). The middle 6 bits (bits 15–20) of the C(Y) are cleared. The contents of the index register are unchanged.

Since indices are usually indicated in a problem analysis by a sequence of letters $(i, j, k, \ldots)$, it is convenient to carry this notation into the symbolic language. In coding, indices are represented by tags on addresses; these tags can be symbolic also: I, J, K, ...   To accomplish this, the following pseudo-operation is useful.

SET.   Consider the following symbolic card:

Location	Oper.	Var. Field
S	SET	T

The HAP assembler assigns to the symbol S the value of the symbolic expression T. All the symbols in T must be defined earlier in the program because this assembly is done during pass 1.

Within the language of the assembler, the action resulting from the use of SET constitutes the assignment of a symbol to a location in memory. In the language of the program, however, this convention permits the use of a symbol to represent a number that may have no significance as a memory location.

Example 8.4 Given a set of n integers in LIST, count the number of negative integers present; n is at most 1000. Place the count in CØUNT.

This problem was analyzed in Section 2.2. A flowchart appears in Fig. 8.2. The loop in this problem is simple, for it consists merely of an instruction to count the negative integers plus the indexing instructions. Let index i count the loop cycles, that is, the number of integers in the set; let index j count the negative integers. XR1 and XR2 will be used for these, respectively. At the end of the program, the C(XR2) is placed in CØUNT. Note that XR2 contains the count of negative integers.

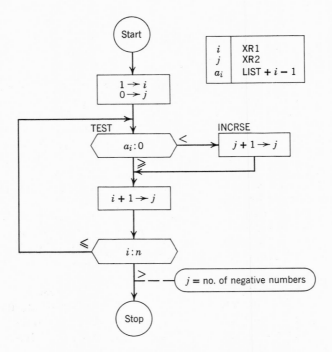

Fig. 8.2.   Counting negative numbers (Example 8.4).

Location	Oper.	Var. Field	
I	SET	1	
J	SET	2	
	SETXR	N,I	SET XRI (XR1)
	LØADXR	ZERØ,J	CLEAR XRJ (XR2)
TEST	LØAD	LIST,I	TEST A NUMBER
	JUMPZE	*+3	
	JUMPPL	*+2	
INCRSE	INCRXM	1,J	J+1 TØ J (CØUNT IF "—")
	INCRXM	1,I	I+1 TØ I
	XJUMP	TEST,I	
	STØRXR	CØUNT,J	
	HALT		
N			
ZERØ	DECML	0	
CØUNT			
LIST	BLØCK	1000	

Example 8.5 Given 80 numbers, find the sum of the tenth powers of the numbers. The numbers are stored in TABLEZ; the sum is to go in SUMZ.

This problem was analyzed in Section 2.4 (page 36): a flowchart appears in Fig. 8.3.

Since the flowchart for this problem has two nested loops, two index registers are required for the two indices i and j. The current value of the accumulator during the multiplication process is called p. The inner loop of this problem, which computes the tenth power of a number, is similar to the loop in Example 8.1. The outer loop, which sums the powers, is similar to the loop in Example 8.2. Summation cannot accumulate in the accummulator, since that register is also used for multiplication. Therefore the computed partial sums are stored in memory (in SUMZ). Symbolic indices are not used here, although they would serve well in this program.

Location	Oper.	Var. Field	
	CLEARS	SUMZ	0 TØ SUM
	SETXRI	80,1	
LØØPI	SETXRI	10,2	
	LØAD	ØNE	
LØØPJ	MULT	TABLEZ,1	P*NUMBER TØ P
INCRJ	INCRXM	1,2	J+1 TØ J
TESTJ	XJUMP	LØØPJ,2	TEST FØR END ØF J-LØØP
SUMI	ADD	SUMZ	SUM + P TØ SUM
	STØRE	SUMZ	
INCRI	INCRXM	1,1	I+1 TØ I
	XJUMP	LØØPI,1	
	HALT		
ØNE			
SUMZ			
TABLEZ	BLØCK	80	

Example 8.6 Given a list of 1000 integers, sort them into negative and positive integers, and compute the sums of the two lists.

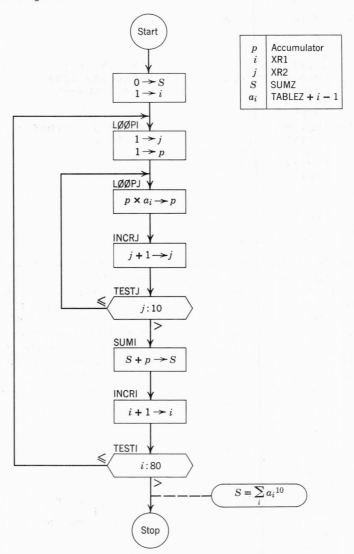

Fig. 8.3.   Flowchart with two nested loops (Example 8.5).

The numbers a_i start at location LIST.   Let the negative integers be placed in the block starting at NEGLST and the positive integers be placed in the block starting at PØSLST.   Let N_j be the jth *location* in the NEGLST block; let P_k be the kth location in the PØSLST block.   Place the sums in NEGSUM and PØSSUM; let S_n and S_p be the negative and positive sums.   A flowchart appears in Fig. 8.4.

Three index registers are to be used.   XR1 is the loop control index register (index i); XR2 and XR3 will be used to store the negative and positive integers (indices j and k),

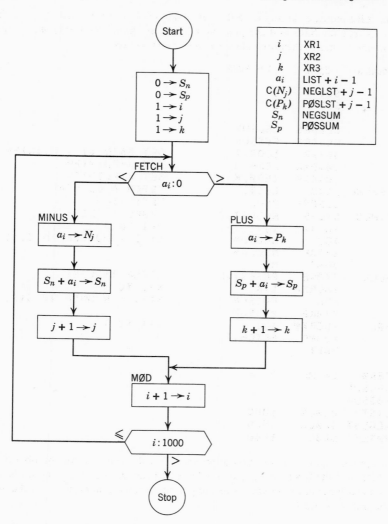

Fig. 8.4. Flowchart of number sorting by sign and adding (Example 8.6).

respectively. To store a positive integer, for example, the following pair of instructions is used:

Oper.	Var. Field
STØRE	PØSLST,K
INCRXM	1,K

The first instruction stores the integer, and the second instruction modifies XR2 so that the next time a positive integer is to be stored it will be placed in the *next word* in the list. Thus XR2 indicates at any time the next available location for storage of an integer. The same is true for XR3 and the positive list. These index registers *point* to the locations in memory; hence they are called *pointers* when so used.

Location	Oper.	Var. Field	
I	SET	1	
J	SET	2	
K	SET	3	
	CLEARS	NEGSUM	
	CLEARS	PØSSUM	
	SETXRI	1000,I	SET MAIN (I-) PØINTER
	LØADXR	ZERØ,J	SET J-PØINTER
	LØADXR	ZERØ,K	SET K-PØINTER
FETCH	LØAD	LIST,I	FETCH A NUMBER
	JUMPPL	PLUS	TEST SIGN
MINUS	STØRE	NEGLST,J	STØRE IN LIST
	INCRXM	1,J	J+1 TØ J
	ADD	NEGSUM	S(N) + NUMBER TØ S(N)
	STØRE	NEGSUM	
	JUMP	MØD	
PLUS	STØRE	PØSLST,K	STØRE IN LIST
	INCRXM	1,K	K+1 TØ K
	ADD	PØSSUM	S(P) + NUMBER TØ S(P)
	STØRE	PØSSUM	
MØD	INCRXM	1,I	I+1 TØ I
	XJUMP	FETCH,I	
	HALT		
ZERØ	DECML	0	
NEGSUM			
PØSSUM			
LIST	BLØCK	1000	
NEGLST	BLØCK	1000	
PØSLST	BLØCK	1000	

One other point to note about this program is that the counts of the number of entries in NEGLST and PØSLST are readily available, if needed, after the program is finished. These counts appear in the modifiers of the pointer index registers; they are the final values of the indices i and j.

The Time-Space Balance

A programmer is often faced with choosing between having a program run as quickly as possible and having it occupy as little space in memory as possible. A choice must be made as he writes his program, of course. Frequently, neither extreme is attainable, since the trouble in attaining cannot be justified by the results. It is, however, worthwhile to consider the possibility of approaching these goals. Let us examine the problem briefly by considering the summation problem coded in Example 8.2. In that problem we now assume $n = 60$. If the program loop is coded so that 3 numbers (rather than 1) are summed each cycle, the coding is:

Location	Oper.	Var. Field	
	CLEARS	SUM	
	SETXRI	60,1	
	LØAD	SUM	
LØØP	ADD	NUMBRS,1	ADD 3 NUMBERS
	ADD	NUMBRS+1,1	
	ADD	NUMBRS+2,1	
	INCRXM	3,1	
	XJUMP	LØØP,1	
	STØRE	SUM	

In each cycle numbers in 3 successive locations are added, and the $C(XR1)_m$ is increased by 3. Note that 3 operand addresses are effectively modified by the change in a single index register.

The same problem can easily be coded so that 2, 4, 6, 10, or 12 numbers are summed each cycle. (The number of summations per cycle must divide 60 without remainder if the loop is to be a simple one.) It is of interest to compare the memory space (exclusive of constants and the numbers to be summed) and the number of instructions executed for each of these possibilities.

If Z equals the number of summations per cycle, S equals the space in memory words, and T equals the "time" in number of instructions executed, then

$$S = Z + 6$$
$$T = 64 + 120/Z$$

Table 8.1 lists a number of values of Z, S, and T. The space is linearly dependent on Z, whereas the time is a constant plus a quantity inversely proportional to Z. This constant represents the 60 summations plus 4 other constants (concerned with initialization and storage of the result). No matter how the summation is accomplished, 60 numbers must be added, and 60 ADD instructions must be executed. The term $120/Z$ represents the index modification and loop-testing instructions; these are "bookkeeping" instructions which provide no direct computational help to the program. Two index register instruction executions per loop cycle are required (INCRXM and XJUMP); the number of loop cycles is

TABLE 8.1 SPACE AND TIME REQUIREMENTS FOR SUMMATION PROBLEM

Z	1	2	3	4	6	10	12
S	7	8	9	10	12	16	18
T	184	124	104	94	84	76	74

Z = number of summations per cycle
S = space in memory words (instructions)
T = "time" in instructions executed

$60/Z$, so that $120/Z$ such instructions must be executed. By increasing the summations per cycle the bookkeeping operations can be made fewer.

Although a simple loop was chosen to illustrate the time-space balance problem, the problem also occurs in complex programs where the choice may be more critical. A savings in time often must be paid for by added space requirements, and vice versa. If we compare the cases of Z equal to 1 and 2, we note that at the cost of 1 memory word (a 14% increase), the running time is decreased by one third.* This might be a worthwhile overall saving. Increasing Z to 3 does not yield as good an additional saving. If the optimal situation is a minimum $S \cdot T$ product, the best value of Z is 3.

Considerations of the type made here are representative, on an elementary scale, of the kind of planning necessary during coding. Further attention is paid to program planning and the use of memory space in Chapter 12.

8.3 NONLOOP INDEX REGISTER USE

The function of an index register is to provide automatic, temporary modification of the operand address of an instruction. Associated with this function is the more general task of loop control, where the following operations are required on the index: it must be set, modified, and tested. Indexing instructions are available to accomplish these jobs quickly and easily. As a consequence of the existence of these instructions, a number of other jobs are readily performable.

The examples studied in this chapter illustrated two of these other jobs. (1) Index registers may be used as counters. (2) Index registers may be used as pointers, for example, to indicate the currently available word in a list. In Example 8.6, XR2 and XR3 were used in both ways simultaneously.

Both these additional functions of index registers can be classified as "nonloop." Although used inside loops here, they are not involved directly in loop control. This section is concerned with further coding techniques involving index registers used in nonloop functions.

Table-Look-at

Another nonloop use of index registers is in the *table-look-at* technique.[1] This method uses the contents of an index register to make a single table reference. The reference is made rapidly, but sometimes a lengthy table is required in memory. The following example indicates one way in which the technique is used; further examples are given in Chapter 15.

An instruction that permits the placement of a portion of the accumulator into an index register is described next. It is useful in Example 8.7.

---

* Not all instructions on computers take the same amount of time for execution, so that a true measure of "time to run" would take into account the various instruction execution times.

PLACE ADDRESS IN INDEX REGISTER MODIFIER (PADDXM) (37). The contents of the address field of the accumulator replaces the contents of the modifier of the specified index register. The C(AC) and the index register tally are unchanged.

No address, immediate or direct, is involved, although a tag is necessary. To indicate that the integer in the variable field is a tag rather than an address, a comma must precede the tag. This is required by the convention described in Section 8.1. An example of one instruction is the following.

Machine Word	Symbolic Instruction
0 37 0006 00000	PADDXM 0,6

Example 8.7 Given 2000 positive integers, all less than 100 in value, determine a histogram as follows. Compute the distribution of integers in ten equal intervals: 0–9, 10–19, ... , and 90–99. The integers are located in the block starting at LIST.

The interval to which each integer belongs can most readily be found by dividing it by 10, discarding the remainder. If the quotient is q, the integer lies in the $(q+1)$th interval.

The value q is used to set an index register and thereby to select one of 10 counters, which is then incremented by 1. These counters count the number of integers in the 10 intervals. A flowchart is drawn in Fig. 8.5. The 10 counts are $n_1, n_2, \ldots, n_{10}$.

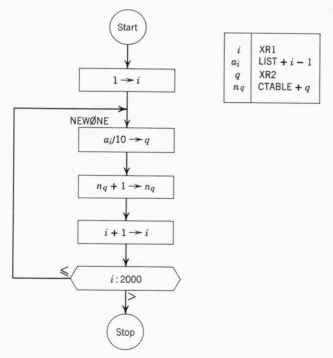

i	XR1
a_i	LIST $+ i - 1$
q	XR2
n_q	CTABLE $+ q$

Fig. 8.5. Determination of a histogram (Example 8.7).

Location	Oper.	Var. Field	
	SETXRI	2000,1	
NEWØNE	LØAD	LIST,1	FETCH AN INTEGER
	DIV	TEN	
	PADDXM	0,2	INTEGER/10 TØ XR2
	LØAD	CTABLE,2	FETCH PRØPER CNTR
	ADD	ØNE	N(Q)+1 TØ N(Q)
	STØRE	CTABLE,2	
	INCRXM	1,1	I+1 TØ I
	XJUMP	NEWØNE,1	
	HALT		
TEN	DECML	10	
ØNE	DECML	1	
CTABLE	BLØCK	10	THE 10 CØUNTERS
LIST	BLØCK	2000	

Selection of the proper counter is made by a reference to a table or list simply by using the head location (CTABLE) as a direct address. Modification by the index register produces the proper effective address for selection of a counter.

Push-Down Lists

Data are sometimes processed after being initially stored into lists. The sorting problem of Example 8.6 has this feature; 1000 integers were placed into two lists, the choice of the list depending on the sign of the integers. As an aid to the storage of the integers, two index registers were used as pointers.

Consider a situation in which numbers are to be both added to and removed from a list. The term *push-down list* refers to a list that has this property. Items for the list are to be stored in some manner and are to be removed later in some other manner. Pointers are used to keep track of the next available position for an entry or of the next item to be removed. The concept of the "next item" or "next location" is essential to the idea of a push-down list. In Example 8.6 this concept was introduced. Another example serves to illustrate the concept further.

Example 8.8 The block of 1000 words starting at PDLIST contains a set of k items (numbers), the first of which is located in PDLIST, the head of the list. The items are stored in successive memory words; the number k is stored in the modifier of XR7.

The following actions occur:

1. An item is added to the bottom of the list, and the $C(XR7)_m$ is increased by 1 to reflect the addition.

2. An item is removed from the top of the list, the list is moved up in its entirety one position, and the $C(XR7)_m$ is decreased by 1 to reflect the removal.*

---

* In practice, there may be no reason for moving up the list; it is done here for illustration.

The sequence of these actions is unknown; they may occur in any sequence, for example, 1, 2, 2, 2, 1, ... This situation may be likened to a purchase order processing scheme, where orders are handled in the order received; new orders go at the bottom while the top order is processed first. This approach is sometimes called "first-in-first-out" sequencing.

The number k may be zero, but we assume it never becomes negative; that is, no more items are removed than are added, if we start with an empty list.

Two subprograms (or *routines*) are required: one to add an item and one to remove an item. These must be coded independently, since that is how they are used. Let the item to be added to the list be stored in NEW; let the item to be removed be stored in ØLD.

The add-item routine (ADDITM) consists of these steps.

1. The C(NEW) must be placed at the bottom of the list; the address of the first free location is given by the tagged address PDLIST,7 since the $C(XR7)_m = k$, the number of items in the list.
2. The $C(XR7)_m$ must be increased by 1.

The flowchart in Fig. 8.6a shows the ADDITM routine. The ith word in the PDLIST is L_i.

The remove-item routine (REMITM) consists of these steps:

1. The C(PDLIST), the first item, must be stored in ØLD.
2. The $k - 1$ remaining items must be moved up one word each. This is accomplished by a loop, which is to be under the control of XR1. The $C(XR7)_m$ must be moved to XR1.
3. The $C(XR7)_m$ must be decreased by 1.

The flowchart in Fig. 8.6b shows the REMITM routine.

Location	Oper.	Var. Field	
ADDITM	LØAD	NEW	PUT ITEM AT BØTTØM
	STØRE	PDLIST,7	ØF LIST
	INCRXM	1,7	K+1 TØ K
REMITM	LØAD	PDLIST	PUT FIRST ITEM IN "ØLD"
	STØRE	ØLD	
	STØRXR	TEMP,7	C(XR7) TØ XR1
	SETXR	TEMP,1	
	INCRXM	-1,1	K-1 IN XR1
MØVE	LØAD	PDLIST+1,1	L(I+1) TØ L(I)
	STØRE	PDLIST,1	
	INCRXM	1,1	
	XJUMP	MØVE,1	
	INCRXM	-1,7	K-1 TØ K

Push-down lists are used in a variety of ways and under a variety of names. In fact, the term push-down, and its counterpart "pop-up," are not standardized. In some varieties of these lists, items are put in at the top and removed from the top, or they are all added to the list, which is then sorted. In any case, index registers are used as pointers to one or more key locations in the list. When

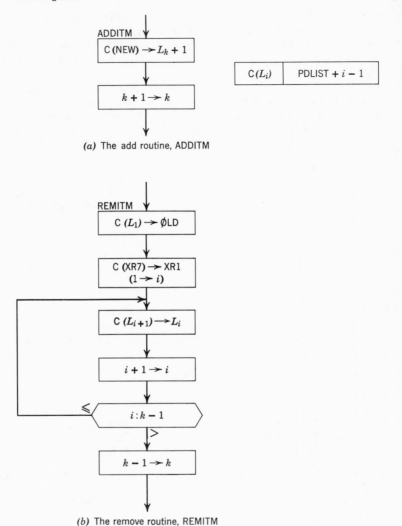

(a) The add routine, ADDITM

(b) The remove routine, REMITM

Fig. 8.6.   Routines for push-down list (Example 8.8).

information is to be added to or removed from the list, the index registers indicate appropriate locations.

8.4 INDIRECT ADDRESSING

Levels of Addressing

A computer is able to perform operations on a sequence of data within a loop
because of its ability to perform address modification on its instructions.   This

modification may be "manual," as explained in Chapter 7, or it may be "automatic," through the use of index registers. The concept of address modification is generalized further in this section with a consideration of *indirect addressing*. This feature is not directly related to the use of index registers, but its action is similar, since it provides another means of automatic address modification.

Zero-level and first-level addressing were discussed in Section 8.1. In zero-level addressing the operand of an instruction is located in the address field. In first-level or direct addressing, the address of the operand is located in the address field; the operand is one level removed from the instruction. An operand may be two levels removed; if so, the addressing is *second-level* or *indirect*. In such cases the address of the operand (the *indirect address*) is located in a word whose address is in the instruction. The situation is pictured in Fig. 8.7.

How Indirect Addressing Works

To indicate that the operand in an instruction is two levels removed, a special mark or digit is required in the instruction. In the DELTA 63 and in some other computers this mark is called a *flag*.

Indirect addressing in the DELTA 63 is indicated by the presence of a 1 in bit 14 of an instruction word. In HAP language, an asterisk immediately following the operation serves this purpose. Following are some examples of indirect addressing.

Machine Words	Symbolic Instructions	
0 01 0000 07700	LØAD	WØRD
0 01 0100 07700	LØAD*	WØRD
0 01 0002 07700	LØAD	WØRD,2
0 01 0102 07700	LØAD*	WØRD,2

Consider an instruction without a flag:

Oper.	Var. Field
LØAD	WØRD

This means "load the C(WØRD) into the AC." If this instruction is flagged

LØAD*	WØRD

we now mean "load the C(C(WØRD)) into the AC." In other words, the C(WØRD) is the operand address of this instruction; Fig. 8.7c illustrates the process.

Next consider the effect of a tag on an instruction.

LØAD	WØRD,2

means "load the $C(WØRD + C(XR2)_m)$ into the AC." If this instruction is flagged

LØAD*	WØRD,2

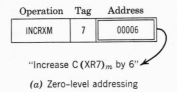

"Increase C(XR7)$_m$ by 6"

(a) Zero-level addressing

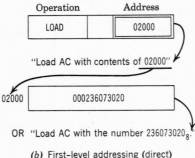

"Load AC with contents of 02000"

OR "Load AC with the number 236073020$_8$."

(b) First-level addressing (direct)

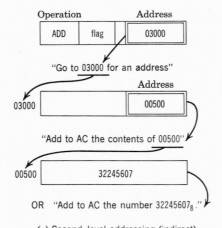

"Go to 03000 for an address"

"Add to AC the contents of 00500"

OR "Add to AC the number 32245607$_8$."

(c) Second-level addressing (indirect)

Fig. 8.7.   Levels of addressing.

we now mean "load the $C(C(W\text{\O}RD+C(XR2)_m))$ into the AC." By this is meant do the following: (1) form an effective address equal to $W\text{\O}RD+C(XR2)_m$; (2) go to that address to find the $C(W\text{\O}RD+C(XR2)_m)$, the indirect address; (3) load the C(indirect address) into the AC.

To illustrate the operation of the tagged and flagged instruction, assume the following, where all numbers are octal:

> WØRD is location 07700
> $C(XR2)_m = 100$
> $C(10000) = 000000022222$
> $C(22222) = 666$

Then the instruction

> **LØAD*   WØRD,2**

causes the following to happen:

> Loaded into the AC is the $C(C(WØRD+C(XR2)_m))$
> $= C(C(07700+100))$
> $= C(C(10000))$
> $= C(22222)$
> $= 666$

It is also possible to have a tag in the word whose address is given in an instruction which is tagged and flagged. If the tag in the instruction word is i and the tag in the addressed word is j, the overall effective address is

$$C(C(WØRD) + C(XRi)_m) + C(XRj)_m)$$

where WØRD is the operand address. Note the role that the tags play at the two levels. They effect modification of the address at which they are located.

Using Indirect Addressing

Indirect addressing provides a means for changing the operand address of an instruction automatically. It is used primarily when it is more convenient or more expedient for the location of an operand address to be given than for the operand address itself to be given. If, for example, a number of references to a particular location must be made, and it is necessary to change the address of the referenced word, each reference must be changed. If, however, these references were made indirectly through another fixed address, the only change needed would be in that fixed address.

To illustrate the usage of indirect addressing in this manner, consider again a list with a pointer to a particular location. A memory word, say PØINTR, might contain that location. There may be ten references to the pointer, that is, there may be ten instructions in the program referring to the list location. If these references are made indirectly, as in these instructions

> **LØAD*   PØINTR**
>
> **STØRE*   PØINTR**
>
> • • •   • • • • •

then only the C(PØINTR) will have to be changed if the list location of current interest changes. The result is a change in the effective addresses of all ten instructions.

If one program provides information to another (as in the case of subroutines, the subject of Chapter 10), the information is frequently provided by giving the locations at which the information is to be found. The latter program can obtain this information by indirectly addressing those memory words containing the addresses of the information.

Another example of the usefulness of indirect addressing is provided by the problem of sorting several blocks of numbers. Suppose it is necessary to sort them so that later they may be processed in an order given by the size of the first number in each block; the block whose first number is smallest is to be processed first. The entire blocks can be moved to place these first numbers in order, but by sorting the *addresses* of these first numbers so that the numbers are in order, indirect addressing through these addresses provides a ready means of processing the blocks in order. The following example illustrates the technique.

Example 8.9 Given five blocks of numbers and a sorted list of the starting addresses of the blocks, write a program to process the blocks in the indicated sequence. The program is to be written so that each number to be processed is loaded into the accumulator and processed in some manner. (This processing is not of interest here and is therefore not coded.)

Let the blocks of numbers be located as follows.

Starting Address	Numbers	
1. 01000	456,3476,91,246,...	(340_8 numbers)
2. 01400	345,9801,23,56,...	(165_8 numbers)
3. 01600	400,390,1897,5676,...	(2100_8 numbers)
4. 03000	289,45,190,4563,22,...	(321_8 numbers)
5. 03700	600,563,22,1111,...	(1005_8 numbers)

When the blocks are "sorted" by sorting starting addresses so that first numbers are in increasing order, we have (at SØRTED):

Location	Contents	
SØRTED	000000	103000
" +1	000000	101400
" +2	000000	101600
" +3	000000	101000
" +4	000000	103700

The starting addresses are located in the address field. The purpose of the 1-tags is explained later.

To process these blocks, it is necessary for their sizes to be available. Assume that in the block at BLSIZE are listed, in an order corresponding to the sorted list, the sizes of the five blocks:

BLSIZE	000000 000321
" +1	000000 000165
" +2	000000 002100
" +3	000000 000340
" +4	000000 001005

The program consists of two nested loops. Each inner loop cycle processes one number, and each outer loop cycle processes one block of numbers. XR1 and XR2, representing indices i and j, respectively, control the inner and outer loops. A flowchart is drawn in Fig. 8.8. The inner loop must cycle 321_8 times for the first block, 165_8 times for the second block, etc. These numbers are located in the BLSIZE block and must be placed in succession in XR1. To effect this, the address of the SETXR instruction is modified by address arithmetic once each outer loop cycle. Initial setting of the SETXR instruction is omitted.

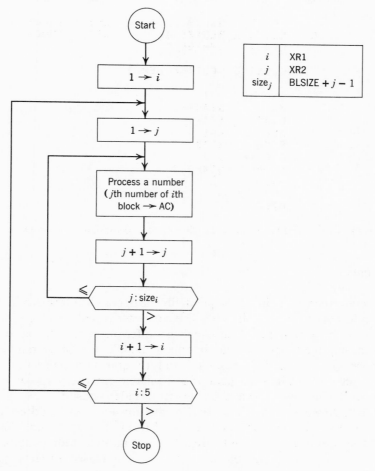

Fig. 8.8. Processing blocks of numbers (Example 8.9).

Indirect addressing may also be used to load the numbers in each block into the accumulator. The instruction

$$\text{LØAD*} \qquad \text{SØRTED,2}$$

has a direct effective address equal to SØRTED + i, since the $C(XR2)_m = i$. When the ith block is being processed, the indirect address of this instruction is the address given in the ith position of the SØRTED list. The 1-tag in each of the words in that list is used to form the sequence of indirect effective addresses required to load the accumulator with the numbers in the block. Thus, if $i = 3$, the addresses so formed are 01600, 01601, 01602, ... These are the addresses of the numbers in the third block. (This program uses an instruction which is tagged and flagged and whose first-level memory reference is also tagged.)

Location	Oper.	Var. Field.			
	SETXRI	5,2	SET	I	INDEX
START	SETXR	BLSIZE,1	SET	J	INDEX
	LØAD*	SØRTED,2			
	(PRØCESSING	RØUTINE HERE)			
	INCRXM	1,1			
	XJUMP	START+1,1			
	LØAD	START			
	ADD	ØNE			
	STØRE	START			
	INCRXM	1,2			
	XJUMP	START,2			
	HALT				
ØNE	DECML	1			

The SØRTED and BLSIZE lists and the five blocks accompany this program.

Summary

The importance of modifying sequentially the operand addresses of instructions in a loop has been well established. The computer is built so that address modification can be automatic. Index registers offer one means for accomplishing this by causing the temporary and automatic modification of operand addresses. This process is rapid and easily coded, and it requires no instruction initialization. A set of indexing instructions is available for the purposes of setting, modifying, testing, and storing the contents of index registers.

Indirect addressing offers a second means for automatic address modification; operands are one more level removed from the instructions that process them. The combined use of index registers and indirect addressing provide the programmer with considerable flexibility and increased program execution speeds.

Notes

1. A paper describing the table-look-at technique in more detail is

P. M. Sherman, "Table-Look-At Techniques," *Comm. Assoc. Computing Machinery,* **4** (1961), pp. 172–174.

PROBLEMS

Section 8.1

8.1. Compare the indexing procedures of this chapter with the corresponding operations in Section 7.1. What operations in the latter correspond to the several indexing instructions described here? How many instructions are saved through the use of index registers rather than address modification?

8.2. What would be the consequences if the SETXR and SETXRI instructions were interchanged in two program loops?

8.3. Distinguish between indexable and indexing instructions. Describe the two uses of tags in these instructions.

Section 8.2

8.4. Write programs to evaluate the five expressions in Problem 7.1 using index registers.

8.5. The mismatch in indexing discussed at the start of the section can be avoided. Rewrite two or three of the programs of Problem 8.4 to do so.

8.6. The numbers a_i, $i = 1, 2, \ldots, 99$, are stored in the block starting at NUMBRS. Compute the averages of each set of 3 adjacent numbers, 33 averages in all, and place them in the block starting at AVRAGE.

8.7. The exponential function is to be approximated by a power series:

$$e^x = 1 + x + x^2/2! + x^3/3! + \cdots$$

(*a*) This series may be considered to be a finite polynomial, if it is terminated after a definite number of terms. Assume that 10 terms are sufficient to yield an accurate answer, and write a program using this approach.

(*b*) The series can be evaluated one term at a time from the left, until the last term added is less than a predetermined amount. Assume this amount is 10^{-6} and write a program using this approach. Scaling must be applied in this program; assume that this has already been done.

8.8. A list is stored at VALUES of a quantity at all intersections of a square mesh grid of size 10×10; there are 121 such points, a_{ij}, i and j running from 0 through 10. Write a program to compute new values of the 81 interior points according to the following formula:

$$a_{ij}' = \tfrac{1}{4}(a_{i+1,j} + a_{i,j+1} + a_{i-1,j} + a_{i,j-1})$$

Thus each new value is determined as the average of its four closest neighbors. The process is to be repeated indefinitely, until the interior values converge. This is assumed to occur when the difference between the sum of the old values and the sum of the new values is less than a predetermined amount, stored in DELTA.

8.9.   Write a looping program to clear as much as possible of the internal memory of the computer, including the program itself. A loading program, of the type described in Section 7.2, is to be used.

8.10.   Given a block of 2000 integers starting at DIGITS, write programs to perform the following.

(*a*) Count the number of times 3 positive integers occur in succession (if 5 integers in a row are positive, this occurs 3 times in the 5);

(*b*) count the number of times a negative number just precedes a positive number;

(*c*) determine if a string of 10 or more successive numbers anywhere in the list are all positive.

8.11.   The following locations in a program are to be set to zero: Q through Q+4, Q+10 through Q+14, . . . , Q+40 through Q+44. The other words in the block are to be left unchanged. Write two programs to accomplish this task.

(*a*) Use five separate loops, none nested;

(*b*) use two nested loops.

Compare the programs with respect to memory space and execution time.

Section 8.3

8.12.   Discuss the differences between the use of index registers as loop-controlling devices and in nonloop situations as pointers to lists. Discuss the similarities.

8.13.   Write a program to determine a histogram over unequal intervals as follows: compute the distribution of integers in 20 intervals of 4 different sizes. The intervals are these:

$$0-9, 10-19, \ldots , 40-49,$$
$$50-99, 100-149, \ldots , 250-299,$$
$$300-399, 400-499, \ldots , 700-799,$$
$$800-999, 1000-1199, \ldots , 1600-1799$$

Use the techniques of Example 8.7 where feasible.

8.14.   Write push-down routines to accomplish the following operations.

(*a*) Sort the entries in a list PDLIST, placing the smallest entry first;

(*b*) enter a new quantity into PDLIST, which may be assumed sorted, such that the enlarged list is still sorted;

(*c*) remove an entry from PDLIST whose position is determined by the $C(XR1)_m$, and close up the gap by moving up all subsequent entries.

9

SEQUENCING IN MEMORY

Sequencing refers to the flow of control through a program. *Normal* flow is the transfer of control from one memory location to the next in numerical sequence; more specifically, it is the transfer of control from one instruction to the next. In order to transfer control in any other way, jump or skip instructions are necessary. Either conditionally or unconditionally, they interrupt the normal flow in some fashion.

In this chapter we study a number of ways in which particular patterns of flow can be effected. Sometimes the programmer can explicitly determine these patterns; at other times, the patterns depend on the structure of the data.[1]

9.1 BRANCHING

Decision Instructions

The term *branching* refers to the variation of transfer of control at a decision point (or *branch point*) in a program. At a conditional jump, for example, there are two ways for the program to branch: control will either jump to a stated location or it will pass to the next sequential address. At a skip instruction, the program will branch to either the next instruction or the instruction after that. Almost all decision instructions in a one-address computer are binary, that is, they have two branches. By combining several instructions, however, any number of branch paths at a point in a program can be created.

167

Some decision instructions have already been studied.   The unconditional jump and four conditional jump instructions were described in Section 5.3.   Two reading skip instructions were described in Section 7.2.   All these were binary-decision instructions.   Another instruction, which compares the relative sizes of two numbers, provides a triple branching.

COMPARE ACCUMULATOR WITH STORAGE (CØMPAR Y) (41).   If the C(AC) is algebraically greater than the C(Y), the computer executes the next instruction in sequence.   If the C(AC) equals the C(Y), the computer skips the next instruction and proceeds from there.   If the C(AC) is algebraically less than the C(Y), the computer skips the next two instructions and proceeds from there.

To carry out the branching, which in general requires sending control to one of three different locations, a series of three jump instructions frequently follows the CØMPAR instruction.

```
Oper.     Var. Field

CØMPAR    WØRD          CØMPARE  AC  WITH  "WØRD"
JUMP      GREATR        JUMP  IF  AC  GREATER
JUMP      EQUAL         JUMP  IF  AC  EQUAL
JUMP      LESS          JUMP  IF  AC  LESS
```

If the CØMPAR instruction is located at 01000 and the C(AC) = $+50$, then

control will go to 01001 (then to GREATR) if the C(Y) = -75
control will go to 01002 (then to EQUAL) if the C(Y) = $+50$
control will go to 01003 (then to LESS) if the C(Y) = $+75$*

The following example illustrates one use of the CØMPAR instruction.

Example 9.1   Given a set of n numbers $(a_1, a_2, \ldots)$, determine the largest number.   The numbers, of which there are no more than 1000, are stored in the block starting at SET; the largest number is to be stored in BIG.

A flowchart appears in Fig. 9.1.   Initially the first number is placed in the AC.   Then the C(AC) is successively compared with $a_2, a_3, \ldots$, until a larger number is found.   When a larger number is found, it is placed in the AC, and the process repeats, the C(AC) being compared to the next numbers in sequence.   After all the numbers are tested, the C(AC) is the largest number in SET; it is stored in BIG.   The flowchart indicates that the index i is initially set to 1, which causes a_1 to be compared to itself.   Although unnecessary, this is done for uniformity with loops in other programs.

```
Location   Oper.     Var. Field

           LØAD      SET          A( 1)  TØ  AC
           SETXR     N,1
FETCH      CØMPAR    SET,1        CØMPARE  C(AC)  TØ  A(I)
           JUMP      NEXT         C(AC)  GREATER
```

(Continued)

---

* Sometimes the coding sequence starting at LESS (or the equivalent) immediately follows the first two jump instructions, so that the third JUMP becomes unnecessary.

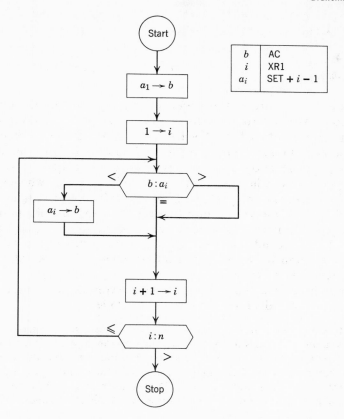

Fig. 9.1.   Determination of largest number (Example 9.1).

```
           JUMP      NEXT                  "     EQUAL
           LØAD      SET,1                 "     LESS,   A(I) TØ AC
NEXT       INCRXM    1,1
           XJUMP     FETCH,1
           STØRE     BIG                   STØRE THE LARGEST NUMBER
           HALT

BIG
N
SET        BLØCK     1000
```

A third JUMP instruction is unnecessary because control simply passes directly to the second LØAD instruction if the C(AC) is less than a_i.

Some computers have skip instructions that test conditions in memory. The operand address in those instructions is used for this memory reference. Examples are "test for zero in location Y," "test for positive number in location Y," etc. If these instructions, the CØMPAR instruction, and others are combined, complex branching points can be created; we next examine some of the methods used to realize such complex branchings.

Fixed Branching

A problem may require that different sequences of operations be performed at the various passes through a loop. For example, operation P may be required on even-numbered loop cycles (the second, fourth, . . . loop cycles), whereas operation Q may be required on odd-numbered loop cycles (the first, third, . . . loop cycles), or operation R may be required whenever a positive number is to be processed, whereas operation S may be required whenever a negative number or zero is to be processed. In the first case, the programmer can code the selection of the several branches into his program; the branch "decisions" are predetermined. This is called *fixed-sequence* branching or *fixed* branching. In the second case, the programmer must provide for testing of the data, since the branch decisions depend on them. This is called *variable-sequence* or *variable* branching.

To illustrate fixed branching, two examples are considered. In these analyses coding is simple when the flowcharts are fully detailed.

Example 9.2   Code a branch point that sends control alternately to operations P and Q.

There are a number of ways to code an alternating branch point, depending on which instructions are chosen. Using instructions already studied, we base the decision on the sign of a number in memory. The sign is reversed every time control passes to the branch point, after which the sign is tested with a JUMPPL instruction. Since the sign is alternately plus and minus, the desired branching results. A flowchart appears in Fig. 9.2.

```
        Location    Oper.      Var. Field

                    • • •      • • • • •
                    LØAD       ZERØ           CLEAR AC
                    SUBT       SIGNWD         CHANGE SIGN ØF "SIGNWD"
                    STØRE      SIGNWD
                    JUMPPL     ØPERP          JUMP TØ ØPERATIØN "P"
                    JUMP       ØPERQ          JUMP TØ ØPERATIØN "Q"
                    • • •      • • • • •
        SIGNWD      DECML      1
        ZERØ        DECML      0
```

If the initial sign of SIGNWD is plus (as indicated here), control will first go to operation Q, since the sign is changed before the test. The C(SIGNWD) will be alternately +1 and −1.*

Example 9.3   Code a branch point that sends control to one of four operations in cyclic sequence: P, Q, R, S, P, Q, ...

---

* Some computers have a single instruction that will load the *negative* of the contents of a memory word into the accumulator.

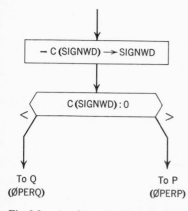

Fig. 9.2. An alternating branch point (Example 9.2).

Here a tagged JUMP instruction is used to produce a cycling transfer of control (with XR1). The effective address of this instruction will be BRANCH, BRANCH+1, . . . , BRANCH+3, in sequence, sending control respectively to ØPERP, ØPERQ, . . . , ØPERS. Control will then go to operations P, Q, R, and S. To produce these effective addresses, the $C(XR1)_m$ is set to 1, 2, 3, 0, 1, 2, ... Increasing the $C(XR1)_m$ is no problem, but following 3 with 0 requires special treatment. By setting the XR1 modifier and tally to 0 and 4 initially, a jump can be effected with the XJUMP instruction as long as the modifier is less than 4. The jump then resets the modifier to 0 and the process repeats. Initially, XR1 must be set by a SETXRI instruction. A flowchart appears in Fig. 9.3.

Location	Oper.	Var. Field	
	SETXRI	4,1	(EARLY IN PRØGRAM)
	...	.....	
	INCRXM	1,1	I+1 TØ I
	XJUMP	JUMPS,1	TEST I ... JUMP IF
	SETXRI	4,1	LESS THAN 4
JUMPS	JUMP	BRANCH,1	JUMP TØ 1 ØF 4 PLACES
BRANCH	JUMP	ØPERP	I = 0
	JUMP	ØPERQ	1
	JUMP	ØPERR	2
	JUMP	ØPERS	3

The program can be made slightly simpler with indirect addressing by flagging the JUMP instruction at JUMPS and removing the JUMP operations from the next four operation fields. The extension of this technique to any number of paths is straightforward.

Another branching situation occurs when an operation P must be performed every nth time through a branch point and not performed at other passes. The program in the last example can be used if n replaces 4 and if the jumps *not* to P are all replaced by jumps to "not P."

Variable Branching

In coding variable branches, the decision instructions that tested counters or constants of the last two examples must be replaced by decision instructions that test data. Occasionally counters must be set and action taken conditional on their contents, but if these settings depend on the data, the branching is classified as variable.

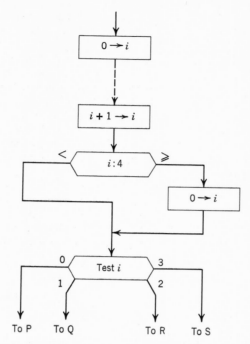

Fig. 9.3.   A four-way cyclic branch point (Example 9.3).

One example of variable branching has already been studied. The problem of sorting 1000 integers by sign, coded in Example 8.6 (page 149), contains a branch point that requires testing the signs of the integers. Another example of variable branching was coded in Example 5.9 (page 95). The values of two quantities a and b were tested; the result was a four-way branch. Two other examples follow.

Example 9.4   Code a branch point that sends control to one of five locations (X1, X2, . . . , X5) if the C(DIGIT) = 1, 2, . . . , 5, respectively.

This problem is similar to the four-way branching problem of Example 9.3, except that the branching depends on the data. [Presumably, the C(DIGIT) is determined during the program execution and thus depends on data.] All that is necessary is that the C(DIGIT) be loaded into an index register and that a jump be effected with a tagged JUMP instruction.*

Location	Oper.	Var. Field
● ● ●	● ● ● ● ●	
	LØADXR	DIGIT,1
	JUMP	JTABLE−1,1

(Continued)

* This program is an example of the table-look-at technique; refer to Section 8.3.

```
JTABLE  JUMP      X1
        JUMP      X2
        JUMP      X3
        JUMP      X4
        JUMP      X5
        ...       .....
```

If the C(DIGIT) $= j$, the effective address of the first JUMP instruction is

$$\text{JTABLE-1+J}$$

Thus if $j = 1$, the jump is to JTABLE as required. Note that no provision is made for values other than 1, 2, ..., 5 for the C(DIGIT). A check on the C(DIGIT) might be necessary to avoid an erroneous jump.

Example 9.5 Code a branch point that sends control to one of eight locations (L0, L1, L2, ..., L7), depending on the signs of three variables, a, b, and c, in the following manner.

Negative c   Positive c

$$a\begin{cases} - \\ + \end{cases}\begin{array}{|c|c|} \hline \text{L0} & \text{L2} \\ \text{L1} & \text{L3} \\ \hline \end{array} \quad a\begin{cases} - \\ + \end{cases}\begin{array}{|c|c|} \hline \text{L4} & \text{L6} \\ \text{L5} & \text{L7} \\ \hline \end{array}$$

(with b columns labeled $-$ and $+$ above each)

Two distinct approaches are possible here. In one, the signs of the three variables are tested in sequence; an eight-way branch results. A flowchart is given in Fig. 9.4a. In the other, a digit j is built up for an eventual jump to location Lj. Weights can be assigned to the algebraic signs of the variables:

$$a: \quad ``-": 0; \quad ``+":1$$
$$b: \quad ``-": 0; \quad ``+":2$$
$$c: \quad ``-": 0; \quad ``+":4$$

As the signs are checked, the appropriate weights are summed to form the proper value of j. Finally, j is used to modify a jump address as in the last example. A flowchart is given in Fig. 9.4b.

The second method is coded now. Accumulation of the sum of the weights can most easily be done in an index register. Indirect addressing can be used to effect the proper jump.

Location	Oper.	Var. Field	
...	.....		
	LØADXR	ZERØ,1	0 TØ J
	LØAD	A	TEST A
	JUMPMI	*+2	
	INCRXM	1,1	J+1 TØ J
	LØAD	B	TEST B
	JUMPMI	*+2	
	INCRXM	2,1	J+2 TØ J
	LØAD	C	TEST C
	JUMPMI	*+2	

(Continued)

```
              INCRXM    4,1              J+4 TØ J
              JUMP*     BRANCH,1
     BRANCH             L0
                        L1
                        L2
                        L3
                        L4
                        L5
                        L6
                        L7
                •••          ••
     ZERØ    DECML      0
```

9.2 SWITCHING

Indicators

The term *switching* refers to branching at a point in a program, where the branch decision is based on the contents of a memory word or register that was previously set during the program execution. That word or register is referred to as an *indicator*. It is also sometimes called a *flag*, but that term has been used in this book for the indirect addressing signal. The only difference between the processes of branching and switching is that the latter is based on an indicator set earlier in the program.

Indicators are of two types: *machine* and *program*. Machine indicators are set automatically by conditions occurring within the computer during program execution. Examples are the overflow indicator (set when the sum of two numbers exceeds the capacity of the accumulator), the divide-check indicator (set when division by zero is attempted), and the end-of-tape indicator (set when the tape reading head is positioned at the tape end). We are not concerned here with these indicators.

Program indicators are used when it is convenient or efficient to test a condition at one point in a program and to act on the result of that test later in the program. One such situation occurs when action on a given decision must be taken at several points in the program. If the test is made once early, it need not be repeated at each branch point based on that test. We may say, of switching, that the original test (at which the indicator is set) is translated into a test of the condition of the indicator. If these two tests are equally easy to make, however, there is little purpose to setting a switch.

Another type of switching process, which does not require a test to be made at the branch point, can be coded. A prior setting, however, is still required. In this case, the form or type of an instruction is set at the branch point earlier in the program. The branch point is called a *switch*, since it resembles a railroad switch which is set at some distance (and time) before the branching occurs.

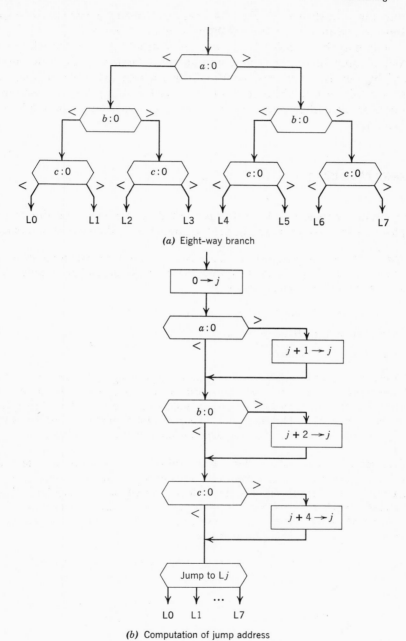

(a) Eight-way branch

(b) Computation of jump address

Fig. 9.4.   Branch point with eight paths (Example 9.5).

The branching illustrated in Fig. 2.4 (page 32), using a variable connector, makes use of a switch; the switch is set by a modification of k.

A switch may be coded by causing an instruction at a branch point to be either a jump instruction or a nonjump instruction. The latter may be achieved by the use of a "no-operation" instruction, available on most computers. In this case the branch point is set either to a jump or no-operation instruction an at earlier point; later, there is no decision to be made at the branch point.

Examples of Switching

A problem is considered here that is treated in two ways and illustrated by examples. In the first approach indicators are used, in the second, switches.

Example 9.6   Five coding sequences are available for use in a computer problem: A, B, C, D, and E. They are to be used in sequence in three ways, depending on which of three conditions is met by data being processed:

> *Case* 1. Use A, B, and D.
>
> *Case* 2. Use A, C, D, and E.
>
> *Case* 3. Use B, C, and D.

A flowchart is drawn in Fig. 9.5 to illustrate the sequencing. Above boxes A, B, C, D, and E are decision boxes in which the question "Is the next box in the sequence?" is asked. The "yes" paths lead directly to the following boxes; they are labeled with the case numbers applicable. The "no" paths bypass the following boxes; they are similarly labeled. The first operation box in the diagram states that either indicators or switches are to be set.

The indicator approach is considered first. Initially it is necessary to determine the case: 1, 2, or 3. When this is done, control goes to one of three indicator-setting sequences which are all of the same form. Five indicators are used, one for each box. They are called INDA, INDB, . . . , INDE. They are set either to zero or nonzero (by storing $+0$ or $+1$ in them) according to the following table; INDj is zero for a particular case if box j is not used in the sequence for that case.

	Case 1	Case 2	Case 3
INDA	$+1$	$+1$	$+0$
INDB	$+1$	$+0$	$+1$
INDC	$+0$	$+1$	$+1$
INDD	$+1$	$+1$	$+1$
INDE	$+0$	$+1$	$+0$

Immediately prior to each box, a pair of instructions of the following form appears.

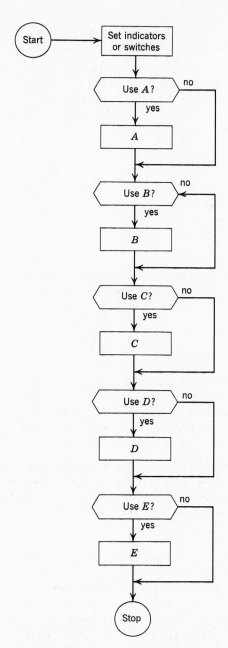

Fig. 9.5. Sequencing through a series of operations.

```
        Oper.      Var. Field

        LØAD       INDA              SKIP "A" IF ZERØ
        JUMPZE     SKIPA
```

SKIPA is the first address past box A. If the A-indicator is zero, box A is skipped. Similar indicators and instructions do the same for other boxes.

The switch approach is considered next. Again it is necessary to test the case number initially. When this is done, five index register modifiers are set according to the following table. Here a setting of 1 corresponds to the skipping of a box, while a setting of 2 corresponds to no skip.

		Case 1	Case 2	Case 3
A:	XR1	2	2	1
B:	XR2	2	1	2
C:	XR3	1	2	2
D:	XR4	2	2	2
E:	XR5	1	2	1

Immediately prior to each box is a pair of instructions. The first is either a jump to the box or a simple transfer of control to the next instruction; the second is a jump to a point beyond the box. The instructions for box A follow.

```
        Oper.      Var. Field

        JUMP       *,1
        JUMP       SKIPA
```

If the $C(XR1)_m = 1$, the first jump sends control in sequence to the second, which in turn causes box A to be skipped. If the $C(XR1)_m = 2$, the first jump causes control to skip the second jump and to go on to box A. If any of the boxes use the first five index registers, it is necessary that their settings remain unchanged; original values must be reset.

The two methods outlined in this example differ very little. We might even argue that there is so little difference that a separate classification is not necessary. No decision, however, is made at the "decision boxes" in the second method, so the term *switch* applies there.

Summary

One of the more important aspects of a computer program is the manner in which control is transferred throughout memory during program execution. Decision instructions are used to effect branchings at points in the program where two or more paths are possible. The decisions made at these points may be predetermined by the nature of the program, or they may depend on the nature of the data being processed. Furthermore, sometimes the outcome

of these decisions is determined earlier in the program than when it is convenient to make them. In that case indicators or switches that are effective at a
later time are set. An indicator is preset and tested at the branch point to effect
a branching. A switch is a coding sequence that is preset to require no testing
to effect a branching.

Notes

1. The following book contains a chapter devoted to the problem of sequencing. A large number of situations are illustrated by flowcharts and coding.

J. Jeenel, *Programming for Digital Computers,* McGraw-Hill, 1959, Chapter 4.

PROBLEMS

Section 9.1

9.1. In Problem 3.11 (page 66) the problem of processing a block of complex numbers too large to fit entirely within memory was flowcharted. Write a complete program, including the reading in of data and printing of results, to realize the operations described: determination of the sum of the numbers and of the number whose
magnitude is the largest.

9.2. Given a block of 2000 integers, starting at TABLE, write routines to perform these
operations:

(*a*) count the number of times an integer is followed by a smaller integer;

(*b*) count the number of times 5 successive numbers form a monotonically increasing sequence (if 8 successive integers are monotonically increasing, this occurs
4 times in the 8);

(*c*) count the number of monotonically increasing sequences of any length in the
list;

(*d*) list the addresses of the 5 largest integers in the list, starting with the address
of the largest integer.

9.3. Code fixed branch points as follows.

(*a*) To send control in cyclic sequence to 6 locations: Q1, Q2, . . . , Q6;

(*b*) to send control to one of three locations (X, Y, or Z), in this sequence: X, Y,
X, Z, X, Y, X, Z, . . . ;

(*c*) to send control to one of four locations (XX1, XX2, XX3, or XX4) in
this sequence: XX1, XX2, XX3, XX4, XX3, XX2, XX1, XX2, ...

9.4. Code variable branch points as follows.

(*a*) To send control to one of 11 locations ($Zi, i = 0, 1, . . . , 10$), where i is the
sum of the C(THING1) and C(THING2);

(*b*) to send control to one of 11 locations ($Yj, j = 0, 1, . . . , 10$), where j is the difference between the largest and the smallest numbers, C(X), C(Y), and C(Z).

Section 9.2

9.5.   Five coding sequences (A, B, C, D, and E) are available for use in a computer problem.   They are to be used in sequence in four ways, depending upon the values of *a*, *b*, and *c*, located respectively in A, B, and C:

   Case 1: *a* and *b* are of the same sign and *c* is zero; use A, B, C, E in that order.
   Case 2: *a* and *b* are of different sign and *c* is not zero; use C, D, C, A in that order.
   Case 3: *a*, *b*, and *c* are all of the same sign; use E, D, C, B, A in that order.
   Case 4: other conditions: use A, B, A, C, A, D in that order.

9.6.   What characteristics are required of a good programmer?   What skills and training does he need?   Consider the tasks of both programming and coding.

10

SUBROUTINES

Any computer of necessity, can execute only a finite number of instructions. A programmer usually requires some operations that are not in the repertoire of instructions for his computer. If these operations occur frequently enough, he can improve his coding efficiency by writing special routines to perform these operations; such routines are called *subroutines*. The programmer writes subroutines and may then consider them to be new "instructions" available for his use throughout his program. Typical subroutines are those that perform the operations of square-root extraction and cosine computation.

Subroutines are usually located in a different part of the program from the place they are used for computation. The problem of how to send information and control properly to and from subroutines is considered in this chapter.

10.1 THE PURPOSE OF SUBROUTINES

What Is a Subroutine?

In most large programs there are processes occurring several times that are not available in the set of instructions of the computer being used. For example, the square-root and cube-root operations needed in the solution of a cubic equation, studied in Chapters 2 and 3, are not available on most computers. In a more complex problem these operations might be needed in dozens of places throughout the program.

Generally these operations occur in scattered locations throughout a program. Both coding time and memory space are saved if the coding sequences comprising the operations are standardized, and the same physical instructions in memory are used.

A standardized coding sequence, written to perform a specific, well-defined operation, is called a *subroutine*. The data supplied to the subroutine and the results computed are also standardized.

Subroutine Operations

In its use a subroutine is considered essentially as a single operation or instruction, operating on the data given to it. It is, in effect, a generalized instruction. For example, the instruction "load the C(A) into the AC"

$$\text{L \O AD} \qquad \text{A}$$

operates on the C(A) only, simply moving it. The instruction "add the C(A) to the C(AC) and place sum in AC"

$$\text{ADD} \qquad \text{A}$$

operates on two numbers and yields the sum as a single result. In a three-address computer the instruction "add the C(A) to the C(B) and store the result in C," which might be written

$$\text{ADD} \qquad \text{A/B/C}$$

also operates on two numbers and stores the sum.

Consider a more complex operation: "sum the squares of the C(A), C(B), C(C), and C(D) and place the result in E." This might be written

$$\text{SUMSQ} \qquad \text{A/B/C/D/E}$$

This instruction operates on four numbers and stores the sum of their squares.

Many similar operations can easily be imagined. If the programmer needs complex operations, he must code subroutines to perform them. The "inputs" to these routines may be the operands to be processed. Because of the manner in which instructions ordinarily refer to operand addresses, however, the inputs are more often the *addresses* of the operands. In the last example of an operation, the operand addresses A, B, C, and D are the inputs. A subroutine supplies an answer, which is placed in one or more addresses, specified in advance. In the last example, E is the address of the answer. A program to realize the SUMSQ operation follows.

Example 10.1   Write a program to evaluate *e*:

$$e = a^2 + b^2 + c^2 + d^2$$

The squares, as they are computed, must be stored temporarily. A three-word block (TEMP) is set aside for this purpose.

Location	Oper.	Var. Field	
SUMSQ	LØAD	A	SQUARE C(A)
	MULT	A	
	STØRE	TEMP	
	LØAD	B	SQUARE C(B)
	MULT	B	
	STØRE	TEMP+1	
	LØAD	C	SQUARE C(C)
	MULT	C	
	STØRE	TEMP+2	
	LØAD	D	SQUARE C(D)
	MULT	D	
	ADD	TEMP	ADD SQUARES
	ADD	TEMP+1	
	ADD	TEMP+2	
	STØRE	E	
	• • •	• • •	
TEMP	BLØCK	3	

Standardization

The form of the input information for a subroutine must be standardized. For example, the implicit assumption in the SUMSQ subroutine is that all numbers are in integer form, placed one to a word. Alternately, they might be floating-point numbers or be placed two numbers to a word. Furthermore, SUMSQ is written so that the four addresses of the data must be given explicitly.

As an example of a slight variation of this subroutine, consider the case where only one data address is given. Probably then the other three addresses are sequentially located in memory. The subroutine statement of operation becomes "sum the squares of the numbers that are stored in the four sequential locations starting at A, and place the result in E." When this is the case, all subsequent use of the SUMSQ subroutine requires the data to be located in four sequential memory locations.

The need for standardization of the form and location of the input and output data of a subroutine is clear. Subroutines, if they are general enough, are used not only by their writers but by others as well. If they are not used properly, chaos can result. One final point on this matter: it is not essential that all subroutines within a class of similar routines be standardized with respect to one another; it is necessary only that each be standardized.

If the SUMSQ subroutine is used in three places in a program, most likely the five parameters (A, B, C, D, E) will vary from use to use. In one case, the numbers involved may be located in X1, X2, X3, X4, and X5; in another, the numbers may be located in DIGIT, RESULT, B12, LIST+50, and XYZ. The structure of the subroutine, however, is the same throughout.

We may liken a subroutine to a mathematical function. Consider the routine coded in Example 10.1 as a representation of the subroutine, rather than a sequence of coding to produce a result. Analogously, the statement of a function can be made in this form:

$$u(w,x,y,z) = w^2 + x^2 + y^2 + z^2$$

To use the function to yield results, we may write

$$u(6,7,10,-2)$$

In the same way, by substituting a set of actual addresses in a subroutine structure, a subprogram is created that will yield results when executed. For example, if we use SUMSQ when the numbers involved are located in X1, X2, . . ., we may represent this use as

SUMSQ(X1,X2,X3,X4,X5)

Assemblers and compilers are capable of accepting an expression essentially in this form and producing the desired coding.

When a subroutine has been written, it may be considered as another "instruction" in the available set. Another programmer may use the subroutine in a similar manner, even though he may not be aware of its coding.

Types of Subroutine

If a subroutine appears physically at each point in a program at which it is used, it is called an *open* subroutine. For example, if SUMSQ were to be used at four places in a program, the subroutine might be placed at those four points. Then 15 instructions would be used four times for a total of 60 for the subroutine. If a subroutine occurs physically just once and is used at several places in the program, it is called a *closed* subroutine. For a closed subroutine to perform its function control must pass to it from the points in the program where the calculation is needed. When the subroutine is executed, control must return to those places. In this case, only 15 words are required for the subroutine in memory in addition to instructions that send control and information to and from the subroutine.*

We have seen the importance of drawing a flowchart or performing some analysis of a problem before coding is done. Part of this job is the identification of subroutines that are used in several parts of the program. It is usually desirable to code the subroutines before the rest of the program is coded, since

---

* The sending of control and information to and from the subroutine is discussed in Section 10.3.

we can then build up a set of operations useful in that program. If a sufficiently large collection of subroutines is available, the ensuing coding job may only involve joining routines into a complete program with additional indexing and decision operations for overall control.

10.2 OPEN SUBROUTINES

Open subroutines are generally quite short. If a subroutine is lengthy, it is usually written in closed form because it would waste space in open form. Another characteristic of an open subroutine is that the locations of data to be processed vary from one occurrence of the routine to another and are coded into each such occurrence. By contrast, since a closed subroutine occurs only once in memory, it cannot make reference to specific data locations. Instead, the locations applicable at each usage of the routine must be supplied at that point.

Example 10.2 Write three open subroutines, each of which computes the sum of a set of numbers; the sets are 50, 100, and 250 in size.

The sets start at locations LIST1, LIST2, and LIST3; place their sums at SUM1, SUM2, and SUM3, respectively. Assume that the latter three locations are cleared.

	Oper.	Var. Field
	SETXRI	50,1
	LØAD	ZERØ
	ADD	LIST1,1
	INCRXM	1,1
	XJUMP	*-2,1
	STØRE	SUM1
	...	.....
	SETXRI	100,1
	LØAD	ZERØ
	ADD	LIST2,1
	INCRXM	1,1
	XJUMP	*-2,1
	STØRE	SUM2
	...	.....
	SETXRI	250,1
	LØAD	ZERØ
	ADD	LIST3,1
	INCRXM	1,1
	XJUMP	*-2,1
	STØRE	SUM3
	...	.....
ZERØ	DECML	0

Macro-instructions

In the routines of Example 10.2 the structure is the same since the function of each is the same: to sum a set of numbers whose locations and size are stated.

Three quantities vary in the routines: the block starting location, the size of the block, and the location of the sum. If a programmer has to code a number of such repetitious routines, it probably occurs to him that there must be an easier way to do this. The repetitive nature of the routines lends itself to computer assistance.

If we were to explain to a clerk the manner in which we wanted this set of routines coded, we would probably describe the basic structure of the sequence and then indicate what sets of quantities or parameters we wanted to include in each routine.

An assembly program can accept precisely this type of information and as a result provides the programmer with a simple way of writing open subroutines. The programmer supplies the basic structure as a sequence of coding with a separate list of all quantities which are to be substitutable. In HAP language, the coding sequence is delimited by two pseudo-operations: MACRØ and MACEND.

MACRØ stands for *macro-instruction*. A subroutine can be considered to be a large (macro-) instruction, as we saw in the last section. The MACEND card indicates the end of the macro-instruction. The sequence of coding is called the *macro-definition*. The routine of Example 10.2 would be written as a macro-definition as follows:

Location	Oper.	Var. Field
SUMBLK	MACRØ	A,B,C
	SETXRI	B,1
	LØAD	ZERØ
	ADD	A,1
	INCRXM	1,1
	XJUMP	*-2,1
	STØRE	C
	MACEND	

Note that the substitutable parameters or *dummy arguments* of the macro-definition are listed in the variable field of the MACRØ card. The arguments A, B, and C represent the list name, list size, and sum location, respectively. The order in which these are listed is irrelevant in the macro-definition. In order to identify the macro-instruction, a descriptive name (SUMBLK) has been assigned; it is placed in the location field.

This macro-definition is given early in the program, before it is used. At those points in the program where the subroutines are to appear, the macro-instruction is called by a *macro-call*. The quantities to be substituted for the dummy parameters in each routine are given with the name of the macro-instruction; they are the *call arguments* or *call parameters*.

Oper.	Var. Field
SUMBLK	LIST1,50,SUM1
...	.....

(Continued)

```
SUMBLK    LIST2,100,SUM2
...       .....
SUMBLK    LIST3,250,SUM3
```

When the assembler encounters macro-calls in the symbolic deck, they are expanded immediately into their equivalent coding sequences. With the three macro-calls just given the subroutines written in Example 10.2 result. Macro-instruction expansion is performed in pass 1 of the assembly process. The resulting symbolic coding is then treated by the assembler in precisely the way that programmer-coded symbolic instructions are treated. We may think of macro-expansions as temporary interruptions of the normal pass-1 process, described in Section 6.3.

Although the order of arguments is not important in the macro-definition, the order in the macro-call must be the same. In the SUMBLK macro-instruction it seems appropriate to specify first a list, then its size, and then its sum location.

The dummy arguments of a macro-definition are symbolic in form but have no significance outside their own particular macro-definition. For this reason any symbols may be used in any number of definitions, regardless of whether they are defined in the program.

The call arguments of a macro-call may be of any form; they may be addresses in the location or variable fields, integers, symbolic operations, or symbolic expressions. In Chapter 17 these features and many others are described.

10.3 CLOSED SUBROUTINES

Transfer of Control

Closed subroutines appear only one time each in memory. If a particular subroutine is to be used, control is sent to that routine, with information on what data are to be processed. The location(s) for storage of the result(s) is also supplied. Generally, if only one operand is given and only one number is the result, the accumulator is used for storage of both the input and the output data. The multiply register (or equivalent register) is sometimes used for a second input argument. An example of a single-input, single-output subroutine is a cosine routine; x is supplied to the routine, and $\cos x$ is the answer.

Within the closed subroutine, because it occurs only once, references to data to be processed are fixed. Adjustments to take into account the variations in data locations from one use to the next must be made within the subroutine. A closed subroutine in this sense is a generalized version of an open subroutine.

The controlling program, which sends control to a series of subroutines, is called the *main program*. It must provide a means for sending control to the subroutine and for supplying information. In addition, it must enable the subroutine to send control and information back to the main program when finished. A special DELTA 63 instruction is used to send control to the subroutine.*

JUMP AND SET INDEX (JUMPSX Y) (30).   The location address of this instruction is placed in the modifier of the specified index register, and the computer takes its next instruction from Y and proceeds from there.   The index register tally is unchanged.

Storing in an index register the location of the jump instruction, that is, the location from which control came, provides a means for the subroutine to return control to the main program.   For example, assume control is to return to the instruction following the JUMPSX instruction, that is, to READY + 1 in the following:

Location	Oper.	Var. Field
READY	**JUMPSX**	**SUBRTE,7**

The following instruction, located within the subroutine, effects the return:

JUMP   1,7

Since the $C(XR7)_m$ is the address READY, the effective address of the JUMP instruction is READY + 1.   The use of the JUMPSX instruction or equivalent instructions to establish a means for the return of control is termed a *linkage*.   Index register 7 is used for this purpose.

The path of control from a main program to a subroutine from three different locations is shown in Fig. 10.1.   In this flowchart control initially passes through box I, then goes to the subroutine SR at point 1, returning just after that point. Control follows line 1a, then 1b, in the process.   Box II follows, and then control follows line 2a to SR and returns on 2b to just beyond point 2.   Box III follows, and the process repeats at point 3.   Note that on each exit from SR control follows a different path.

In Fig. 10.1 the three exits from the SR box are not drawn in the conventional manner. Although the decision of the path to take is actually made within the box, the branch point is shown outside, at SW.   As far as the subroutine is concerned, there is one exit. Nevertheless, XR7 is set prior to entry, and the effect is that the tagged JUMP instruction that returns control to the main program is a multiple-branch point.   This point is a switch in the sense of Section 9.2, since the decision instruction is set at an earlier place in the program.

Transfer of Information

The means by which information is supplied to a closed subroutine varies from one routine to another.   As we noted, if the subroutine has a single argu-

* This instruction is very similar to the equivalent instruction in the IBM 704-709-7090 computers.   Other computers have instructions for similar purposes; the IBM instruction is among the more flexible.

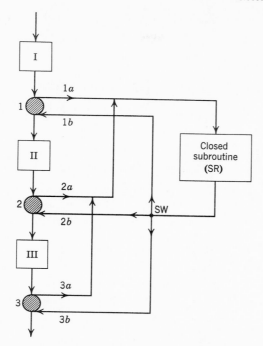

Fig. 10.1.   Flow of control with a closed subroutine.

ment, the accumulator may be used.   A relatively simple means for supplying this information is to list the arguments in succession in the address fields of the words immediately following the JUMPSX instruction.   Such a sequence is a *calling sequence*.   These arguments correspond closely to the call arguments of a macro-instruction written for the same purpose.

As an example, if a closed subroutine SUMBLK is written to sum a set of numbers, as coded in Example 10.2, the calling sequence might be

Location	Oper.	Var. Field
MØVE	JUMPSX	SUMBLK,7
		LIST1
		50
		SUM1

As seen here, the information stored in the calling sequence may be of several types: (1) the address for a result or the address of one data word may be given (for example, SUM1); (2) the starting address of a block of words may be given (for example, LIST1); (3) the size of a block of words may be given (for example, 50).

The subroutine has the job of obtaining the information for its use from the calling sequence.   The effective address of the first word following the JUMPSX instruction is given by "1,7," so that the following instructions are equivalent.

```
LØAD      1,7

LØAD      MØVE+1
```

These instructions load the address LIST1 into the accumulator. Similarly, the other arguments in the calling sequence can be addressed with "2,7" and "3,7."

A Subroutine Obligation

A subroutine has an obligation to the main program in addition to providing the answer. The subroutine is, in effect, a single operation to the main program and most likely is used within a loop. Therefore it should be possible for a programmer to use the routine without giving any thought to its effect on the index registers in the main program. In other words, the subroutine should not disturb these registers. For example, if an index register must be used by the subroutine, its original value must be restored. This is accomplished by initially saving the contents of all the used index registers. When the subroutine has completed its computations, the index register contents must be restored. By convention, it is usually not assumed that the contents of the accumulator and multiply register are untouched by the subroutine.

Index register 7 is, of course, changed by the JUMPSX instruction so that its value need not be saved for the main program. The subroutine requires, however, that XR7 be unchanged so that it can return control to the main program. If XR7 is used by the subroutine, its contents must then also be saved and later restored.

Examples

Example 10.3 Write the SUMBLK macro-instruction of Section 10.2 as a closed subroutine.
Since all parameters are given in the calling sequence, they must be placed in the body of the routine. Three instructions of the form

```
LØAD      M,7
```

where M is 1, 2, and 3, load the contents of the address fields of the calling sequence into the accumulator. STØRAD instructions store these addresses in the proper places in the routine. The heart of the subroutine, which computes the sum of the numbers in the block, is the same in form as in the macro-instruction. Because XR1 is used by the subroutine, its contents must be saved.*

---

* The use of ** as an address is a convention within the HAP language. It assembles as a zero address and indicates that an address will be supplied during the execution of the program. An address of 0 would do as well, but the ** acts as a signal to the programmer that an address is to be supplied. The parenthesized items in the "remarks" column are supplied during program execution by the STØRAD instructions.

```
        Location     Oper.      Var. Field

        SUMBLK    STØRXR     SAVEX1,1        SAVE XR1
                  LØAD       1,7             FETCH LIST ADDRESS
                  STØRAD     SUB1
                  LØAD       2,7             FETCH LIST SIZE
                  STØRAD     SUB2
                  LØAD       3,7             FETCH SUM ADDRESS
                  STØRAD     SUB3
        SUB2      SETXRI     **,1            (SIZE)
                  LØAD       ZERØ
        SUB1      ADD        **,1            (LIST ADDRESS)
                  INCRXM     1,1
                  XJUMP      SUB1,1
        SUB3      STØRE      **              (SUM ADDRESS)
                  LØADXR     SAVEX1,1        RESTØRE XR1
                  JUMP       4,7             RETURN TØ MAIN PRØGRAM

        SAVEX1
        ZERØ      DECML      0
```

This subroutine is generalized so that any calling sequence in the proper form can call on it. The following calling sequence results in the summation of the 100 words at LIST2.

```
                Oper.     Var. Field

                JUMPSX    SUMBLK,7
                          LIST2
                          100
                          SUM2
```

Indirect addressing is useful in a closed subroutine for obtaining the necessary information for its use. In a calling sequence the locations of operands are frequently given. If the subroutine indirectly addresses the words in the calling sequence, the operands in those locations can be addressed through that sequence. The SUMBLK subroutine is recoded using indirect addressing.

Example 10.4 Write SUMBLK as a closed subroutine. Since the size of the block, rather than the address of a location containing the size, is given in the calling sequence, indirect addressing is not used to obtain that parameter. The tag on the ADD instruction (see Example 10.3) must be placed in the calling sequence.

The calling sequence:

```
                Oper.     Var. Field

                JUMPSX    SUMBLK,7
                          LIST2,1
                          100
                          SUM2
```

(Continued)

The subroutine:

Location	Oper.	Var. Field	
SUMBLK	STØRXR	SAVEX1,1	
	LØAD	2,7	FETCH LIST SIZE
	STØRAD	SUB2	
SUB2	SETXRI	**,1	(SIZE)
	LØAD	ZERØ	
	ADD*	1,7	ADD C(LISTX,1)
	INCRXM	1,1	... X = 1, 2, ØR 3
	XJUMP	*-2,1	
	STØRE*	3,7	
	LØADXR	SAVEX1,1	
	JUMP	4,7	
SAVEX1			
ZERØ	DECML	0	

The flexibility offered by the combined use of indirect addressing the index registers is illustrated.

Comments on the comparison of the two versions of the SUMBLK subroutine are appropriate here. The second version (Example 10.4) is shorter than the first version (Example 10.3) by 4 instructions. It is, however, slower. The number of instructions executed in the two versions are $12 + 3n$ for the first and $8 + 3n$ for the second, but indirect addressing requires additional time. A flagged instruction requires a double memory reference. In the IBM 7090, indirect addressing requires 50% more time for a fixed-point addition instruction than direct addressing for that instruction does.

It is possible to combine the advantages of a closed subroutine and a macro-instruction by defining the latter as a call for the former. Thus we write:

Location	Oper.	Var. Field
SUMBLK	MACRØ	A,B,C
	JUMPSX	SUMBLK,7
		A
		B
		C
	MACEND	

The macro-call

SUMBLK LIST1,50,SUM1

has the same effect as in Section 10.2, except that now a closed subroutine is used. Notice that SUMBLK is used in two ways here: as the name of the macro-instruction and as the address of the subroutine. Since naming a macro-definition does not constitute "symbol definition" there is no ambiguity here.

As another example of a closed subroutine, consider the problem of computing the sum of the squares of four given numbers (Example 10.1).

Example 10.5   Write a closed subroutine for the evaluation of e:

$$e = a^2 + b^2 + c^2 + d^2$$

The calling sequence:

	Oper.	Var. Field
	JUMPSX	SUMSQ,7
		A
		B
		C
		D
		E

The subroutine:

Location	Oper.	Var. Field
SUMSQ	LØAD*	1,7
	MULT*	1,7
	STØRE	TEMP
	LØAD*	2,7
	MULT*	2,7
	STØRE	TEMP+1
	LØAD*	3,7
	MULT*	3,7
	STØRE	TEMP+2
	LØAD*	4,7
	MULT*	4,7
	ADD	TEMP
	ADD	TEMP+1
	ADD	TEMP+2
	STØRE*	5,7
	JUMP	6,7
TEMP	BLØCK	3

In this example the use of indirect addressing does not slow down the subroutine. In Example 10.4 flagging is effective within a loop that cycled n times. In this subroutine no loop is present.

Example 10.6   Write a program to evaluate

$$F = \sqrt{x} + \sqrt{x^2 - y^2} + (x^2 + y^2 + z^2 + u^2)$$

Two subroutines are assumed available for this purpose: SQRØØT, which computes the square root of the C(AC) and leaves the result in the AC, and SUMSQ (see Example 10.5).

Location	Oper.	Var. Field
LØAD	X	X TØ AC
JUMPSX	SQRØØT,7	
STØRE	TEMP	STØRE SQ.RT. ØF X

(Continued)

```
        LØAD     Y
        MULT     Y
        STØRE    TEMP+1              STØRE Y{2
        LØAD     X
        MULT     X
        SUBT     TEMP+1              X{2 - Y{2
        JUMPSX   SQRØØT,7
        STØRE    TEMP+1
        JUMPSX   SUMSQ,7
                 X
                 Y
                 Z
                 U
                 TEMP+2             (FØR RESULT)
        LØAD     TEMP
        ADD      TEMP+1
        ADD      TEMP+2
        STØRE    F
        HALT

TEMP    BLØCK    3
X
Y
..
```

The symbols SQRØØT and SUMSQ must be defined. When the subroutines are added to the program, this will be done.*

In Section 8.4 it was pointed out that indirect addressing may be used with tags on both the direct and the indirect addresses. This technique is illustrated by an example.

Example 10.7 The block at LISTA contains 100 numbers whose cube roots are to be computed; the results are to be placed in the block at LISTB. Write a routine to perform the operations, making use of a CBRØØT subroutine.

It is assumed that CBRØØT has two addresses in its calling sequence, the address of the argument (to be cubed) and the address for the result. A loop is established containing the calling sequence. The addresses in the calling sequence are tagged. Within the subroutine, a flagged reference places one of the arguments in LISTA in the AC; because of the tag on the LISTA address, all arguments are fetched in sequence.

```
       Location   Oper.    Var. Field

                  SETXRI   100,1
       BEGIN      JUMPSX   CBRØØT,7
                           LISTA,1
                           LISTB,1
                  (Continued)
```

---

* Several instructions can be saved in using SUMSQ if it is noted that the subroutine leaves the result in the accumulator. There is actually no need for the final STØRE instruction in the subroutine or the LØAD instruction immediately following the calling sequence.

```
                    INCRXM   1,1
                    XJUMP    BEGIN,1
                    HALT

            LISTA   BLØCK    100
            LISTB   BLØCK    100
```

Within the subroutine, the argument is placed in the AC and the result is subsequently stored in LISTB by the instructions

```
                    LØAD*    1,7
                    • • •
                    • • •
                    STØRE*   2,7
```

Common Storage

Sometimes a subroutine requires the use of some space in memory during its execution that is not needed when the computation is completed. If this is true of several subroutines used by one program during its run, space can be shared by the subroutines. For this purpose some portion of the computer memory is designated as *common* storage. If a subroutine, or any program for that matter, uses common storage, no results may be left there and be presumed to be available for later use. A subsequent routine may use the space freely. An advantage of this approach is that less total space is then required by the program and its subroutines.

Multiple Entries

All the subroutines described and illustrated in this section have had one *entry point* or starting location. Sometimes two or more desired operations are so similar in nature that a single subroutine can perform all of them. For example, since it is true that

$$\cos x = \sin (90° + x)$$

a single subroutine can be used to compute both trigonometric functions. The subroutine might begin with the following coding, provided the argument x is located in the accumulator.

Location	Oper.	Var. Field	
SINE	ADD	NINETY	ADD 90
CØSINE	STØRE	ARG	
	• • •	• • • • •	

The argument (ARG) must be given in degrees here. (More commonly, an angular measure in radians is required.) ARG contains the value of the argument which is to be operated on. This subroutine has two entry points; control passes to either of them in the usual manner, using a JUMPSX instruction.

Multiple Returns

A particular subroutine might be used only for the purpose of making a decision, for example, whether or not the algebraic sum of a set of numbers is positive, negative, or zero. In this case, the information desired by the main program is not the sum but rather some information about it. This may be provided within the subroutine by (1) actually supplying the sum, which can then be tested by the main program, (2) setting a specific register or word equal to 1, 2, or 3 for the three alternatives, or (3) providing three separate returns to the main program.

For example, in the case of the SUMBLK subroutine, the following sequence might replace the jump instruction in Example 10.4.

```
      Oper.   Var. Field

      JUMPZE   5,7              ZERØ RETURN
      JUMPPL   6,7              PØSITIVE RETURN
      JUMPMI   7,7              NEGATIVE RETURN
```

Since the sum is still in the accumulator, it is tested there. Note that zero must be tested for first, since $+0$ and -0 are treated differently by JUMPPL. In the main program, control is then caused to return as desired in these three possible outcomes.

It is evident that for a subroutine, whether closed or open, to be useful, it must work properly under all allowable circumstances for which it was designed. Since a subroutine will very likely be used by programmers other than its writer, it must not only be correct for proper usage but must also allow for improper usage. For example, if a subroutine computes the quantity x^n only for values of x and n that do not cause the capacity of a single word to be exceeded, it must do something positive if, for example, the user supplies $x = 450$ and $n = 25$. It cannot merely stop or plow ahead with improper calculations. If the user of the subroutine did not write it, he cannot necessarily tell what went wrong if he is unaware of his error.

To allow for such erroneous usage, one or more checks must be coded into the subroutine and applied as needed. If an error is detected, generally an additional return to the main program is supplied. For example, a fourth return in the last example is provided by

```
      JUMP     8,7                    ERRØR RETURN
```

The main program then should take appropriate action.

In addition to exceeding the capacity of a subroutine, there may be other errors. For example, (1) certain combinations of data might be considered erroneous because of physical situations that the subroutine simulates, (2) the quantities in the calling sequence might appear in an incorrect order, (3) required tags in the calling sequence might be omitted, or (4) insufficient data cards might have been provided. It is possible to provide a number of error returns so that the type of error can be identified. Alternately, a comment can be written on the output tape indicating the error type and a single error return might be provided.

10.4 LIBRARIES

Many subroutines are used by persons other than their writers. The reason for the widespread use of such subroutines is that most are written to perform fairly frequently used operations, such as the computation of the square root or cosine of a quantity, or the solution to a set of simultaneous, linear, algebraic equations. The more commonly used subroutines are placed in a *library* associated with a particular computer installation. A programmer wishing to use such a routine should therefore check at his library to see if it is available.

A subroutine library generally takes two forms; some subroutines are placed in each form. A *library tape* is generally associated with the computer. It contains the most commonly used subroutines, each of which may be called by an appropriate pseudo-operation. Library tapes usually provide the common trigonometric functions, several root extraction operations, exponential functions, etc.

Some subroutines are available as decks of source programs or object programs; these are generally available in the library at a computer installation. If these decks are used, they are placed with the main program deck. They are called as the subroutines on the library tape are called.

Libraries from several installations having the same model of computer frequently share their subroutines by submitting information on them to *users' organizations*. These organizations, in turn, prepare brief write-ups of these subroutines and send them to all member installations. This insures still wider spread use of subroutines.

When a program, be it a subroutine or not, is submitted to a library, it should be documented; that is, all pertinent information related to the subroutine should be explicitly provided. The programmer must know precisely how the program is to be used and what its limitations are. Other information of interest is a description of the method(s) used, the time for execution, the space required in memory, a flowchart of the program, and a listing of the program.

All programs should be documented, whether they are to be placed in a library or not. It is not uncommon for a program, although presumably completed, to be revised by another programmer after time has passed. Without a full description of the methods used and appropriate flowcharts, the task of the second programmer is difficult. If the flowcharts are drawn before the problem is coded, the documentation problem is a simpler one. A verbal description, which is usually written after the program is completed, is also valuable.

Summary

Subroutines are, in effect, single instructions and are so used. In reality they are special routines that perform well-defined operations. If a programmer finds that a particular operation is fairly common in his program and there is no instruction for it, he very probably writes a subroutine.

Subroutines take two forms, open and closed. An open subroutine is placed physically at each point in the program where the desired operation is performed. A macro-instruction, one form of open subroutine, is a specially defined sequence of instructions that is coded once in a program in general terms; later, as the subroutine is needed, particular addresses are substituted to yield specific coding sequences.

A closed subroutine exists physically only once in a program, but it may be used at any desired number of points in the program. By standardizing the form of the data, the manner of presenting information to the subroutine, and the manner of receiving information from the subroutine, a main program may readily be written to use the routine. In order to transfer both control and information to the subroutine, the calling sequence is used. This includes the use of a special jump instruction to set a return switch and a sequence of addresses that constitute the parameters of the subroutine at the point of usage. On completion the subroutine supplies answers or appropriate information for action by the main program.

Collections of commonly used subroutines are called libraries and make the routines available to a wide audience.

PROBLEMS

Section 10.1

10.1. What are some operations that occur frequently enough to warrant being coded as subroutines? Consider the problems mentioned in the examples and problems of earlier chapters. Indicate whether each subroutine ought to be written in open or closed form. In each case list the parameters of the subroutine, for example, the addresses that must be supplied each time the subroutine is used.

10.2. A great deal of emphasis is placed on the standardization of subroutines and the structure of their input and output. Why?

Section 10.2

10.3. Write macro-instructions to accomplish the following operations.

(*a*) Zero the contents of a block of words whose starting and ending addresses are specified;

(b) form the sum of all the negative numbers in a specified block of words, placing the sum in a specified location;

(c) move a specified block of words to a new location;

(d) place the square, cube, and fourth power of the C(AC), assumed an integer, in 3 specified locations;

(e) place the largest and the smallest of a set of 4 numbers in specified locations in the accumulator and the multiply register, respectively.

10.4.   What are some possible uses for macro-instructions? Consider situations where closed subroutines are of less value than macro-instructions.

10.5.   In what way might the assembler treat macro-definitions and macro-calls, on encountering them in a symbolic program?

Section 10.3

10.6.   The subroutine linkage described in the text is only one approach to the problem of transferring control and information between a main program and a subroutine. Devise other methods for transferring them.

10.7.   Write closed subroutines to accomplish the operations in Problem 10.3.

10.8.   Code the SQRØØT subroutine mentioned in Example 10.6. Use the iterative approach described in Section 2.2, assuming that the argument is an integer. A desired accuracy should be assumed.

10.9.   Assume that the following closed subroutines are available:

SQRØØT	square root
SINE	sine
LØG	natural logarithm
EXPØN	exponential function

In the first three the function argument is to be placed in the AC; in the fourth, the base and exponent are to be placed in the AC and MR respectively. In all, the result is placed in the AC by the subroutine. Write programs to evaluate the following expressions.

(a) $F = \sqrt{a + bx + cx^2} + \dfrac{\sin x^2 + \cos x^3}{\ln (a + b)}$

(b) $G = \dfrac{a^3 + \sqrt{\sin x + \cos ax}}{1 + a^x + b^{\sin cx}}$

10.10. Write four subroutines for the performance of complex arithmetic, one for each of addition, subtraction, multiplication, and division. The arguments of the subroutines are to be placed in locations specified when the routines are used. The real and imaginary parts of the arguments may be assumed to be in adjacent locations; the real and imaginary parts of the results are to go into the AC and MR, respectively.

10.11. Code a third entry to a SINE-CØSINE subroutine for the computation of the tangent of an argument: TANGNT. Write the sequence at the TANGNT entry so that switches or indicators are set for use of the following ratio:

$$\tan x = \frac{\sin x}{\cos x}$$

This problem is similar to Example 9.6, except that a few extra steps are required to yield the tangent function.

10.12. Code a sequence for an exponential-function subroutine to determine whether the numbers x and n are too large; x^n is to be computed. The test need not be precise (this might require performing the actual computation); a reasonable, not necessarily precise, test is desired.

10.13. What are some other reasons (besides the one of Problem 10.12) why an error return from a subroutine might be provided? Consider the subroutines in Problems 10.7 and 10.9 and others.

11

INPUT-OUTPUT OPERATIONS

The problem of performing input-output operations on a computer was introduced in Chapter 7. Now a closer look is taken at the several tasks involved—loading the program, reading in the data to be processed, and printing out results. Another task, mentioned only in passing, is the use of magnetic tapes for intermediate results.

In the introductory material on input-output a single program was considered. The usual procedure, however, on large-scale computers, is to have in memory at all times an *input-output monitor program*. One function of the monitor program is to perform the several input-output tasks with a minimum of coding effort on the part of the programmer. In his source program, the programmer specifies the manner in which data are to be read in, the portions of memory into which they are to be placed, and the manner in which results are to be printed.

11.1 MONITOR PROGRAMS

The Running of Programs

In Section 3.2 we had a brief look at the operations involved in running computer programs. Both in that section and in Section 7.2 the emphasis was on the problem of running a single computer program. The steps in the process may be summarized as follows.

1. The assembled object program is loaded into the memory, either from the on-line card reader or from the input magnetic tape. In the latter case, the program had to be read onto tape from the program deck.

2. Data called for by the program are read into memory, also either from the card reader or from the magnetic tape.

3. The program is executed. It stores its intermediate results either in memory or on intermediate tapes connected to the computer.

4. Answers are supplied by the program and are placed on punched cards, on the on-line printer paper, or on the output tape. In the latter case, the answers must be subsequently printed if they are to be read.

In this chapter our attention turns to the execution of a collection of programs. Our primary concern is still just one program, but we now look at the manner in which a sequence of programs is run. For this purpose an *input-output monitor program* or *monitor* is frequently used.*

Program Execution with a Monitor

When a monitor is used, it remains in memory at all times. Program execution using a monitor proceeds according to the following steps (which should be compared with the steps listed before).

1. Off-line, a sequence of perhaps 10 to 100 programs are loaded, with their data, on the input tape.

2. On-line, one program from the input tape is loaded into memory. The monitor does this loading, using information punched on the program deck (now written on the input tape). The monitor then turns control over to this program.

3. The data are read in by the monitor, using information supplied to it by the program in memory. The format of the data to be read and the memory locations into which they are read are specified by the programmer.

4. The program is executed. It stores its intermediate results either in memory or on intermediate tapes. Actual writing of information on these tapes is done by the monitor.

5. Answers are computed by the program. The monitor writes these on the output tape, using information supplied to it by the program in memory. The format of the results and the memory locations from which they are to be read are specified by the programmer.

6. When a program is completed, control is returned to the monitor, which loads the next program. The cycle, starting at step 2, repeats until no programs are left on the input tape.

7. Off-line, all results are printed from the output tape.

* Other terms used for this kind of program are *monitor system* or *system.*

An examination of these steps indicates the way in which the monitor and the object program in memory interact during the loading and execution of a program. Figure 11.1 diagrams their interaction more clearly. In that diagram each box represents one operation. The boxes are numbered to correspond to the steps we have listed. Box 2 consists of step 2. Box 2a is not actually indicated in the series of steps, because it usually consists of very few instructions, if any at all. Control actually passes to the object program after it is loaded, but usually control is immediately returned to the monitor for data reading. Boxes 3, 4, and 5 correspond to steps 3, 4, and 5. Again control is actually returned to the object program after answers are written on tape, but almost immediately thereafter it is returned to the monitor.

When a program has been executed, it must send control to the monitor program so that the latter can load the next program. If a HALT instruction is used to terminate a program, the monitor will not obtain control; instead, the computer will stop. Therefore programs run with a monitor are terminated with a jump to the monitor, to a specified "end of job" location. In the programs listed in this book, HALT is used, however, for simplicity.

Program Assembly with a Monitor

Before programs can be run, they must be assembled (or compiled) into object program decks. For this purpose the assembler is used; its usage is normally under the control of the monitor. If, on the input tape, a symbolic source program is present, then the following procedure is used.

1. The assembler is loaded into memory by the monitor.
2. The symbolic cards of the source program are assembled by the assembler. The monitor writes the assembled program on the output tape. It should be recalled that the role of the assembler here is that of an object program, for which

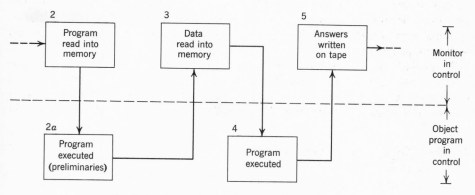

Fig. 11.1.   Interaction of monitor and object program.

the symbolic cards are data. The purpose of this object program is to translate the symbolic cards into machine form. Since assembly is a two-pass process, an intermediate tape is used to hold the results of pass 1.

3. When assembly is completed, an object program in machine language is written on a "punch tape" for later punching. At this point the assembled program is located on an intermediate tape. If the programmer has indicated that he wants to execute this program, the monitor loads it into memory. If he has not done so, the monitor proceeds to the next program.

At this point, if the program is to be run, the procedure continues with step 3 of the list we gave earlier.

The Roles of the Monitor

The programmer need not be directly concerned with the manner in which the monitor performs its functions. The monitor may simply be viewed as an automatic operator, input-output facility, subroutine librarian, and debugging service. Its role as an automatic operator has just been examined. Its role as an input-output facility is described in Section 11.2. Its role as subroutine librarian was mentioned in Section 10.4, where a library tape was described. The library tape is under the control of the monitor; the monitor is directed by the object program to load subroutines into memory. Finally, the role of the monitor as a debugging service is described in Section 11.3.

Monitor Control Cards

In order to convey information to the monitor, it is necessary to include with the program deck several *monitor control cards*. These cards are similar to assembler pseudo-operations, because they direct the monitor to take certain specific actions concerning the loading of programs, tape operations, and debugging. Several typical control cards are described here only briefly. Monitor systems vary widely in their structure and use, probably more so than do assembly programs.

To provide a reference for each control card, we imagine a deck of cards whose contents are loaded onto the input tape (and later into memory). The deck consists of an assembled program and its data and associated control cards. The sequence of cards is pictured in an "exploded view" of the deck in Fig. 11.2.

The deck (for program execution):
1. Job card.
2. Load card.
3. Object program deck.

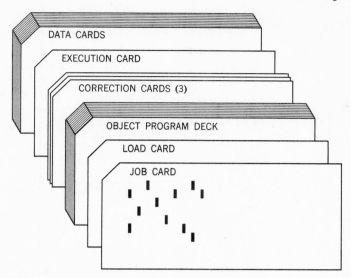

Fig. 11.2.   A deck for program execution.

4. Correction cards.
5. Execution card.
6. Data cards.

The purpose of the control cards is explained shortly.

Let us imagine a second deck that contains a symbolic deck to be assembled as well as a subroutine object program deck.   After the symbolic deck is assembled, the resulting object program is to run with the subroutine deck (already assembled).   The deck is pictured in Fig. 11.3.

The deck (for program assembly and execution):
1. Job card.
2. Assembler call card.
3. Symbolic deck.
4. Load assembler card.
5. Object program deck (subroutine).
6. Tape card.
7. Debugging cards.
8. Execution card.
9. Data cards.

Job card.   Every computer "run" is referred to as a *job*, whether it consists of an assembly, execution, or both.   Each deck must begin with a job card, which indicates the start of a new job to the monitor.   This card often contains identifying information, such as the programmer's name.   Sometimes separate tape files are used for separate jobs.

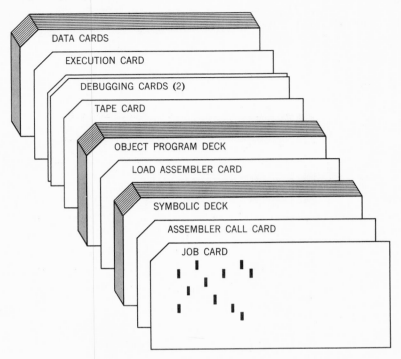

Fig. 11.3.   A deck for program assembly and execution.

Load card.   An object program deck is preceded by a load card, which directs the monitor to load the program into memory as indicated on that deck.

Correction cards.   If a program is found to contain an error, the error may be corrected without reassembly.   Instead, one or more correction cards are placed directly behind the deck they are intended to correct.   These cards, which are interpreted by the monitor, may be octal, decimal, or alphanumeric in format.* Their contents are loaded into memory at the locations stated on the cards.   The result is that whatever was present in those memory locations is overwritten by this newer information; thus assembled instructions can be changed prior to program execution.

Execution card.   After the program is loaded into memory and other control cards are read and interpreted, a signal must be given to the monitor to start program execution.   This is the purpose of the execution card.   The starting address of the program to be executed is usually present in the program deck. In a symbolic deck the starting address of the program may appear on the END card (see Section 6.2).

---

* The word *alphanumeric* is almost self-explanatory; it is short for "alphabetic or numeric" and refers to letters, digits, or a combination of both.

Assembler call card. If a programmer wishes to assemble a symbolic program, he uses the assembler call card to direct the monitor to load the assembler into memory. This must precede each symbolic program.

Load assembler card. This card is similar to the load card, except that it directs the assembler to load the assembled program, which is located on one of the tapes, into memory. In Fig. 11.3, it also serves as a load card.

Tape cards. The programmer may direct the monitor to rewind, move forward or backward, load into memory the contents of, or otherwise affect, a tape unit; tape cards are so used. Tape instructions within a program accomplish the same thing, but separate cards offer somewhat greater flexibility.

Debugging cards. To indicate the use of the debugging facilities of the monitor in a particular job debugging cards are used. Their use is described in Section 11.3.

If the monitor roles of input-output facility and automatic operator are distinct, as they sometimes are, the monitor may do little more than execute control cards. In so doing, it performs its several functions by calling into memory from tape any required routines.

11.2 INPUT-OUTPUT DATA TRANSMISSION

Data Formats

Data are accepted by a monitor program in several forms: octal or decimal integers, fixed-point numbers, floating-point numbers, and alphanumeric information. Examples are

$$56 \qquad 20047 \qquad 56.6701 \qquad .0000342$$

$$56.10E+45 \qquad .3342895E-2 \qquad 500 \ TERMS.$$

In these examples E stands for "exponential"; for example, $56.10E+45$ means 56.10×10^{45}. The base 10 is understood.

Data may be punched on cards in many ways. For example, consider 16 decimal numbers (1) punched 16 to a card with 4 colunms allotted to each number and (2) punched 4 to a card with 5 columns allotted to each number. These two cases are pictured in Fig. 11.4. Other data cards are pictured in Fig. 11.5.

Generally, if a number of items appear on one card, the same number of columns is allotted per item; the group of such columns is called a *field* on the card. Floating-point numbers generally require fields of 10 or 12 spaces, if reasonable accuracy is desired. A monitor may consider numbers as being "right-adjusted," that is, moved to the extreme right of their allotted fields; if blank spaces appear at the right of card fields, an error may result.

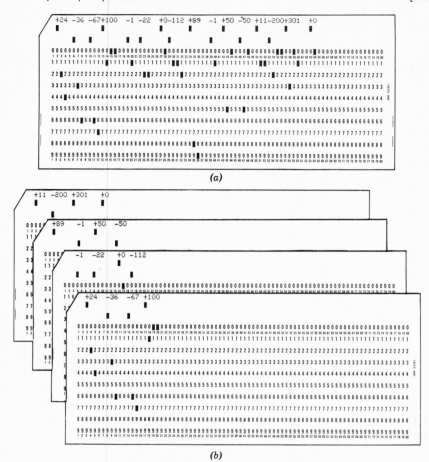

Fig. 11.4.   Two data formats. (*a*) 16 numbers, 4 columns each; (*b*) 16 numbers, 4 numbers to a card, 5 columns each.

Alphanumeric Information

The various characters that are permitted in a computer form a finite set, consisting generally of the digits, the letters, the more common arithmetic operators, and several other special symbols.

In the DELTA 63 there are 48 permitted characters, listed in Table 11.1.*   These are coded in binary fashion, 6 bits being used for each character.   The coding is done by the card reader in order to put information on tape or in memory.   The code is termed *binary-coded-decimal* or *BCD*.   For compactness, the codes are generally expressed as 2-digit octal numbers, as in the table.   The term *Hollerith* is used synonomously with *BCD*.

* The codes are essentially those used in many computers, such as IBM and Philco equipment.

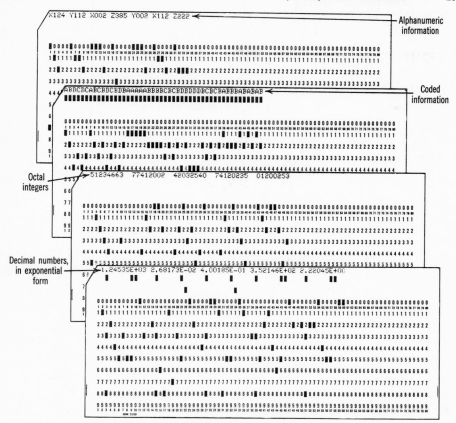

Fig. 11.5.   Several data cards.

TABLE 11.1 BCD CHARACTER CODES*

Character	BCD Code	Character	BCD Code	Character	BCD Code
0	00	F	26	Q	50
1	01	G	27	R	51
2	02	H	30	$	53
3	03	I	31	*	54
4	04	.	33	(blank)	60
5	05	)	34	/	61
6	06	=	35	S	62
7	07	"	36	T	63
8	10	—	40	U	64
9	11	J	41	V	65
+	20	K	42	W	66
A	21	L	43	X	67
B	22	M	44	Y	70
C	23	N	45	Z	71
D	24	Ø	46	,	73
E	25	P	47	(	74

* The letter b (not capitalized) is often used manually to indicate a blank.

Note that all the codes for integers, when written as binary numbers, occupy the right-most 4 bits in the code, whereas all other codes occupy at least one or the other of the leftmost 2 bits. This is useful in distinguishing internally between symbols (which contain at least one letter) and integers (which contain no letters).

As an example of BCD information, consider the following alphanumeric string of characters:

TØDAY THE DATE IS ØCTOBER 24, 1961.

This string, counting from the initial T to the final period, consists of 35 characters. Since 6 bits are required to code and store 1 character, 6 characters can be stored in one 36-bit word. Therefore 6 words are required for this string, with 6 bits left over which are filled with a blank. Strings of BCD characters are usually stored in successive memory words. The string we have given appears in memory as follows:*

Octal Words	Alphanumeric Words
634624217060	T Ø D A Y –
633025602421	T H E – D A
632560316260	T E – I S –
462363462225	Ø C T Ø B E
516002047360	R – 2 4 , –
011106013360	1 9 6 1 . –

Note that numbers may be stored in memory in a binary computer in two basically different forms. For example, the number 25110 can be stored as a binary number whose octal form is 61026, or as a BCD word whose octal form is 000205010100. In succeeding chapters the uses of these two forms will be investigated.

The HAP assembler language includes a pseudo-operation for the introduction of BCD information into a symbolic program.

BCD. The first character in the variable field of this pseudo-operation is a decimal digit n, from 1 to 9. The following BCD string of characters (after a comma) of $6n$ characters is stored in the n successive computer words in memory at the point in the program at which this card occurs. Thus to store the 6 words of BCD information we have given, we write:

Location	Oper.	Var. Field
STRING	BCD	6,TØDAY THE DATE IS ØCTØBER 24, 1961.

The symbol STRING is assigned to the first word containing this information.

If the count n is insufficient to account for the entire string, only the first $6n$ characters

* The contents of words containing BCD codes are usually shown as *unsigned* octal numbers. The dash (" – ") indicates a blank here.

are stored in *n* words. If the count is too large, blanks fill up remaining spaces to a total of *n* words.

Input-Output Subroutines

In order that the monitor may perform its input-output functions, control is sent to its subroutines by the object program. The calling sequence of those subroutines specifies two types of information: (1) the addresses of the memory locations into and out of which information is to be read (to or from tapes) and (2) the format of the data, as it appears or will appear on tape. To illustrate the structure of input-output subroutine calling sequences, the 63-monitor program is assumed to have two subroutines, one for input and one for output. Two new pseudo-operations are introduced for use in these calling sequences.

Two HAP pseudo-operations are used to set special indicators for use by the monitor in executing input-output operations.

ZERØ. This pseudo-operation directs the assembler to assemble 0-bits into bits S and 1–8 of a computer word. If an address and tag are given in the variable field, they are assembled as on an instruction card.

MZERØ. This pseudo-operation directs the assembler to assemble 1 into the S-bit (a minus sign) and 0-bits into bits 1–8 of a computer word. If an address and tag are given in the variable field, they are assembled as on an instruction card.

The purpose of these pseudo-operations is to permit the signs of words in subroutine calling sequences to be set to either plus or minus. In all the calling sequences described in Chapter 10 these signs were plus. Additional information, however, may be conveyed to the monitor in this manner. Note that the instruction HALT has the same meaning to the assembler as ZERØ; the latter pseudo-operation is introduced for uniformity with MZERØ.

The structure of an input-output calling sequence follows.

1. A JUMPSX instruction to send control to the subroutine.
2. In the first word following, the address of the format statement in memory. (Format statements are described later.)
3. In succeeding words, the addresses of words involved in the input or output process of data transmission.
4. A termination word.

It is possible to refer to blocks of memory words and to individual words. These must be listed in the order in which they are involved in the data transmission process. For example, if 24 items of data are to be placed in order in NAME1, NAME2, NAMEX, NAMEY, and the 20-word block starting at BLØCK, these addresses must be listed in that order. To distinguish between individual word addresses and block addresses, the ZERØ and MZERØ pseudo-operations are used. ZERØ is used for individual addresses. Blocks are identified by giving the starting and ending addresses, both of which are accompanied by MZERØ. Since the calling sequence is of variable length, a terminating word is necessary; MZERØ with a blank variable field is used.

Example 11.1   Write a 63-monitor calling sequence to read 24 data items from the input tape into NAME1, NAME2, NAMEX, NAMEY, and the 20-word block at BLØCK. The format of the data is given in the format statement at FMT.

Both the object and source programs are listed.

Object Program	Oper.	Var. Field
0 30 0007 03300	JUMPSX	INPUT,7
0 00 0000 04000		FMT
0 00 0000 05500	ZERØ	NAME1
0 00 0000 05503	ZERØ	NAME2
0 00 0000 05411	ZERØ	NAMEX
0 00 0000 05412	ZERØ	NAMEY
-0 00 0000 06001	MZERØ	BLØCK
-0 00 0000 06024	MZERØ	BLØCK+19
-0 00 0000 00000	MZERØ	

The addresses in the object program are arbitrarily chosen.

It is possible for information to be transmitted between other than the input or output tapes and memory. To signal this choice to the monitor, a tag is used in the first word of the calling sequence (the format word). The tag used corresponds to the tape designators listed in Section 7.2: 1 for tape B, 2 for tape C, etc. Tape A is the monitor tape.

Example 11.2   Write a calling sequence to write 10 words on tape G from WØRD1, WØRD2, the 5-word block at NUMBRS, X1, X2, and ZZZ. The desired format of the data on tape is given in the format statement at FØRMAT.

Oper.	Var. Field	
JUMPSX	ØUTPUT,7	
	FØRMAT,6	"6" = TAPE G
ZERØ	WØRD1	
ZERØ	WØRD2	
MZERØ	NUMBRS	
MZERØ	NUMBRS+4	
ZERØ	X1	
ZERØ	X2	
ZERØ	ZZZ	
MZERØ		

If an address in the calling sequence of an input-output 63-monitor subroutine is tagged, the tag is interpreted by the monitor as an address modifier in the usual manner. The index register involved is the one specified, and the modifier value used is the one set outside the calling sequence, in the main program. The following coding sequence causes the printing of every other word from LIST to LIST+8:

Location	Oper.	Var. Field
	SETXRI	10,1
LØØP	JUMPSX	ØUTPUT,7
		FØRMAT

(Continued)

```
ZERØ      LIST,1
MZERØ
INCRXM    2,1
XJUMP     LØØP,1
```

Format Statements

A very useful feature of a monitor program is its ability to accept a wide variety of data formats to be used in input and output. The short loading program coded in Example 7.5 (page 131) did not have this feature. The formats for data may vary in many ways. First, information may be placed on cards or tape in various densities: short items may be packed 12 to a card, longer numbers may be punched only 4 to a card. Second, the information may be octal, decimal, alphanumeric, or a combination of these. Third, the output results may be tabulated and may be headed with titles and comments; blank lines may be used for the separation of lists. There are many other possibilities. If a monitor system were not available, each programmer would have to provide his own means for reading and writing data in this variety of structures; the coding task would be formidable in many cases.

Format statements are used to specify the precise format of the data, both for input (on punched cards, usually) and for output (on printed pages). The format statements used in the FORTRAN language are described here, because their structure is used in a number of assembly languages.* This is true for compatibility within the monitor.

The format statement lists, as a series of *field specifications,* the type and number of data items to be read in or written out; also specified is the width of the field allotted to each item on cards or on a printed page. These specifications are of the form

$$nCw$$

where *n* is the number of items involved, C is a *control character* indicating the type of data word, and *w* is the field width in alphanumeric characters.

The character C may be one of the following:

Character	Significance
A	Alphanumeric information
E	Floating-point decimal numbers
F	Fixed-point decimal numbers
N	Decimal integers
Ø	Octal integers

---

* FORTRAN, described in Chapter 14, is a special coding language that is widely available for computers.

A monitor has the ability to convert the data appearing on cards in one of these forms to an appropriate internal representation and to do the reverse on output.* Specifically, the following conversions on input are performed by the monitor, under the command of the specification control characters. Output conversions are similar, but in reverse order.

A. Alphanumeric information on cards is read directly into memory "without conversion." Actually, a conversion to BCD codes is accomplished by the card reader. The monitor itself does no conversion.

E. Floating-point decimal numbers on cards are converted to floating-point internal numbers. The form of the numbers on cards is as follows: 56.10E+45.

F. Fixed-point decimal numbers on cards are converted to floating-point internal numbers.

N. Decimal integers on cards are converted to integers in machine form.

Ø. Octal integers on cards are converted to integers in machine form.

Following are some examples of field specifications.

Spec.	Significance
5A4	5 fields of 4 characters each are treated as alphanumeric information.
2F12	2 fields of 12 characters each are treated as fixed-point decimal numbers to be converted to floating-point form.
20N4	20 fields of 4 characters each are to be treated as decimal integers.
Ø12	1 field of 12 characters is to be treated as an octal integer. (If n in a field specification is 1, it may be omitted.)

A complete format statement consists of a sequence of field specifications, listed with intervening commas.

Example 11.3 Write a format statement that directs the monitor to read into memory the information pictured on the card in Fig. 11.6; vertical lines separate fields. The first 12 columns contain an octal number, the next 12 columns contain a second octal number, the next 2 fields of 4 columns each contain 2 alphanumeric strings, and the next 20 fields of 2 columns each contain decimal numbers.

The proper format statement is:

$$(\text{Ø}12,2A4,20N2)$$

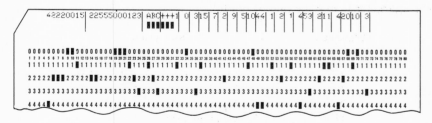

Fig. 11.6.   Data card (Example 11.3).

---

* Although we say data "on cards," we really mean data "on cards or on tape." The card fields spoken of are usually converted to fields on tape, but it is easier to picture data on cards.

Such statements are enclosed in parentheses and must be inserted in alphanumeric form into a symbolic program. If this format statement applies to the calling sequence of Example 11.1, we would write

Location	Oper.	Var. Field
FMT	BCD	3,(2Ø12,2A4,2ØN2)

The assembler would store this BCD string in three successive words in memory, in locations FMT through FMT+2.

After execution of the INPUT subroutine, as called in Example 11.1, the following would be the contents of the designated memory locations:

Location	Contents (Octal)
NAME1	000042220015
NAME2	022555000123
NAMEX	606060212223
NAMEY	606020202001
BLØCK	000000000000
BLØCK+1	000000000003
BLØCK+2	000000000017
BLØCK+3	000000000007
• • •	• • • • •

Other Input-Output Features

The monitor program written for a particular real computer performs operations in a manner very similar to those described for the DELTA 63 and, in addition, may have more flexibility. Since we are concerned primarily with programming and coding and only incidentally with input-output, no further details on the 63-monitor are given. Since actual characteristics and functions of a monitor vary widely, little is gained by supplying these details. Rather, several other features that are usually available are listed.

1. It is possible to print a number of lines using one format statement. This is useful for the production of tabular information. If the calling sequence indicates that M words are to be written out and only N words ($N < M$) are called for by the format statement, the latter is scanned sufficiently often to exhaust the number M. The sequence of field specifications normally represents one line of printing. If a format statement is scanned n times, it produces n lines of print. For example, if a format statement is (8Ø10) and a block of 800 words is indicated in the calling sequence, then 100 lines of print, each containing eight 10-character octal numbers, are the result.

2. In the specification code sequences it is possible to insert sequences of alphanumeric strings that are later printed with other information. For this purpose another control character is used: H (for Hollerith). The string

NHXXXXXXXXXXXXXXX

where the number of X's is N represents such an alphanumeric insertion. The X's each represent any alphanumeric characters, including blanks. The format statement

(16HANSWERS... SUM =N5,12H,   PRØDUCT =N6,8H, RØØT =N5)
⎣←——— 16 char. ———→⎦   ⎣←——12 char. —→⎦ ⎣←8 char.→⎦

results in a printed line of this form:

ANSWERS... SUM = 4562,   PRØDUCT = 56786, RØØT =   213

3. In order to indicate the number of decimal places that are to be printed to the right of the decimal point, additional information is provided with certain field specifications. The specifications for the control characters E and F are then of this form:

$$nCw.d$$

where d is the number of places to the right of the point. For example, the code 2F10.2 would direct the monitor to print out 2 fixed-point numbers of 10 characters each, with 2 digits to the right of the decimal point; one such number is 1984009.36.

4. It is possible for a monitor to accept data that are not punched on cards with a fixed format. For example, blank spaces can be used to delimit items on data cards. The monitor must then scan each card until a blank is encountered, signaling the end of one item. The several types of items can be identified as follows: (a) octal integers can begin with a qualifier, such as /Ø/; (b) decimal integers can be written with no special mark; (c) fixed-point decimal numbers can be written with decimal points; (d) floating-point decimal numbers can be written with an E; (e) alphanumeric information can be written with at least one special letter or other mark. These conventions are arbitrary; they merely serve to show that a format statement is not essential. This approach makes the coding effort and data preparation easier, but it requires a more complex card-scanning routine.

A sample printout shown in Fig. 11.7 indicates many of the features explained in these paragraphs on the variations of data formats.

Reading in Data

Once a programmer has decided on the format of the data for his program, there are still a number of questions that he must answer on the matters of data and tapes for intermediate results.

Should all the data be read in at once or should they be read in in batches? Should the data be marked with the number of items present or should an end-of-data card be used? Should intermediate tape storage be used?

```
GAIN CØNSTANT  =   0.1110011E+05


NUMERATØR PØLYNØMIAL ...

CØNSTANT MULTIPLIER = 0.5091821E+04

RØØTS ØF NUMERATØR

              REAL PART          IMAG PART
     1       -1.50000E-01        0.0
     2       -3.05812E+00        0.0


DENØMINATØR PØLYNØMIAL ...

CØNSTANT MULTIPLIER = 0.4587180E-00

RØØTS ØF DENØMINATØR

              REAL PART          IMAG PART
     1       -4.01962E+00        9.77462E-01
     2       -4.01962E+00       -9.77462E-01
     3       -4.09195E+00        3.25395E-01
     4       -4.09195E+00       -3.25395E-01
     5       -3.87192E+00        1.63356E+00
     6       -3.87192E+00       -1.63356E+00
```

Fig. 11.7.   Sample computer printout.

These questions cannot be answered once for all situations; they must be answered for each particular program. Several comments can be made, however, that are general in nature.

Clearly, if only 20,000 words of memory are available for data and 100,000 10-digit numbers are to be processed, only part of the data can be read in at one time. A general rule of thumb is that as much data as possible should be read into high-speed memory at one time. Tape-reading time is then minimized, since less time is wasted bringing the tape unit to reading speed and in stopping it. Since the contents of one data card are read into one tape record by the card reader, the more information placed on each card, the faster the tape-reading time as data are loaded into memory. Some computer systems permit the regrouping of information on tape so that large records are produced prior to memory loading. In this way even greater speed is obtained, because less time is wasted while the reading head is positioned over record gaps.

Preceding a set of data an additional item of information may be given: the number of data items to be read. If this is done, the program reads in that many and proceeds to other work. Alternately, a blank card or a card with a special end-of-data number or character may be used. In this case, the program reads in data until this special card is encountered. There is little difference in these approaches, either in execution time or in memory space.

The question whether to use scratch tapes for intermediate results is the most difficult of the three questions to answer. Consider the problem of producing 50,000 integers, all relatively small (having under 5 digits each), during a calculation. Some of these may be put on tape for later usage, but this involves tape-writing time, which may be quite large. Alternately, these numbers may be "packed" two to a memory word; they will fit in 25,000 words. It takes time, however, to pack and unpack the numbers. The packing method is the faster of the two approaches, but there may not be room if an additional 5000 words are needed for the actual processing (besides the 25,000 needed for storage). The choice here is relatively easy to make compared to some actual situations that arise in computation problems. Further discussion of efficient use of storage is given in Chapter 12.

11.3 MONITOR DEBUGGING

Debugging a program is important because it is essential that the program work correctly, and for the program to work correctly all errors must be removed. Sometimes as much as 80 or 90% of program development time is spent on debugging. A few of the approaches to debugging offered by monitor programs are considered in this section. Further discussion appears in Chapter 19.

Preliminary Checking

By introducing the topic of debugging as a facility of the monitor program, we do not imply that a programmer first turns to the monitor for debugging help. Computer time can be expensive, and a programmer should attempt to locate his errors by hand, by looking closely at his coding.

Errors can be made at every step of the program-writing process; these steps were outlined in Section 1.2. Most errors occur in the coding stage, however, since so many operations are involved. If an error is known to be present, instruction-by-instruction checking is often one of the best ways of detecting it.

Memory Dumps

A *memory dump* is a printout of the contents of a portion of memory or of a magnetic tape. Usually the dump consists of one or more blocks of memory words or records on tape; if it is the former, a printout of the contents of the console registers is usually given. Dumps may be of two kinds. *Snapshot dumps* indicate information that exists at a specified point in the program, that is, when control passes to that point; *post-mortem dumps* indicate information present at the conclusion of a run, whether the program stopped normally or otherwise.

The execution of a snapshot dump does not affect the program in any way; the program may continue running from that point on.

Debugging control cards, mentioned in Section 11.1, are used by the programmer to indicate a request for dumps. As shown in Fig. 11.3, these cards are placed after the program deck being debugged. Because a programmer rarely wishes to examine all of memory, but rather wants a dump of certain portions only, the debugging cards specify the desired locations for dumping.

In the 63-monitor the snapshot and post-mortem dump request cards have the following formats.

	Location	Oper.	Var. Field
Snapshot request:	L	SNAP	C,A,B
Post-mortem request:		PØSTM	C,A,B

Here C is a control character: Ø for octal, D for decimal, H for BCD (Hollerith), and F for floating-point. A and B are the starting and ending addresses (in octal) of the block to be dumped. L is the location (in octal) at which the snapshot dump is desired. Thus the following control card

Location	Oper.	Var. Field
00427	SNAP	Ø,00500,02000

supplies a snapshot dump of locations 00500 through 02000 inclusive, every time control passes to 00427, the output being printed in octal format.

Examination of a sequence of snapshot dumps located at a point in a program through which control passes a number of times reveals the changes in the specified block that have occurred since the last time through. This information can be quite helpful in analyzing the effect of repetitious processing on a program.

Some snapshot routines provide greater flexibility in their use by permitting the programmer to state the conditions under which the dumps are to be provided. Some possibilities follow.

1. Dump only the first N times control passes through location L, dump only the Nth time, dump after the Nth time, dump from the Mth through the Nth times, etc.

2. Dump only if the C(AC) is zero, nonzero, positive, negative, etc.

3. Dump only if a specified index register contains a number less than K, equal to K, greater than K, between K_1 and K_2, etc.

4. Dump only if the contents of a specified location in memory is zero, nonzero, positive, negative, less than K, equal to K, etc.

Conditional dumping is useful if an error is known to exist within a loop. If the loop cycles 100 times, it is usually sufficient to examine a dump for each of the first 3 or 5 cycles. The statement "dump only the first 5 times control passes through L" can be used for this situation. Similarly, it may be known that a process occurs satisfactorily the first 10 cycles of a loop, and fails the 11th. Then "dump after the 10th time . . ." is useful. (This second case, incidentally, is far rarer than the first.) Other situations can arise, at which times the other listed conditional dumps may be of value.

For the monitor to execute snapshot dumps, it must temporarily obtain control at those points in the program at which dumps are requested. After executing the dump, the monitor then returns control to the object program so that it can continue running. The instruction at the location of the snapshot request must be executed before control is returned. Control may be sent to the monitor by means of a special feature, available on many computers: the *trap*. The instruction at the point of request is modified in some way and the computer is trapped by the monitor. Details of the trapping feature and the flow of control during the process are described in Chapter 19.

Examples of Dumps*

In Fig. 11.8 two snapshot dumps are given. They apply to the problem coded in Example 10.6 (page 193), the evaluation of a function of four variables. It is assumed here that the program is assembled starting at location 00100. The following cards were used to obtain these dumps.

Location	Oper.	Var. Field
00100	SNAP	0,00100,00200
00125	SNAP	0,00124,00200

The first snapshot occurs at the start of the program, and the complete program is dumped. The second snapshot occurs at the end, and only part of the program is dumped. In addition to supplying the information in octal, the symbolic operation codes of all the instructions are given as an aid to the programmer. Any constants that can be interpreted to have operation codes are so interpreted; therefore a number of HALT instructions appear, since their operation code is 00.

Several things should be observed in the snapshot dumps of Fig. 11.8. Many of these are representative of dumps from any monitor, but details vary.

1. Locations are indicated at the left; the address in the first column applies to the first word on the line.

2. The initial contents of the registers in the console (AC, MR, and XR's) are irrelevant here, since the first dump occurs before the program is run.

3. Blocks of words of size greater than 4 (1 line of print) all of which contain

* The DELTA 63 and its debugging cards are used for illustration in these examples.

```
00100    SNAP    0,00100,00200

MR +000000000000    AC +000000000000              XR1 00000 00000   XR2 00000 00000
XR3 00000 00000    XR4 00000 00000    XR5 00000 00000    XR6 00000 00000   XR7 00000 00000

00100  LØAD  10100000131    JUMPSX 03000701000    STØRE 00200000126    LØAD   00100000132
00104  MULT  00600000132    STØRE  02000000127    LØAD  00100000131    MULT   00600701200
00110  SUBT  00500000127    JUMPSX 03000701000    STØRE 02000000127    JUMPSX 03000701200
00114  HALT  00000000131    HALT   00000000132    HALT  00000000133    HALT   00000000134
00120  HALT  00000000130    LØAD   01000000126    ADD   00400000127    ADD    00400000130
00124  STØRE 02000000135    HALT   01000000000    HALT  00000000000    HALT   00000000000
00130  HALT  00000000000    HALT   10000000000    HALT  00000000000    HALT   00000000000
00134  HALT  00000000004    HALT   00000000015    HALT  00000000014    HALT   00000000002
00135 TØ 00200 ALL CØNTAIN ZERØ
```

```
00125    SNAP    0,00124,00200

MR +000000000000    AC +000000000507              XR1 00000 00000   XR2 00000 00000
XR3 00000 00000    XR4 00000 00000    XR5 00000 00000    XR6 00000 00000   XR7 00000 00113

00124  STØRE 02000000135    10000000000    HALT 00000000003    HALT 00000000005
00130  HALT  00000000477    HALT 00000000015    HALT 00000000014    HALT 00000000002
00134  HALT  00000000004    HALT 00000000507
00136 TØ 00200 ALL CØNTAIN ZERØ
```

Fig. 11.8.   Two octal snapshot dumps.

zero are not printed individually (in order to save space); rather, a comment about their extent is printed.

4. The 1's in bit 2 of locations 00100 and 00125 (an initial octal digit 1) are concerned with the trapping feature and are discussed in Chapter 19.

With reference to the program dumped (Example 10.6), we can observe the effects of program execution.   A comparison of the two dumps reveals changes in the contents of locations 00126 to 00130 and 00135; these locations are TEMP to TEMP+2 and F, respectively.   By following the program calculations, we can understand the reasons for these changes.   Note that the arithmetic is of integers, and fractions are ignored.   Note also that the answer remains in the accumulator, as seen in the second dump.

Two other snapshot dump formats are indicated in Fig. 11.9; a floating-point dump and a BCD dump.   Because less room is required for each word in these formats, 6 words per line are printed in floating-point format and 12 words per line are printed in BCD format.   No symbolic operation codes are supplied in either case.

In a floating-point dump the contents of the accumulator and multiply register are also given as floating-point numbers.   Sometimes a dump provides the contents of these registers in both fixed- and floating-point form.   If a word in memory has a zero characteristic, that is, if bits 1–8 are all zero, the number if considered to be an integer and is printed in that form, in octal.   This is a valid assumption, since all floating-point numbers have nonzero characteristics.

In a BCD dump everything is interpreted as BCD information except for illegal BCD codes, such as 14 and 37; in these cases blanks are printed.   Thus instructions and constants as well as alphanumeric strings are interpreted in this manner.   In the dump in Fig. 11.9 locations 01100 through 01105 (6 words) contain instructions; the associated printout has an odd appearance.*   Following this, in locations 01106 through 01121 (12 words) are 2 comments for use by the program.   Then in locations 01122 through 01130 (7 words) a format statement for output printing appears.   In locations 01131 through 01134 (4 words) there are 4 constants.   Finally, in locations 01135 through 01141 (5 words), a binary pattern of 0's and 1's, in BCD, is stored.

Snapshot dumps are very useful for the gross checking out and debugging of a program, when the location of the error is not known with any accuracy. Then it is helpful to place a snapshot request at the end of every segment of the program, perhaps 6 or 8 in all, dumping large portions of the program.   This procedure is to be avoided if a loop is to be studied in detail, because large amounts of printout result.   If, for example, a request is made for an octal dump of 4000 words of memory, all of which are nonzero, the dump printout might fill about 18 pages.   If this request is placed in a loop and 40 dumps are provided, 720 pages of printout result.

* These 6 words were actually obtained by taking locations 00104 through 00111 of Fig. 11.8 and converting them to their BCD equivalents.

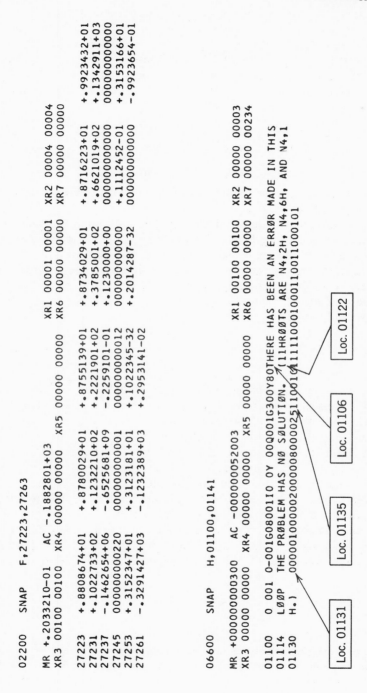

```
02200  SNAP  F,27223,27263

MR +.2033210-01  AC -.1882801+03              XR1 00001 00001   XR2 00004 00004
XR3 00100 00100  XR4 00000 00000  XR5 00000 00000   XR6 00000 00000   XR7 00000 00000

27223   +.8808674+01   +.8780029+01   +.8755139+01   +.8734029+01   +.8716223+01   +.9923432+01
27231   +.1022733+02   +.1232210+02   +.2221901+02   +.3785001+02   +.6621019+02   +.1342911+03
27237   -.1462654+06   -.6525681+09   -.2259101-01   +.1230000+00   00000000000    00000000000
27245   00000000220    00000000001    00000000012    00000000000    00000000000    00000000000
27253   +.3152347+01   +.3123181+01   +.1022345-32   +.2014287-32   +.1112452-01   +.3153166+01
27261   -.3291427+03   -.1232389+03   +.2953141-02                                 -.9923654-01
```

```
06600  SNAP  H,01100,01141

MR +000000000300  AC -00000052003            XR1 00100 00100  XR2 00000 00003
XR3 00000 00000  XR4 00000 00000  XR5 00000 00000  XR6 00000 00000  XR7 00000 00234

01100   0 001 0-001G080011O OY 00Q001G300Y8OTHERE HAS BEEN AN ERRØR MADE IN THIS
01114      LØØP  THE PRØBLEM HAS NØ SØLUTIØN. (11HRØØTS ARE N4,2H, N4,6H, AND N4,1
01130   H.) 00000100000200000800002511001Ø111100010001100110000101
```

Loc. 01131 Loc. 01135 Loc. 01106 Loc. 01122

Fig. 11.9. Floating-point and BCD snapshot dumps.

For detailed debugging, snapshot dumps are requested at intervals close together, perhaps several times in one portion of a program. This approach is taken when the location of the error has been more closely pinpointed. Conditional requests for dumps within a loop are desirable such as dumps "until the fifth time." Generally, smaller areas of memory are dumped. It is usually possible to request two small areas of memory at one location, through the use of two cards:

Location	Oper.	Var. Field
03000	SNAP	0,04000,04400
03000	SNAP	0,12300,12450

This avoids having to request a single dump from 04000 through 12450, which would result in needless printout.

Therefore we use dump requests closer together and perhaps of smaller areas of memory as the error is bracketed. Post-mortem dumps, not discussed at any length here, are useful in seeing the final disposition of a program. Dumps of records on tape are used in the same manner as dumps of memory; intermediate results are sometimes written on tape, and it is useful to study them. If a very detailed analysis of a portion of a program is needed, other debugging techniques should be used.

Summary

An input-output monitor program is usually available at computer installations having large-scale machines. This program is used primarily for the automatic loading and running of programs and the production of results. The programmer views the monitor in other ways as well. It provides him with input-output facilities that he can utilize with little coding effort on his part. It contains a library of commonly used subroutines that he may call on. Finally, it offers him some facilities for debugging his program.

Aside from helping to run a program, the most important of the services is the input-output facility. By calling on monitor subroutines for this purpose, the programmer is able to accept and provide a wide variety of data formats. If the programmer had to code his own input-output operations and perform the associated conversion of data, his work would be greatly increased.

PROBLEMS

Section 11.1

11.1. Programs may be loaded, run, and have their answers supplied without the assistance of a monitor program. Describe the differences between using and not using a monitor.

11.2.   Draw a flowchart of the monitor operations, indicating what happens when each of the control card types is encountered in the programmer's deck.

11.3.   Describe in some detail the nature of the routines within the monitor used to perform the monitor's functions as described in the text. Consider the monitor roles listed.

Section 11.2

11.4.   Data may appear on punched cards in various formats. Discuss the reasons for this variation. What are the advantages of placing many numbers on one card and of placing few numbers on one card?

11.5.   Write the INPUT and ØUTPUT subroutines described in the text. Ignore the format statement, however, and assume that information on the input tape can be stored directly into memory, 6 characters to a word; make a similar assumption on output. Use the tape instructions and conventions of Section 7.2. Assume that 20 words (120 characters) fill each output record.

11.6.   Write format statements to read information from punched cards in the following formats.

(a) Cols. 1–24: 4 octal integers of 6 digits each;
        cols. 25–37: 1 decimal integer;
        cols. 38–67: 5 alphanumeric words of 6 characters each;
        cols. 68–72: 5 single digits.

These are to be read into 15 words in memory.

(b) Cols. 1–40: 10 decimal integers of 4 digits each:
        cols. 41–72: 4 floating-point numbers of 8 characters each, having 3 decimal places each.

These are to be read into 17 words in memory.

Assume appropriate INPUT subroutine calling sequences. Show, in octal form, the contents of associated memory words after reading in, assuming any data cards of the proper format.

11.7.   Tape F contains 1000 20-word records. Write routines

(a) to count the records containing at least 1 zero word;

(b) to sort the 20 numbers in each record, putting the largest first, and placing each sorted record on tape G;

(c) to form a 20,000-word table in memory, composed as follows: the first word of each record, taken as a group, filling the first 1000 words; the second word of each record, taken as a group, filling the second 1000 words; etc.

Section 11.3

11.8.   Discuss the several sources of error in computer problem solving: machine errors, operator errors, programming errors, and coding errors. Compare the likelihood of occurrence of each and the ease of detection and correction of each.

11.9.   Prior to placing a program on the computer, what kinds of error checks can be made at the several stages of program writing?

11.10. Examine some of the examples and problems in earlier chapters and imagine a number of errors to be made in the coding of each.   Discuss the possible consequences of these errors and the debugging approaches that might be taken to locate them.

11.11.   What are some errors that can be readily detected by an examination of the postmortem dump and the snapshot dumps of a program?   What are some errors that cannot be so readily detected by these means?

11.12.   Discuss other debugging aids besides the dumps discussed in the text.   What other types of information about a program would be helpful in debugging it?   Under what circumstances would these other approaches be useful?

PART THREE
CODING TECHNIQUES
AND LANGUAGES

PART II was devoted to a development of several fundamental coding concepts. These concepts were introduced in general terms and illustrated by the use of a symbolic language. In this language there was essentially a one-to-one correspondence between symbolic and machine instructions.

In Part III we turn to a study of more advanced coding techniques and coding languages. The first chapter in this part considers the overall planning of a computer program, unifies the topics studied earlier, and offers several new concepts. Later chapters are devoted primarily to an examination of coding languages that are frequently termed *higher-level* languages. These languages are designed for particular classes of problems; they permit the programmer to code in a form closely allied to his problems. Some consideration is given also to certain classes of problems and the particular problems they offer. The problem of debugging is considered in greater detail.

12

PROGRAM PLANNING

Computer programs, despite any attempt to classify them, are all to an extent unique. Many programs have similarities to one another, particularly if they solve similar problems, but each has its own set of characteristics. Variations among computers exist also, but to a much lesser extent. The fundamentals of computer organization and language can readily be characterized, but characterizing programs is more difficult, and writing down rules for planning programs is subject to the same difficulties.

Despite these difficulties, some general principles in program planning can be stated. The first planning phase examined in this chapter is the preparation of a program for coding. Associated with this problem is the selection of a "point of view" or programming goal. The next phase considered is the problem of planning the coding in an efficient manner. Next, an examination is made of some useful operations that frequently occur in programming. Finally, a technique for automatically automatic loading programs into memory and linking main programs and subroutines is examined.

12.1 PREPARATION FOR CODING

Problem Definition

Prior to coding a programmer must define his problem precisely, select a method for its solution, and perform an analysis (perhaps draw a flowchart) of the problem. In this section further attention is paid to the first two of these steps; the third was discussed extensively in Chapter 2.

A computer program must be explicit in all its aspects; every possible alternative must be allowed for, and all actions to be taken must be coded. The computer cannot make decisions on its own. For this reason the problem to be coded must be precisely stated. Furthermore, the nature and format of the data to be processed must be precisely known.

The following information must be provided before a program can be coded and run: (1) a statement of what information is given; (2) a statement of what information is wanted as results; (3) information on the accuracy of results; (4) the format (on cards, tape, or other input medium) of the given data; (5) the format (on cards, tape, or paper) of the results; (6) information, if applicable, on what to do if the results diverge in an iterative problem; (7) miscellaneous information, such as the number of problems to be run and the amount of data printed out (if this is a variable).

As an illustration of a complete problem definition, consider this example.

Example 12.1   A set of 16 simultaneous linear equations is to be solved for the 16 unknowns of the set.

Given: 256 coefficients and 16 constants, those of the set of equations, appropriately identified.

Accuracy: All unknowns are to be determined to within a relative accuracy of 0.01%.

Data format: 8 coefficients appear on each of 32 cards, followed by 2 cards containing the 16 constants. One extra card, placed first, has the number 16 punched in columns 1 and 2. Each number is given in the form .XXXXXE$\pm$YY (10 columns), where XXXXX is a fraction and YY is an exponent. The coefficients in the first equation appear on the first 2 cards; the coefficients of the second equation appear on the next 2 cards; etc.

Output format: The 16 unknowns are to be printed in the same format as the input data, printed 8 to a line with three intervening blanks between adjacent results.

Although this information is of the proper form, it is too specific. If a programmer were to code a program to solve simultaneous equations, he would generalize the program to accept any number of equations, up to some limiting number. It should also be noted that this problem is so common that most computer libraries have it available as a subroutine. If so, such matters as data format and accuracy are usually specified in the subroutine description and are therefore not part of the problem definition.

Although all information must be available eventually for a problem (unless use of a library subroutine obviates some of it), it is evident that a programmer can begin to code before any information on format and accuracy is used. Because these items actually belong in the definition of the problem, however, they are mentioned here. The program will read data from cards or tape and the form of this data must be included in the program, probably in the format statements of the input calling sequences. Similarly, the answers must be provided and the form of the results must be included in the program.

Selection of a Method

We saw in Section 1.1 that the best approach to a problem on a computer is not necessarily the same as (and may be quite different from) the best manual or desk calculator approach. The ideal method for a computer solution takes advantage of the high speeds available on a computer and is therefore fast, requires no storage space outside the high-speed memory, and is easy to code. In a particular case, if the problem is even slightly complex, the ideal method is hard to identify.

We cannot list a set of rules for selecting a method that will apply to all problems; it is even difficult to do this in general terms. Nonetheless, the following rules are given to serve as a guide to making the selection. They take into consideration characteristics of computers and standard programming techniques.

1. The method should not generate intermediate results in very large quantities, that is, in tens of thousands of numbers. High-speed memory space, although large, is limited.

2. Iterative or other methods that can be expressed in terms of indices or subscripts are desirable because of the automatic indexing features of modern computers and languages for them.

3. The method should not rely on extreme accuracy of calculations unless this is essential. Memory words carry 8 places in a floating-point number (in a 36-bit machine) or 10 places (in a 48-bit machine).

4. It is highly advantageous if the program that realizes the method can be broken down into a series of parts or subroutines that can be individually coded and checked.

5. Many subroutines are readily available. A method that utilizes subroutines already written or other programs is desirable, since less coding and debugging are then required.

6. A number of assemblers, compilers, and interpreters have been written. Some methods are well suited to the use of one or more of these, and such a choice may be advantageous.

A consideration sometimes paralleling the selection of a method is the choice of a computer. Most programmers do not have this choice, since their college or place of employment has only one computer for their use. Sometimes, however, we can choose among two or more computers, and if so, there are additional considerations.

Although it is true that most computers within a given price or size range have similar characteristics, there are some variations. Most of these are minor, however, having to do with special instructions, number of index registers, etc. Some variations are more significant, such as the number of addresses per instruction or whether the word length is fixed or variable. When we compare computers that differ greatly in size or speed, however, larger differences can be noted. We cannot describe these here, because of space limitations, but they should be considered if the choice exists. Perhaps the single outstanding difference among computers is their identification by the manufacturer as either "business" or "scientific" computers. This distinction generally reflects the difference in the types of problem in the two areas.

The Next Steps

The steps numbered 3, 4, and 5 in Section 1.2 are these: (3) problem analysis, (4) coding, and (5) debugging. Chapter 2 is devoted to an examination of step 3. Coding is the topic most widely discussed and illustrated; most of Parts II and III are devoted to it. Finally, debugging is treated in two places in this book: Section 11.3 uses the framework of the monitor program to introduce the topic; Chapter 19 explores other approaches to the problem.

Program Segmentation

When a program is coded, it is usually desirable to consider the problem as being composed of a number of *segments,* each of which may be coded individually. A segment is any identifiable portion of a program large enough to be considered largely independent of other portions. This approach is called *segmentation.*

Some operations within a program are best coded as closed subroutines, particularly if they are used frequently throughout the program. Segmentation implies identification of chronological sequences, whereas putting things into subroutines implies identification of frequent operations whose use is scattered throughout the program. These two approaches are not disparate; a programmer should first identify subroutines and then segment the program.

If a programmer codes and checks out each segment of his program in turn, he can be reasonably sure that earlier segments are correct. If adding later segments leads to errors, most likely the errors are in those segments. If segments are small, the likelihood of two or more errors in each is very low. Identification of two errors is usually twice as much trouble as the identification of one error. For these reasons, segmenting a program for the purpose of coding is generally efficient.

Since the purpose of segmentation is to provide efficient coding, the associated problem of debugging merits a few comments at this point. It is wise to assume that a program will not perform correctly the first time it is run. Therefore a programmer ought to plan to use snapshot dumps at the end of all segments in an attempt to check them. Some of the techniques described in Chapter 19 may also be used for this purpose. If a programmer considers the possibility of errors and means for debugging during coding, he may save himself a great deal of work later.

12.2 PROGRAM EMPHASIS

When a programmer starts to write a program, he usually gives some thought to his goals. For example, he might not care how long the program runs on the computer or how much space is required. Or he might be writing a subroutine for general usage; such a program ought to be fast and require little memory space.

A few primary goals in program writing are these.

1. The programmer may want the program to run correctly as quickly as possible after he begins to code; his goal is minimal coding and debugging time.

2. He may want the program to be executed in the shortest possible time.

3. He may want the program to occupy as little space as possible in memory.

4. He may want to minimize debugging efforts, since debugging is so time consuming.

5. Finally, the programmer may want to write the program in such a way that it is easy to modify as changes become necessary; program flexibility is his goal here.

A particular program will not, in all likelihood, emphasize just one of these goals; it will rather emphasize two or three. In a given program one may be most important, but others must seriously be taken into account as well. Some goals are usually mutually incompatible, such as the minimizations of both time and space. Others are not as a rule incompatible, such as the minimization of both debugging efforts and overall preparation time.

Making the Program Work

The most common goal is probably that of making the program work correctly as quickly as possible after the job of programming has begun. This goal is very hard to characterize by the series of steps to be taken for it, because they vary from person to person a great deal. For one programmer, writing all the coding and then debugging each part in turn is the speediest. For another, coding and debugging each part separately is the best. For still another, spending a great deal of time and care on the coding followed by relatively few debugging runs is fastest.

There may be a number of reasons for wanting to minimize overall programming time. It may be necessary to use the results of the program in some other work that is waiting for them. Perhaps other programmers are working simultaneously on different programs, and later the collection of routines will be consolidated. Another possibility is that to meet a schedule answers must be obtained as fast as possible.

Minimizing Running Time

Minimizing the running time of a program on a computer is perhaps the second most sought-after goal. A frequent approach is to achieve the first goal, and after the program has been proved to work satisfactorily, to modify the coding so that running time is decreased. It is not unusual for a programmer to be able to improve running time by a factor of 10 or more by subsequent coding changes.

One type of program that must invariably run at high speed, if possible, is a subroutine that will be used frequently. Examples are mathematical operations that appear in monitor libraries, such as the sine or cosine. In general, the more often a program is used, the more important it is that it run fast. If by recoding we can save the execution of 5 instructions in a loop that is used 500 times in a routine, the saving is only negligible if the program is used 10 times in a program on a modern computer. If, however, it is used 100,000 times, as might be the case if a program calls on the routine to process 100,000 items, the savings are appreciable.

The table-look-at technique described in Section 8.3 is designed to minimize execution time. In general, if a programmer can store information for program use within the program and make references to tables instead of making calculations during execution, much time can be saved. If, for example, we store trigonometric functions as tables, listing arguments with function values, a simple searching procedure replaces a time-consuming calculation. For high accuracy, such tables may be very lengthy, unless interpolation or similar methods are used.

Another means of increasing the speed of processing is concerned with the relative times spent in "bookkeeping" and "useful" operations. In Section 8.2 this problem was considered. A summation loop was coded several ways, and execution times were considered. If several additions are performed each loop cycle, execution time is decreased, since the ratio of bookkeeping to arithmetic operations is decreased. Arithmetic operations are fixed in number in this problem, so that the improvement is achieved by decreasing loop control operations.

Descriptions of instructions in computer manuals differ in one important respect from the descriptions in this book. The execution time of each instruction is given in manuals. It was noted in Section 5.3 that multiplication takes about three to five times as long as addition (in fixed-point arithmetic). If minimization of time is important, such execution times must be considered.

In a problem involving addition and multiplication, like that in Example 5.6 (page 92), efforts to minimize multiplication operations tend to be more significant than efforts to minimize addition operations.

The DELTA 63 instructions can be classified by assumed execution times. If we consider a unit of time, the following list indicates execution times for most of the instructions already studied; the list may be considered typical of real computers.

One time unit:	JUMP, SETXRI, INCRXM, PADDXM
Two time units:	LØAD, STØRE, ADD, SUBT,
	LØADM, STØREM, JUMPPL, JUMPMI,
	JUMPZE, JUMPNZ, CLEARS, SETXR,
	LØADXR, STØRXR, JUMPSX
Three time units:	XJUMP, CØMPAR
Six time units:	MULT, DIV

Minimizing Memory Space

If several programs are to be placed in memory at the same time, it may be necessary that each occupy as little space as possible. This is true particularly if the room required for data storage is extensive. Magnetic-tape memory is not as high in access speed as internal memory and is to be used with caution when much reading in and writing out is required.

The use of closed subroutines goes far to save space, as pointed out in Section 10.1. A sequence of coding used many times throughout a program should be converted to a closed subroutine and used as needed, being stored only once in memory. This might require extra time spent on the transfer of information and control to and from the subroutine.

An approach similar to the use of a closed subroutine is the sharing of sequences in the main program. For example, three long sequences of coding might be so similar that they differ only in a few of their instructions. It is possible to combine the three by writing a single routine and providing for initial setting of perhaps 6 or 8 instructions before the routine is used. This is an example of the method of switching (Section 9.2). An illustration of this method follows.

Example 12.2 Assume that at location PUT in a routine the contents of the accumulator is to be stored in BLØCK if the sequence is being used for a particular purpose and is to be stored in LIST otherwise.

The decision on which version of the routine to use is made just before its use. If the C(NUMBER) is nonzero, the version containing the following instruction is used.

STØRE   LIST

The sequence to set the STØRE instruction is the following.

```
Location      Oper.      Var. Field

              LØAD       NUMBER                    TEST C(NUMBER),
              JUMPZE     ZERØ                         JUMP IF ZERØ
              LØAD       WØRD1
              STØRAD     PUT
              JUMP       PAST
ZERØ          LØAD       WØRD2
              STØRAD     PUT
PAST          •••        ••••                      (THE RØUTINE)
              •••        ••••
PUT           STØRE      ••
              •••        ••••
WØRD1                    LIST
WØRD2                    BLØCK
```

This approach has its limitations. To modify one instruction in this example at least four instructions are required. To modify m instructions, $2 + 2m$ instructions may be required. If a routine is used under k different circumstances where m instructions are different in each case, about $2mk$ setting instructions are required. Therefore this method is useful only if $2mk$ is not large compared to the size of the routine.

Facilitating Debugging

We have already seen how the segmentation approach tends to allow the programmer to determine and eliminate his errors more readily than coding his program all at once does. Other coding techniques can be used to help in the location of errors.

A program is often checked by an examination of intermediate results; snapshot dumps are frequently so used. Hence it is generally desirable for those results to be saved in memory through the entire execution of the program. Later results should be placed in different memory locations, unless it is known for certain that the early portions of the program are error-free. Subsequently those early results can be checked (perhaps with a post-mortem dump). This approach is not possible if many intermediate results are produced and space is at a premium. Then the intermediate results may simply be printed as though they were part of the output; later this printing can be suppressed.

A number of error checks can be incorporated into the program. As results are computed, their magnitudes or their quantity may be checked. If an error is detected, a comment to that effect can be printed.

If a program is well annotated by remarks, as in many examples in this book, it is easier to follow the coding. As an error is being tracked down, it is very helpful to be able to understand quickly what each coding sequence is supposed to do. If the coding was done far in the past, or by another person, such notations can be invaluable. In any event, the programmer is urged to sprinkle comments freely throughout his program. Even after a program is completely debugged, these comments aid in further study of the program.

Programs should be well organized. The plan used throughout this book is to place all instructions first, and to follow these by constants, the input data, and space for answers. Any scheme is reasonable, provided like quantities are grouped. For example, one program may use a number of indicators throughout a program. If they are grouped, it is easy to check the course of the program by a glance at the group. The examination of dumps is far easier if data and results are carefully blocked off into distinct areas of memory.

Incorporating Flexibility

A programmer should write a program considering the possibility of future changes. Usually his goal is to obtain a working program quickly even though a restricted set of conditions applies to it and future changes are certain. Sometimes programs can be coded with the knowledge that they will almost certainly never need modification. An example is a square-root subroutine. Other programs exhibit a steady growth and modification process, so that they never seem to stabilize. It is important for these to be written in a manner that readily allows the inevitable changes.

To provide flexibility we code with the expectation that any aspect of the program will be changed, extended, or modified in some way. For only 6 cases that exist now, 12 may exist later. Lists may be 1000 long now but 3000 long later. Integer powers of numbers are needed now, but fractional powers may be required later. Incorporating flexibility may require more time and space initially, but if the potential changes are realized, undoubtedly there will be overall savings.

12.3   STORAGE ALLOCATION

When a program is about to be coded, some thought must be given to the problem of the efficient use of available storage space. Storage is generally of two types, internal (high-speed) memory and auxiliary memory. Of the latter type, magnetic tape is the most common.

Let us first consider two factors in coding: execution time and storage space. Maximal speed of execution and minimal space for a program and its data are often incompatible ends. If, however, the space required to run a program is doubled from 1000 to 2000 locations, and the latter size still fits within computer memory, we cannot truly say that twice as much space is required. All the memory space was "used" in both cases, since the "unused" portion could not otherwise be used at the same time. On the other hand, if the execution time of that program is reduced from 30 seconds to 15 seconds, a true savings results.

Thus if we have a situation wherein time and space can be freely interchanged (for example, if the product of time and space is a constant), all the available internal memory space of the computer should be used.

If the problem of the use of computer space were always this simple, no more would have to be said of the use of storage space. There are, however, several considerations that make the problem more complex.

1. Input-output operations are far slower than internal computation operations.

2. Internal memory space is finite; this space must be shared by the program, its data and working space, and probably a monitor system.

3. A particular program in one application may require a set of blocks of words different in size or number than in another application, although both cases may require all available space.

4. Most computers have a variety of available storage space: internal memory, drum memory, magnetic-tape memory, etc; each has different capacity and speed of access. The manner of storage is also different; internal memory generally has random access, whereas tape memory has its information strung along a line.

5. Certain program segments interact frequently with certain blocks of data and working space and should be placed simultaneously in memory, if possible. Other portions interact less frequently or not at all, and they can be placed in memory at different times.

The problem of the optimum use of all available space is the problem of *storage allocation.* It is concerned with the assignment of programs, data, and blocks for computations to the various memory spaces of a computer during a run in order to minimize running time. If an attempt is to be made to achieve this, the following factors must be taken into account for a particular computer. (1) The speeds of access of all types of associated memory. (2) The space available in all types of memory. (3) The use in time of each portion of the program, including closed subroutines. (4) The space requirements of each portion of the program. (5) The interaction of all program segments, data, and working space.[1]

The storage allocation problem is attacked in two general ways. One is termed *preplanned;* the other is termed *dynamic.* In the first approach the allocation is determined as the program is assembled or compiled and is ready to run. In the second approach the allocation is determined during the course of the program and is subject to change at a later time during execution.

Storage allocation may be achieved at several levels of complexity. So for example, we may simply reserve the space needed in memory through the use of block-saving pseudo-operations (for example, BLØCK in HAP). This simple approach to the problem may be all that is needed. On the other hand, a storage-allocating program can be conceived that would make all space and time assignments of segments, data, and working storage. To illustrate the techniques at a fairly simple level examples of preplanned and dynamic storage allocation are presented.

Preplanned Allocation

Suppose that 4000 positive integers, all no greater than 1,000,000, are to be sorted in memory into 10 lists: 1–100,000 into the first list, 100,001–200,000 into the second list, etc. Since it is possible that as many as 4000 entries might be made into one list, it would be desirable to reserve a block of 4000 words for each list. This would require 40,000 words, however, more than many computers have in memory.

One approach to the allocation of space is to reserve 1000 words for each list, a total of 10,000 words in all. There is a chance that a block may be filled before all the integers are sorted, so that a check must be made every time an integer is sorted to see if 1000 integers are stored in any list. When they are, extra blocks reserved for this purpose can be used for the overflow; these blocks might also be 1000 words in size. Only three overflow blocks are required, since no more than three original blocks can overflow. Thus only a total of 13,000 words is required.

This problem is relatively simple. No external memory space is required, since the entire program can fit within the computer at one time. The allocation procedure here might be considered a mixture of a preplanned and a dynamic approach, since not all the space is allotted when the program is coded. The extra 3000 words are allotted during the program.

Dynamic Allocation

Next we consider a problem which, during the course of its execution, uses four blocks for data and other numbers. A characteristic of this problem is that the relative sizes of the four blocks vary with the data. If we identify the four blocks by the letters A, B, C, and D, the block requirements in number of words are the following, where p, q, and r are three parameters of the problem, supplied to the program with the data.

$$\text{block A requires } 1000p + 2000q \text{ words}$$
$$\text{block B requires } 2000p + 1000r \text{ words}$$
$$\text{block C requires } 2000q + 2000r \text{ words}$$
$$\text{block D requires } 1000p + 3000r \text{ words}$$

The range of values of the three quantities p, q, and r is 0 through 3.

One approach here, the preplanned approach, is to set aside the maximum-sized blocks. If this were done, however, for $p = q = r = 3$, 42,000 words would be required. Another approach is required (for most computers) if all the numbers are to be placed simultaneously in memory. Here this is assumed to be highly desirable. Despite overflow of memory in the maximum case for all three parameters, it is still possible to place all blocks within memory in many other cases.   For example, if $p = q = r = 1$, only 14,000 words are required.

An approach is needed here for assigning these blocks so that the problem may be run for small values of p, q, and r.   Since these quantities are parameters of the data, it is necessary for the program, at the start of execution, to make the assignment using the current values of the three parameters.   A method for accomplishing this is considered in the following example.

Example 12.3   Assume that the quantities p, q, and r are read initially into memory from data cards, into locations P, Q, and R.   Write a program that assigns blocks of words to blocks A, B, C, and D.

It should be noted that a test must be made at the start to see if memory capacity will be exceeded.   Assume that 24,000 words of memory are available for the blocks; other memory space is required by the program, its constants, and the monitor system.   The total number of words required is

$$4000p + 4000q + 6000r$$

This must not exceed 24000, so we can write the following condition as a requirement:

$$2p + 2q + 3r \leqslant 12$$

The following coding accomplishes the test.

Oper.	Var. Field			
LØAD	P	FØRM	2P + 2Q + 3R	
ADD	P			
ADD	Q			
ADD	Q			
ADD	R			
ADD	R			
ADD	R			
CØMPAR	TWELVE			
JUMP	TØØBIG			
JUMP	*+1			
...	.....			

TØØBIG, to which control is sent if the given requirement is not met, is a routine that prints an appropriate comment and stops the program.

The next coding sequence calculates the following quantities and stores them as indicated.

the number $1000p + 2000q$ is stored in ASIZE
the number $2000p + 1000r$ is stored in BSIZE
the number $2000p + 2000r$ is stored in CSIZE

Following that it is necessary to assign the starting addresses to the four blocks:

Location	Oper.	Var. Field
ASSIGN	LØAD	BEGINA

(Continued)

```
              ADD      ASIZE
              STØRE    BEGINB
              ADD      BSIZE
              STØRE    BEGINC
              ADD      CSIZE
              STØRE    BEGIND
              ...      .....
BEGINA                 A
BEGINB                 **
BEGINC                 **
BEGIND                 **
A             BLØCK    24000
```

Note that it is not necessary to compute the size of block D since no address is set following that block. Since the test that checks the total size of the blocks has already been performed, it is known that block D will fit within the allowed space.

As an example, if $p = 1$, $q = 1.5$, and $r = 2$, the sizes of the first three blocks are as follows:

block A: 4000 (7640_8) words
block B: 6000 (13560_8) words
block C: 7000 (15530_8) words

The last sequence here supplies the following addresses, if block A is assembled starting at 02000:

BEGINB: 11640
BEGINC: 25320
BEGIND: 43050

Since block D requires 7000 or 15530_8 words, the first address not used by the blocks is 60600.

In this problem, space for the four blocks is assigned after the program is assembled, as the data are read in. Note that the starting address of the first block can be fixed at assembly time. As the data varies the locations of the blocks vary. If maximum-size blocks were allowed, there would be insufficient room in memory for them. The dynamic approach used here is more flexible, allowing some large problems to be run which could not be run if storage allocation was preplanned.

This application of dynamic storage allocation is relatively simple, since no memory space outside the computer is required. The problem is complicated somewhat if the block assignment varies during the run of the problem. For example, it may be that for the second half of the computation the parameters p, q, and r are different in value. Then it may be necessary to reassign blocks at that time. Care is needed here to see that intermediate results carried over to the second half are not moved to incorrect locations as a result. Reassignment changes the starting addresses of blocks in name, not in fact, and the words within them do not move.

12.4 INFORMATION PACKING AND UNPACKING

Logical Instructions

Digital computers are equipped to perform a set of operations that are generally described as *logical* or *nonnumerical.** These operations on computer words are not concerned with the numerical values of the quantities in the words. Rather, the quantities are treated as ordered collections of digits (in a decimal machine) or bits (in a binary machine). The instructions used to perform these operations are *logical* instructions.

The purpose of the logical instructions is to permit processing of individual portions of a computer word. With one exception, all the instructions we have studied that move words between memory and the accumulator operated on the entire word. (The exception is the STØRAD instruction, which moves only bits 21–35 of the accumulator.) The logical instructions permit individual digits or bits or collections of them to be processed. A group of adjacent bits is called a *bite*.†

Assemblers, compilers, and monitor programs use this facility. As an example consider the problem of translating a symbolic expression to an address in memory. If the expression is

BLØCK+50

it is necessary for the assembler to (1) identify the symbol BLØCK by scanning the expression left to right, character by character; (2) identify the plus sign; and (3) identify the integer 50 by scanning. Once these pieces are identified, they must of course be processed, but that is not of concern here. The important point here is that the expression being scanned is variable in size and position. The integer 50 may begin and end anywhere over a wide range of column positions. As a result, it is necessary to scan one character at a time in order to make proper identification.

In the following discussions logical operations are assumed to apply to binary word structures, although the same processes apply equally well to decimal machines. As individual bits are processed, so would individual decimal digits be processed. It is generally true that logical instructions are present on binary machines; they are less frequently found on decimal machines.

Shifting

A computer is able to operate on individual bits or bites of bits within a word because it can *shift* the bits in that word to the left and right. Shifting is usually

---

* The reason for the term *logical* is explained in Chapter 15.
† The spelling *byte* is sometimes used.

accomplished within the accumulator and the multiply register. Another means of obtaining bits or bites for processing is to *mask* parts of a word, retaining certain bits while eliminating others. Several logical instructions are introduced for accomplishing shifting and masking.*

ACCUMULATOR RIGHT SHIFT (RSHIFT Y) (42). The C(AC), including the sign, are shifted right Y bit positions. Bits shifted out at the right are lost; vacated bits are filled with zeros.

ACCUMULATOR LEFT SHIFT (LSHIFT Y) (43). The C(AC), including the sign, are shifted left Y bit positions. Bits shifted out at the left are lost; vacated bits are filled with zeros.

LONG RIGHT SHIFT (LRSHFT Y) (44). The C(MR) and the C(AC), considered as a single 72-bit word, are shifted right Y bit positions. Bits shifted out at the right are lost; vacated bits are filled with zeros.

LONG ROTATE LEFT (RØTATE Y) (45). The C(MR) and the C(AC), considered as a single 72-bit word, are shifted left Y bit positions in an "end-around" fashion. Bits shifted out of the leftmost bit position (the MR S-bit) reappear at the right (the AC 35-bit). No bits are lost.

Other shifting operations can readily be conceived, and various computers have instructions for performing them. For illustrative purposes, however, these four instructions suffice. Examples of shifting operations follow.

If the C(AC) are (in binary)

$$011000000110111000110101011111000110$$

then execution of the instruction

$$\textbf{RSHIFT}\quad \textbf{10}$$

changes the C(AC) to

$$000000000001100000011011100011010101$$

If the C(MR) and the C(AC) are, respectively (in octal),

$$\textbf{003266012200}\quad \textbf{004322777111}$$

then execution of the instruction

$$\textbf{RØTATE}\quad \textbf{24}$$

(which means "rotate left 8 octal digits") changes the contents of these registers to

$$\textbf{220000432277}\quad \textbf{711100326601}$$

Masking

The DELTA 63 contains a special register for masking, the *mask register* (MK). It contains 36 bits, labeled 0, 1, . . . , 35. It masks out any selected combination of bits from

---

* Note that shift instructions are of the immediate-address type (refer to Section 8.4).

a word during the process of loading the accumulator from memory or storing its contents in memory. If bit 11 (the *mask bit*) of a LØAD or STØRE instruction word is 1, only those bits whose corresponding positions in the MK are 1 are transferred.

With the addition of the mask bit, the complete DELTA 63 instruction word format has been described. The fields of an instruction word, pictured in Fig. 12.1, are the following: bits 3–8, operation code field; bit 11, mask bit; bit 14, indirect addressing bit; bits 18–20, tag field; bits 21–35, address field. Other bits are not used.

As an example of the use of the MK, we assume

		Octal		Binary

$$C(AC) = 033200577740 = 000011011010000000010111111111100000$$

$$C(MK) = 007777777400 = 000000111111111111111111111100000000$$

Then a STØRE instruction, if its 11-bit is 1, causes the following word to be stored in memory:

$$003200577400 = 000000011010000000010111111111100000000$$

Thus only those bits of the AC are stored in memory whose corresponding positions in the MK are 1; other bits in the memory word are set to 0. The same sort of thing happens with a LØAD instruction.

To indicate masking in HAP language, the character $ is used after the operation code. Indirect addressing may be used simultaneously.

	Machine Words		Symbolic Instructions	
0	01 1000 04440	LØAD$	NUMBER
0	01 1001 04440	LØAD$	NUMBER,1
0	01 1107 04440	LØAD$*	NUMBER,7

The $ and * may be interchanged.

Two instructions for moving masks in and out of the MK follow.

LOAD MASK REGISTER (LØADMK Y) (46). The C(Y) replaces the C(MK). The C(Y) is unchanged.

STORE MASK REGISTER (STØRMK Y) (47). The C(MK) replaces the C(Y). The C(MK) is unchanged.

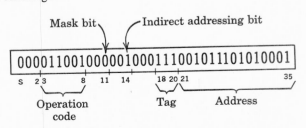

Fig. 12.1.   Format of a DELTA 63 instruction word.

Packing and Unpacking

Numbers may be *packed* by placing two or more in one word. If there are more numbers to be stored in memory than there are words for them, packing offers a way out of the dilemma, provided the numbers are small enough. For example, a 36-bit binary word will hold 2 signed 17-bit numbers ($2^{17} = 131,072$), 3 signed 11-bit numbers ($2^{11} = 2048$), or 4 signed 8-bit numbers ($2^8 = 256$). Sometimes data are stored in packed form and must be *unpacked*, that is, each item within a computer word must be separated and placed in a separate word. Numbers packed during a computer program must be unpacked before they are used. The logical instructions of a computer are very useful in packing and unpacking numbers.

Example 12.4   Four positive 9-bit integers are stored in successive words starting at WØRDS. Write a routine to pack them into a single 36-bit word, PACKED. The C(WØRD) is to be placed in the leftmost 9 bits of PACKED, the C(WØRD+1) is to be placed in the next 9 bits, etc.

The MR will be used to accumulate the 4 numbers; they will be packed there from the right. To accomplish this each number will be placed in the leftmost portion of the AC, and the MR-AC double register will then be shifted left, to place the number in the MR. If this is done 4 times, all 4 numbers will be packed in the MR. A computer flowchart is drawn in Fig. 12.2; it is drawn specifically for the DELTA 63. The program follows; a detailed analysis of the packing procedure is also given.

Location	Oper.	Var. Field	
	LØADM	ZERØ	CLEAR MR
	SETXRI	4,1	
GETWRD	LØAD	WØRDS,1	NUMBER TØ LEFT
	LSHIFT	27	PART ØF AC
	RØTATE	9	SHIFT NUMBER TØ MR
	INCRXM	1,1	
	XJUMP	GETWRD,1	
	STØREM	PACKED	
	HALT		
ZERØ	DECML	0	
PACKED			
WØRDS	BLØCK	4	

The contents of the MR and AC throughout the execution of this program follow; the 4 loop cycles are shown. The action of the indexing instructions is omitted, and effective addresses are listed. The 4 numbers being packed are assumed to be (in octal) 510, 327, 222, and 106.

Instruction		C(MR)	C(AC)
LØAD	WØRD	000000000000	000000000510
LSHIFT	27	000000000000	510000000000
		(Continued)	

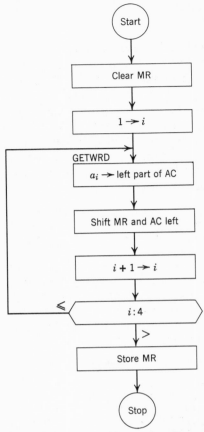

Fig. 12.2.   Flowchart for packing routine (Example 12.4).

```
RØTATE  9              000000000510   000000000000
•••         ••••
LØAD    WØRD+1         000000000510   000000000327
LSHIFT  27             000000000510   327000000000
RØTATE  9              000000510327   000000000000

•••         ••••
LØAD    WØRD+2         000000510327   000000000222
LSHIFT  27             000000510327   222000000000
RØTATE  9              000510327222   000000000000

•••         ••••
LØAD    WØRD+3         000510327222   000000000106
LSHIFT  27             000510327222   106000000000
RØTATE  9              510327222106   000000000000
```

At the end of this sequence the numbers are packed in the MR.

Unpacking information is a necessary operation in the analysis of an alphanumeric string, as in program assembly or compilation. One standard approach
to unpacking such information is to store each character (6 bits) in a separate

word and then process them.   A disadvantage of the method is the space required; analysis of a 72-column punched card requires 72 words.   Advantages are the ease of coding it and the ease with which the information can be subsequently used in this form.

Example 12.5   Given a 72-character alphanumeric string, stored in a block from STRING to STRING + 11 (6 characters to a word), write a routine to unpack the string, placing each character in the rightmost 6 bits of a word in the block UNPAKD, in the order of appearance in the string.

Each word in the STRING block must be unpacked, its contents being placed in 6 words in UNPAKD.   This requires a loop of the form in Example 12.4, except that now unpacking is required.   It can be accomplished by loading a word from STRING into the MR and rotating the MR-AC pair left 6 bits, putting 1 character at the right of the AC.   After that is stored in UNPAKD and the AC is cleared, another rotation puts the next character into the AC.   Surrounding this loop is an outer loop that fetches a new word STRING each cycle.   After that word is unpacked, the next word from STRING is placed in the MR.   A flowchart is drawn in Fig. 12.3.

In this program XR1 and XR2 are used for the inner and outer loop indices, i and j, respectively.   XR6 is used as a pointer (k), indicating the next available location in UNPAKD for an unpacked character.   Note that symbolic indexing is used.   After each character is stored, the AC must be cleared for the next one.   (The indexing discrepancy, described in Section 8.2, should be recalled.)

```
Location    Oper.     Var. Field

K           SET       6
I           SET       1
J           SET       2
            LOADXR    ZERO,K          1 TO K
            SETXRI    12,1            1 TO I
            LOAD      ZERO            CLEAR AC
LOOP1       LOADM     STRING,I        WORD TO MR
            SETXRI    6,J             1 TO J
LOOP2       ROTATE    6               1 CHARACTER TO AC
            STORE     UNPAKD,K
            LOAD      ZERO            CLEAR AC
            INCRXM    1,K             K+1 TO K
            INCRXM    1,J             J+1 TO J
            XJUMP     LOOP2,J
            INCRXM    1,I             I+1 TO I
            XJUMP     LOOP2,I
            HALT

ZERO        DECML     0
STRING      BLOCK     12
UNPAKD      BLOCK     72
```

12.5 RELOCATION

During the assembly of a program, addresses are assigned to each assembled instruction, each item of data, and each block for storage.   When the resulting

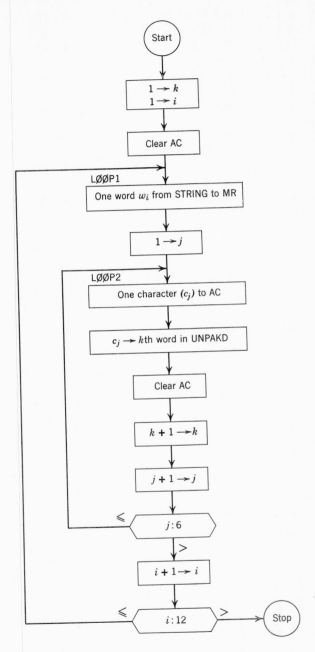

Fig. 12.3.   Unpacking a string of characters (Example 12.5).

object program is loaded into the computer, the program is placed in these assigned addresses. It is often desirable to be able to load an object program into
a different set of locations without recourse to reassembly, that is, to move the
program "up" or "down" in memory, otherwise leaving it unchanged.   This
ability is sometimes a necessity, as it is when several independently assembled
programs must be run together, like a main program with its subroutines. If
these programs have been assigned overlapping areas in memory, such movement of programs is clearly necessary.

Programs can be assembled in a manner that permits "movement" at the time
of loading, so that they occupy nonoverlapping areas and can be run without
reassembly. This technique is referred to as *relocation*, and the object programs
so produced are *relocatable*. The problem that may arise when programs are
assembled with absolute addresses (such programs are *absolute)* can be appreci-
ated by considering an example.

Example 12.6   Assume that the following four absolute programs have been independently assembled and that they are to be loaded into the computer at the same time for
execution; the addresses assigned to them are listed:

> main program (MAIN):   locations 00100 through 01765
> subroutine 1 (SUBR1):   locations 00500 through 00722
> subroutine 2 (SUBR2):   locations 01000 through 01777
> subroutine 3 (SUBR3):   locations 01600 through 02220

Clearly it is not possible to load all four programs into memory at the same
time and expect them to work properly. If they were so loaded, SUBR1 would
overwrite 223_8 locations of MAIN, SUBR2 would overwrite 766_8 locations of
MAIN, etc.

To avoid this problem, assemblers can produce relocatable object programs
which, on loading, can be placed anywhere in memory. Unless the monitor is
directed otherwise, a sequence of relocatable programs in a single job is loaded
so that each occupies a memory area immediately following the preceding program. In the object deck and its associated listing, however, the starting address
of all programs is 00000. It is the job of the monitor to relocate program addresses, as shown in the following example.

Example 12.6, Continued   The addresses of the four programs considered earlier, both in
the object decks produced and subsequently in memory, are listed next. The first
memory location used is 00100.

	Assembly Time	Loading Time
MAIN:	locations 00000–01665	locations 00100–01765
SUBR1:	locations 00000–00222	locations 01766–02210
SUBR2:	locations 00000–00777	locations 02211–03210
SUBR3:	locations 00000–00420	locations 03211–03631

A relocatable object deck must contain information about the addresses to be relocated. All operand addresses that are symbolic must be relocated, since the location addresses to which they refer are relocated. Absolute operand addresses, however, are not to be relocated. For example, the operand address of a SETXRI instruction is an absolute number that is not to be changed when the program is relocated.

The Loading of Programs

The job of assigning memory locations to a sequence of programs as they are loaded into memory is accomplished by a loading program or *loader*. The loader is either a routine within the monitor or is located on magnetic tape and called in as needed. In addition to this address assignment, the loader provides automatic means for the linkage of main programs with their subroutines, relieving the programmer of that responsibility. Automatic linkage provides a great convenience to the programmer; without it, he would have to determine all subroutine entry points at the time he assembled the main program.

Programs that are to be linked together, such as a main program and its subroutines, do not in general make absolute references to one another. References are usually symbolic, and information of this type is required by the loader if the linkage is to be effected. It is necessary for the assembler to provide some symbolic information so that the loader can subsequently relate the programs.

Program cards accompany assembled relocatable object decks; these cards convey symbolic information to the loader as follows. Main-program program cards indicate the locations of all subroutine calls and the symbolic names of those subroutines. Subroutine program cards indicate the entry points of the subroutines and the symbolic names of the entry points. After all programs are in memory, the loader, having noted the symbolic information, the subroutine call locations, and the entry points, can provide all the required linkages.

Summary

In program writing the steps taken prior to coding are significant, because they have an appreciable effect on the coding. A problem must first be stated explicitly; the format of the data and the results, the nature of the results, and any additional information must all be known. The choice of a method of solution must take into account both the mathematical algorithms available and the structure and operation of a computer. As an aid to efficient coding and debugging, a program is frequently segmented. With this approach errors tend to be fewer and, more significantly, are probably easier to identify.

In coding a program a programmer usually selects one or two goals; among the goals most commonly sought are completing the program in overall minimal time, coding the program to run in minimal time or with minimal space, coding for ease of debugging, and coding for ease in modification of the program.

Another step in planning a program is the allocation of the several storage areas of a computer to the program, its data, and space for computed results. Storage allocation is simple if internal memory alone is required but complex if auxiliary memory must also be used. Allocation may be preplanned and coded into the program; it may be dynamic and established during the running of the program, when it is dependent on the data.

The techniques of packing and unpacking data are useful both for more efficient use of memory space and for the analysis of a string of alphanumeric information. The operations of shifting and masking are useful for the purpose; computer instructions are available for these operations. In this way individual bits or digits or any selected group of them in a computer may be processed.

In order that assembled programs be easily moved in memory, otherwise remaining unchanged, relocation techniques are used. In this way several programs may be automatically linked together and loaded into memory in nonoverlapping areas with no wasted space between them.

Notes

1. One dozen papers on storage allocation were published in a special issue of the *Comm. Assoc. Computing Machinery*, **4** (1961), October.

PROBLEMS

Section 12.1

12.1. Give complete problem requirements for the following problems, assuming any required information.

(*a*) Determine the square root of x.

(*b*) Convert a given set of fixed-point numbers to floating-point format.

(*c*) Multiply two given matrices.

(*d*) Evaluate a given integral using Simpson's rule.

12.2. List considerations in the selection of a method for problem solution other than those given in the text.

Section 12.2

12.3. Consider some problems involving tape-reading and -writing, such as Problems 7.7, 7.8, 7.9, and 11.7, and consider how each might be modified to realize each of the programming goals we listed. Assume as each goal is considered that all others are secondary. In which cases is this last assumption invalid?

Section 12.3

12.4. Describe the structure of a program designed to provide automatic, preplanned, storage allocation facilities. The program must consider memory size (that is, size of space for data), auxiliary memory size, input-output reading and writing speeds, relative interaction of segments of the program being analyzed, etc.

12.5. Describe techniques that might be used to provide automatic, dynamic, storage allocation facilities. These techniques might be incorporated into the assembler or into the program being analyzed.

12.6. Write a program to sort 4000 positive integers, all no greater than 1,000,000, into 10 lists, as described in the text.

12.7. If it is necessary to sort more than 4000 integers into 10 lists, the program must be modified to increase the space available for each list. Consider the difficulties imposed by an increasing number of integers. How many integers can be so sorted when 30,000 words of memory in all are available?

12.8. If there is insufficient space available within the computer, it may be necessary to utilize tape storage for some or all of the lists being prepared in a sorting problem, such as Problem 12.7. Assume that the time to execute any computer instruction is 1 unit and that information can be written on tape or read from tape at the rate of 5 units per word plus 100 units per record (regardless of record size). Optimize a procedure for sorting 100,000 integers, each no more than 1,000,000 in size.

Section 12.4

12.9. Thirty 12-bit unsigned integers are stored, three to a word, in locations XXLIST through XXLIST+9. Write routines to (a) unpack them, placing 1 integer per word in a block at ØPEN, and (b) pack them, 2 integers per word, in a block at CLØSED.

12.10. By using masking instructions it is possible to store bites of any size from one word in part of another word. Write a routine to store the bite consisting of bits 13–22 of THINGA in bits 13–22 of THINGB, in bits 17–26 of THINGC, and in bits 26–35 of THINGD. The other bit positions should be left unchanged.

12.11. Consider each of the 8 words starting at BLØCK as consisting of 9 4-bit bites. Write a routine to count the bites that contain at least three 1's in their 4 bits.

12.12. Nine 8-bit integers are packed into the 72 bits of LEFTWD and RITEWD; the middle integer has half of its bits in each word. Write a routine to add the 9 integers, placing the sum in SUM, and to reverse the order of the 9 integers, although not by bits within each integer.

13

NUMERICAL PROBLEMS

Many problems solved by computers are concerned primarily with arithmetic processes. In these problems addition, subtraction, multiplication, division, exponentiation, root extraction, and logarithmization are the basic operations. Problems that arise from using algebra and calculus to solve problems in physics and engineering are very often in this category. Generally these problems are characterized by the fact that the method of solution can be expressed in the form of a set of equations or formulas.

Numerical problems are usually solved with numbers in floating-point form, and computers have floating-point instructions for this purpose. Sometimes the word size in a computer memory is insufficient for desired accuracy; two words can be jointly used to greater precision. In this chapter these aspects of arithmetic are considered.

The question of accuracy in computation always merits consideration, but particularly so in numerical problems, because of the many possible sources in error in numerical quantities. These sources are examined in this chapter.

Numerical problems can be characterized by the fact that nearly all their operations involve simple arithmetic. More specifically, their operations occur in evaluating a sequence of formulas. The solution of a cubic algebraic equation is an example; this problem was analyzed in Section 2.1. The four basic operations are sufficient to solve it. This characterization of numerical problems is crude at best, but it serves us at this time.

Many of the numerical problems put on computers result from numerical analysis, an approach to the solution of problems in mathematics that uses approximate formulas. These formulas involve arithmetic operations; when such problems are solved by computers, the four basic arithmetic operations are used primarily. Approximate solutions are used because exact solutions are either too cumbersome or cannot be achieved.

The solution of numerical problems is not the topic of this chapter. Rather we merely indicate a few of their characteristics in an attempt to justify the use of special coding languages for their solution; two such languages are considered in Chapter 14. The methods employed to translate such problems into equations require complete texts of their own. We can only hope to get the flavor of the problems here.[1]

Problems may be classified into three groups: *numerical, nonnumerical,* and *business* problems. Nonnumerical problems consist primarily of logical operations, some of which were examined in Section 12.4. Another term for such problems is *symbol manipulation,* since the operands are frequently symbols or characters. Nonnumerical problems are considered in Chapter 15.

Business problems are sometimes called *data-processing* problems; the latter term, modified somewhat in meaning, is used in this book. Typical operations in such problems are combining, modifying, and updating files of information, the production of tabular information for printing purposes, and relatively simple arithmetic. Data-processing problems are considered in Chapter 16.

All computer programs have some nonnumerical aspects; they are frequently confined to input-output operations. Data must be read in; their conversion and placement in memory is largely a nonnumerical problem, particularly if unpacking is required. When results are printed they are usually accompanied by titles or headings; the preparation of this material is a nonnumerical process.

Any classification leaves us open to criticism, since many problems are hybrid in structure. The classifications established here, however, serve our purposes.

13.1 FLOATING-POINT OPERATIONS

We saw in Section 4.2 that floating-point number representation permits a wide range of numbers to be stored in a fixed-length computer word. For example, in a 10-digit decimal word, numbers in the approximate range of 10^{-50} to 10^{50} with 8 significant digits can be stored; in a 36-bit binary word, numbers in the approximate range of 10^{-38} to 10^{38} with about 8 significant decimal digits can be stored.

Floating-point numbers in the DELTA 63 are of the form described in Section 4.2, which is the following. Bits 1–8 of a computer word hold the characteristic; bits 9–35 hold the fraction. The characteristic is formed by adding 128 (200_8) to the exponent when the fraction is in normalized binary form and the exponent is a power of 2. Exponents from -128 to $+127$ can be represented; the range of numbers possible is therefore approximately 2^{-128} to 2^{+127}, or approximately 10^{-38} to 10^{+38}. A normalized number is one having a 1 in the leftmost bit of the fraction, bit 9.

To incorporate floating-point numbers into a symbolic program, the DECML pseudo-operation is used with decimal points in the variable field. To assemble the number 75 as an integer we write

Oper.   Var. Field

DECML   75

which assembles as $+000000000113$ (octal). To assemble this number as a floating-point number we write

DECML   75.

which assembles as $+210446000000$ (octal). Alternately, the exponential form described in Section 11.2 may be used:

DECML   .75E+2

Regardless of the form given, provided a decimal point is included, the number is assembled in normalized floating-point format.

The four floating-point arithmetic instructions are described next. In all, the operands are treated as floating-point numbers (not necessarily normalized), and the result is a normalized floating-point number. In the process of normalizing a number after the operation, zeros fill in vacant bits on the right.

FLOATING ADD (FLADD Y) (14). The C(Y) is added algebraically to the C(MR), and the sum is placed in the MR and the AC; the more significant half of the sum is placed in the MR. The characteristic of the AC is adjusted so that it is 27 less than the characteristic of the MR.* The C(Y) is unchanged.

FLOATING SUBTRACT (FLSUBT Y) (15). The C(Y) is subtracted algebraically from the C(MR), and the difference is placed in the MR and the AC; the more significant half of the difference is placed in the MR. The characteristic of the AC is adjusted so that it is 27 less than the characteristic of the MR. The C(Y) is unchanged.

FLOATING MULTIPLY (FLMULT Y) (16). The C(Y) is multiplied algebraically by the C(AC), and the product is stored in the MR and the AC; the more significant half of the product is stored in the MR. The characteristic of the AC is adjusted so that it is 27 less than the characteristic of the MR. The C(Y) is unchanged.

FLOATING DIVIDE (FLDIV Y) (17). The C(AC) is divided algebraically by the C(Y), and the quotient is placed in the AC. The remainder is placed in the MR. The C(Y) is unchanged.†

To illustrate these operations we show an addition. Consider the addition of the following two numbers, which are approximately 560 and 13.8:

$+212430010231$

$+204570023322$

If they are to be added with no loss of significant bits, a separate register must be used to catch the overflow as one number is shifted; the shift is performed to equate the char-

---

* The reason for the arrangement of the result in this and the following two instructions is explained shortly.

† It was pointed out in Section 4.2 that fixed-point division often results in loss of accuracy. This problem is largely avoided in floating-point division. The two operations should be compared in this respect.

acteristics. Since the difference in the characteristics is 6, the fraction portion of the smaller number must be shifted 6 bit positions to the right; the result of this shift is

$$+212430010231$$
$$+21200570023322$$

The sum of these numbers is

$$+21243571046422$$

The AC (on the right) is used to hold the shifted bits, the 22 of the sum. After the summation the result is

$$C(MR) = +212435710464 \qquad C(AC) = +157220000000$$

The difference in the characteristics of the MR and AC is 33_8 (27). The product in a multiplication operation is placed in the MR and the AC in the same manner.

The form of the sum deserves further attention. Consider the following number:

$$0.49236236 \times 10^7$$

This number can be written as the sum of two numbers,

$$0.4923 \times 10^7 + 0.6236 \times 10^3$$

where each number contains half of the significant digits of the original number. The second number was produced from the right half of the original number after a decimal-point shift of four places to the right; the exponent was therefore reduced by 4. This is precisely the form of the sum in a floating-point addition and the form of the product in a floating-point multiplication. The answer in either case is the sum of the C(MR) and the C(AC); each part may be stored separately. Note that the less significant portion (in the AC) is not necessarily normalized.

Double-Precision Arithmetic

The reason for producing a floating-point sum, difference, or product in the form described is to allow a structure for the maintenance of increased accuracy during a program. Increased accuracy is not automatically produced by this process; it is merely maintained. The manner of realizing greater accuracy is now examined.

Sometimes the 8-digit accuracy possible with a 36-bit or 10-decimal-digit floating-point number is insufficient. Even when only 5 or 6 places are meaningful in a particular problem, the limitation may be serious. Intermediate calculations are limited to 8 places, and errors may accumulate to invalidate perhaps half of these. (This problem is considered in some detail in Section 13.3.) In order to avoid this difficulty, *double-precision* calculations can be made. In this method two words are used to contain a number as the MR and

AC do after a floating-point multiplication. These words are generally consecutive in memory, although they need not be. The form of the words is as we have described, with a reduced characteristic accompanying the less significant portion of the fraction. With 2 words, approximately 16 digits can be retained, and overall 8-place accuracy is almost certain.

Arithmetic performed as described previously is *single-precision*. All double-precision operations are performed using combinations of single-precision operations.

13.2 CONSIDERATIONS IN ANALYSIS AND CODING

A programmer must consider a number of things as he selects a method for solving his problem and as he analyzes it. Some of these matters have already been discussed in Chapter 12. A few more are examined here; these considerations are primarily directed towards numerical problems, but they may apply equally well to many nonnumerical problems.

Subtraction offers a problem. This was pointed out in Section 4.2, where we saw that the subtraction of two almost equal numbers may result in the loss of several significant figures. Sometimes it is possible to avoid subtraction. For example, if the quantity $(1 - \sin^2 x)$ is to be computed, the quantity $(\cos^2 x)$, the same function, can be computed instead. Let $x = 85°$; $\sin 85° = 0.9962$ and $\cos 85° = 0.0872$. From these 4-significant-digit values, we can compute

$$1 - \sin^2 x = 0.0076$$
$$\cos^2 x = 0.007603$$

The first result has only two significant digits; the second result has three.

If a problem is analyzed into a sequence of formulas to be evaluated, it is frequently true that particular algebraic expressions occur in several places in the analysis. As an example consider the analysis of the cubic equation given in Section 2.1. The two expressions

$$b^2/4 + a^3/27$$
$$2\sqrt{-a/3}$$

each appear in at least two equations. If these two expressions are coded early in the program, coding time, execution time, and memory space can all be saved. The values of these expressions would be computed once, so the coding required would be present only once. (The cubic equation problem is coded in Section 14.2, where this technique is used.)

The identification and early coding of such expressions is similar to the use of macro-instructions, but there is an important difference. In using macro-instructions coding of repetitious sequences is saved, but when the macro-instructions are expanded they require as much space and subsequent execution time as if they had been written out in full.

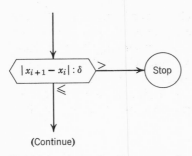

(Continue)

Fig. 13.1.   A test for divergence of estimates.

If an iterative method is used in a computation, the sequence of estimates obtained may diverge, that is, they may increase without a bound, thereby failing to approach the correct answer. If this is possible in a particular program, a check must be made. The flowchart in Fig. 13.1 shows a decision box that might be included for this check. Here a sequence of estimates x_i is assumed. If the difference between two successive estimates exceeds the value δ, the program is stopped; otherwise the computation continues.

Another, similar source of trouble is division by zero or a very small quantity. It is possible, for example, for roundoff errors to cause a number that is small to become zero. If this situation is possible a check should be incorporated.

Sometimes a cumulative product or sum is required in successive loop cycles or within a single computation. For instance, the powers of x (x, x^2, x^3, . . .) may be needed. It is faster to store each power as computed for later use than it is to compute the separate powers. This approach was incorporated into the coding of a polynomial (see Example 8.3, page 147).

The several considerations given here illustrate the type of analysis that ought to be made before a numerical problem is coded; they are only illustrative, and the programmer will have others suggested to him. Sometimes these techniques can save considerable computer running time.

13.3 ERRORS IN COMPUTATION

Sources of Error

Errors are of two general types: "unconscious" and "conscious." The first category includes mistakes due both to computer malfunction and to programmer errors; these errors are the *bugs* in a computer or a program.

The second category includes a variety of errors introduced by the approximations made in the method selected for programming and by the limitations of the computer. In this section we are concerned only with conscious errors. Several types are now considered.

Physical errors are introduced when numerical values are used for physical quantities. No physical quantity can be measured precisely, and the number used to represent its measurement is somewhat in error. Physical errors do not concern us here, because they are completely unrelated to the programming problem.

Formulation errors arise when approximate methods are used to solve problems. An integral may evaluated as a sum of numbers; since the sum is only an approximation, an error is introduced. By taking more and more terms in the sum the error can be made as small as desired. This is a characteristic of formulation errors; they can be made arbitrarily small, if there is no limit to the number of steps performed in the computation on the computer.

Truncation errors are similar to formulation errors in that they are created when a mathematical process is approximated on the computer. They are caused by the use of a finite sum as an approximation to an infinite sum. For example, trigonometric functions may be represented as infinite series. In a computation, only a finite number of terms may be calculated; the error due to dropping the others is one of truncation. These errors can also be made as small as desired.

Roundoff errors arise from the restrictions imposed by fixed-length computer words. In a 36-bit word no more than 35 bits can be retained in the representation of a number, unless double-precision arithmetic is used. The term *rounding* is used to describe the process of dropping digits or bits beyond the capacity of a word. If a programmer is aware of the manner in which roundoff errors accumulate in his program, he may be able to formulate his coding to minimize them. His aim here is to develop an approach to a given problem that performs the operations of addition, subtraction, multiplication, and division in a sequence that reduces roundoff errors to a minimum. Formulation and truncation errors can be reduced until they are less than roundoff errors.

Computational errors are due to the inexactness of computer operations. Fixed-point division may introduce errors if there is a remainder that is ignored. Floating-point operations often involve approximations even in addition and subtraction.

Roundoff Errors

Only roundoff errors are investigated further here, because they are caused by word size limitations and can be reduced by appropriate coding. If a programmer is to interpret his results properly, he must be aware of the manner in which roundoff errors propagate. If both operands in an operation are approximate, the result is approximate. Since the result may be used in other operations, errors may build up until they become quite large.

The error caused by an individual operation is relatively easy to determine in a particular computer. Nevertheless, the propagated error in a complex operation is difficult or almost impossible to estimate. We look briefly at the roundoff errors in individual operations. First, let us examine the roundoff error in one word.

While numbers are being stored in memory by a program such as a monitor, they may be rounded either up or down. For example, if the number $.5620153968 \times 10^{12}$ is to be stored in a 10-decimal-digit word (which holds 8 digits plus a characteristic), it should be stored as $.56201540 \times 10^{12}$ (properly converted to machine format). Then the roundoff error is minimized. This is not necessarily done; the actual number stored depends on the coding incorporated into the monitor. The monitor may simply scan the digits from the left, stopping after 8 digits; in the example here, $.56201539 \times 10^{12}$ might be stored.

When an operation is performed, *rounddown* usually occurs, that is, digits or bits beyond the word capacity are simply dropped. In the material that follows we assume rounddown. The binary words of the DELTA 63 will again be used for illustration.

The 36-bit binary words each use 27 bits for the fraction in a floating-point number. The roundoff error may be as great as the number represented by a 1 in bit 35. If the floating-point number is normalized, the error may be as large as 1 part in 2^{26} (about 6.7×10^7). The expected error will be half of this, 1 part in 1.34×10^8. Note that the error in a word is nonpositive, that is, the true value is no less than the value in memory.

Assume that two quantities, a and b, are to be stored in memory. If a' and b' are the actual values stored in memory, and δ_1 and δ_2 are the errors in a' and b' then

$$a = a' + \delta_1$$
$$b = b' + \delta_2$$

The following equations represent the relation between exact results and their approximations due to roundoff:[2]

$$a + b = a' + b' + (\delta_1 + \delta_2)$$
$$a - b = a' - b' + (\delta_1 - \delta_2)$$
$$a \times b = a' \times b' + (\delta_2 a' + \delta_1 b')$$
$$\frac{a}{b} = \frac{a'}{b'} + \left(\frac{\delta_1 b' - \delta_2 a'}{b^2}\right)$$

Here all the second- and higher-order terms, those involving the product of at least two δ's, are dropped.

As an example of the analysis needed to evaluate the error in an algebraic formula, consider the expression

$$axy + bx + cy$$

Assume that the following relations hold between true and stored values:

$$a = a' + \delta_a$$
$$b = b' + \delta_b$$
$$c = c' + \delta_c$$

$$x = x' + \delta_x$$
$$y = y' + \delta_y$$

Then the following equation indicates the extent of the error in the evaluation of the polynomial:

$$axy + bx + cy = a'x'y' + b'x' + c'y'$$
$$+ (a'x'\delta_y + a'y'\delta_x + x'y'\delta_a + x'\delta_b + b'\delta_x + c'\delta_y + y'\delta_c)$$

A similar analysis for a large problem would be extremely tedious and probably not worth the trouble. It might be possible instead to make estimates of the overall error using these concepts.

Assume, in the polynomial problem, the approximate values

$$a = 6, \quad b = 8, \quad c = 4, \quad x = 10, \quad y = 12$$

The exact value of the polynomial is 848. If the roundoff error in every word is 1 part in 1.34×10^8, the error in the result is -1.81×10^{-5}, or 1 part in 2.15×10^8, which is 1.6 times as large as the individual errors. In more complex expressions, the accumulated errors can be correspondingly larger.

Summary

Numerical problems are concerned primarily with arithmetic calculations. The numbers in the problems may run over a wide range of values, and hence floating-point arithmetic is used. Special computer instructions are available to perform calculations in floating-point form. Since computer words frequently have insufficient accuracy, double-precision arithmetic is sometimes used.

When a programmer codes numerical problems several considerations of analysis and coding should be made in an attempt to decrease errors and improve running time. Several types of error result when numerical problems are coded and run. The most important of these to the programmer is roundoff error; it can be reduced by appropriate coding techniques.

Notes

1. The following two books on numerical analysis consider the difficulties associated with placing problems on the computer. The first text is of particular interest to the programmer, since each topic is followed by a flowchart and description of the program as it might be written.

A. Ralston and H. S. Wilf, *Mathematical Methods for Digital Computers,* Wiley, 1960.
J. Todd (ed.), *Survey of Numerical Analysis,* McGraw-Hill, 1962.

2. The formulas for errors are derived in the following.

G. W. Evans II and C. L. Perry, *Programming and Coding for Automatic Digital Computers,* McGraw-Hill, 1961, p. 211.

PROBLEMS

Section 13.1

13.1. Write two closed subroutines for double-precision addition (*a*) to sum two numbers, and (*b*) to sum a sequence of numbers. The calling sequences should specify
the addresses of the first and second (or last) numbers to be added and the location of the sum.

13.2. Write two closed subroutines for double-precision multiplication of the form specified in Problem 13.1.

13.3. Write double-precision routines for subtraction and division.

Section 13.2

13.4. Consider the problem of solving a quadratic equation by the quadratic formula.
Draw a complete flowchart for the problem, taking into account all the possible
values of the coefficients. Write a routine to evaluate the formula, assuming the
existence of the SQRØØT subroutine, coded in Problem 10.8.

Section 13.3

13.5. The path of a projectile, after it is fired, can be roughly approximated by a parabola.
If it is desired to determine the points at which the projectile is a given height above
the ground, a quadratic equation can be used. Discuss all the possible sources of
error, such as the approximate formulation of the problem, the computation of
the square root, and the roundoff errors.

13.6. It is desired that a cubic equation be solved to an accuracy of 1 part in 10^6. How
accurately must each coefficient in the equation be known? Refer to the cubic-
equation analysis of Section 2.1, and assume that *a* in Eq. 4 (page 18) is positive. How accurately can the solutions be determined if the only source of error
is roundoff in the DELTA 63?

13.7. Determine the roundoff error in the evaluation of the following expression:

$$w = ax^2y^2 + bx^3y + cxy^3 + dxy + ex + fy + g$$

The parameters and variables have these values (approximately): $a = 12, b = -8,$
$c = 6, d = 12, e = 20, f = 4, g = -6, x = 10,$ and $y = 13$. The roundoff error in
one word is 1 part in 1.34×10^8.

14

ALGEBRAIC LANGUAGES

Numerical problems can often be solved by methods consisting of several expressions of formulas to be evaluated. Algebraic computer languages have been developed to take advantage of this fact. To code in these languages a programmer writes formulas as instructions; the latter are written in sequence as dictated by an analysis or flowchart. The concepts of loops, indexing, and subroutines, among others, have their counterparts in these languages.

Computer programs that translate algebraic-language coding into machine language are called compilers. A description of the structure of algebraic languages and their compilers is given in this chapter. The FORTRAN and ALGOL languages are used as illustrations, and a number of problems are coded in them.

14.1 THE STRUCTURE OF ALGEBRAIC LANGUAGES

Compiler languages offer a number of advantages over symbolic languages. Symbolic languages are modified machine languages that reflect the structure of a computer to a large degree, although they avoid reference to specific memory locations. Compiler languages generally reflect the structure inherent in problems and largely avoid being tied to computer structure and organization. They are "problem oriented" since they accept the language and operations of a large class of problems. Theoretically, a program coded in a compiler language may be run on any computer for which that compiler has been written. In practice, variations among computers are reflected in these languages.

Algebraic compilers form perhaps the largest class of compilers; certainly they are currently the most widely used. Other classes of compilers exist; among them are COBOL, a business problem language, LISP and IPL-V, special languages for handling lists, and COMIT, a language written with language translation facilities.* This chapter is devoted to a study of algebraic languages only, which typify the class.

There are a number of features of algebraic languages (and other compiler languages too) that make the coding and debugging task easier. Most of these features will probably be evident as the descriptions of FORTRAN and ALGOL are studied. In general, since fewer statements are written than in a symbolic language, fewer coding errors tend to be made, although the statements are often very long. Furthermore, since the statements usually resemble algebraic formulas, one step in problem translation is avoided.

If a programmer decides that his problem is a hybrid with both algebraic and nonalgebraic aspects, he may have to use a nonalgebraic language. There is no language generally available that permits much more than limited facilities in both areas. One way around this problem is to code subroutines or segments of the program in one type of language and other portions in the other; when the object decks are produced, they will frequently be compatible. Such interaction of assembler and compiler depends largely on the monitor program used.

One basic difference between assembler and compiler languages is that the latter uses whole words or specific portions of words as operands. In a symbolic language any bits, characters, or groups of digits may be processed individually. Operations such as packing, unpacking, shifting, and masking are generally not possible in an algebraic language.†

Statements

An algebraic program consists of a sequence of *statements* that can be classified into two types: executable and nonexecutable. These classes correspond to the categories of (1) machine instructions and (2) pseudo-operations and constants of a symbolic language.‡

Executable statements can be further classified into four types: arithmetic, decision, indexing, and input-output. These are the designations given to machine instructions, but they are not truly descriptive of algebraic statements. Such statements are more complex and are not as readily classified.

---

* References to the literature on these languages are given in appropriate chapters.[1]

† One exception is NELIAC, a compiler that is a version of ALGOL.

‡ The term *symbolic language* is used to refer to the symbolic coding language of an assembly program, where machine instructions are written symbolically. The adjective "symbolic" actually might be applied to algebraic languages as well.

Arithmetic statements are algebraic formulas and are of the form

$$a \rightarrow b$$

which means "compute the value of the expression a and assign its value to b." This is precisely the significance attached to this notation in Section 2.2. In mathematics we would write

$$b = a(x_1, x_2, \ldots)$$

and ask that the value of the function b be determined, given values of the variables $x_1, x_2, \ldots$.

The quantity b is the name of a memory location and is thus equivalent to a symbol in symbolic coding. The variables x_i represent other locations. As in symbolic coding, reference is made to the locations of the operands, but there is a subtle distinction. Although in practice reference to locations is made, in theory reference is made to the names of the variables. For example, a statement may be of the form

$$\frac{-b + \sqrt{b^2 - 4ac}}{2a} \rightarrow r$$

We mean here that the values of the variables a, b, and c are to be substituted in the expression on the left, and the value of the expression is to be assigned to the variable r. In computer terms, however, a, b, c, and r are locations in memory.

Decision statements are similar to those in a symbolic language, except that they are usually complex and offer multiple paths of control. In some languages only simple conditions may be tested; in others, complex conditions may be stated for testing.

Indexing statements are combined with statements expressing loop control in some manner. The full extent of the loop is usually expressed initially (prior to the loop) in a form such as "Execute all the statements from the next one to statement X inclusive, until condition Y is met." Usually an index is used to control the loop and to refer to a sequence of subscripted variables. Loops may be nested.

Input-output statements cannot easily be characterized, for their structure varies considerably. In general, they are more compact than the equivalent coding sequences in symbolic language.

Nonexecutable statements provide additional information to the compiler (as do pseudo-operations). Examples are format statements and statements about arrays. An *array* is analogous to a multi-dimensional matrix; it is a collection of subscripted variables. It is necessary to indicate the extent of the subscripts, that is, the size of the array. Array statements (also called *dimension* statements) are used to reserve space for the full extent of the array.*

---

* Array statements are analogous to the BLØCK pseudo-operation of the HAP assembler.

Addressing

In order to transfer control to various parts of a program it is necessary to address statements, since the point to which control is to be sent must be identified. Therefore statements are addressable; they may be named and referenced by other statements. These statement names are distinct from variable names, although both in practice refer to memory locations. To keep the distinction clear, it is probably best to think in abstract terms of variable names and of statement names, rather than of memory locations. In a symbolic language symbols are used in one way only: to refer to the locations of memory words.

Subroutines

Subroutines are written and used in a manner that is analogous to their treatment in symbolic languages. They may be compiled separately (as closed subroutines) or with the main program (as open subroutines). It is this feature which permits the preparation of "mixed" routines, that is, object decks prepared in both assembly and compiler languages.

Complex Numbers

All numbers stored in a digital computer are real. A complex number $a + ib$ must be stored as a pair of real numbers (a,b), and the real and imaginary parts must be individually processed. All operations must be written in terms of real operations, the only type available on digital computers.

Consider complex multiplication. The product of two complex numbers is given by

$$(a + ib)(c + id) = (ac - bd) + i(ad + bc)$$

To carry out this multiplication, a routine must be coded to perform all the individual operations of real addition, real subtraction, and real multiplication.

This approach is required whether the coding language is symbolic or algebraic, unless special subroutines are available for complex arithmetic.

The Compilation Process

The compilation and assembly processes have both similarities and differences. They are similar in the basic function they perform: the translation of a coding language into a machine language, accompanied by the production of an object program (and an object deck). During compilation the compiler is in memory, usually under the control of a monitor program, and source program statements are treated as data during the translation process.

The primary difference between a compiler and an assembler lies in the nature of the translation process. An assembler converts each symbolic instruction into a machine instruction, in a one-to-one manner: symbolic operation into operation code, symbolic address into numeric operand address, etc. Exceptions to the one-to-one correspondence are pseudo-operations, which act as special commands, and macro-instructions, which introduce an additional translation step into the process.

A compiler, in contrast, converts a single executable statement into a sequence of coding in such a manner that, when the sequence is executed subsequently, the statement operation is performed. If it is an arithmetic statement, the written expression is evaluated. This procedure can be illustrated by the following statement, given earlier:

$$\frac{-b + \sqrt{b^2 - 4ac}}{2a} \to r$$

A HAP sequence that evaluates r is the following:*

Oper.	Var. Field	
LØAD	A	
MULT	C	
MULT	FØUR	
STØRE	TEMP	
LØAD	B	
MULT	B	
SUBT	TEMP	
JUMPSX	SQRØØT,7	THIS SUBR. TAKES
SUBT	B	SQ.RØØT ØF C(AC)
DIV	A	
DIV	TWØ	
STØRE	R	

The action of the compiler, on encountering the statement, would be to generate coding of this form (in machine language). Floating-point arithmetic, however, would most likely be used.

The coding produced by a compiler is not as efficient in execution time and memory space as similar coding produced "by hand," that is, by coding in a symbolic language. Efficiency is lower for a number of reasons. First, there is usually no attempt on the part of the compiler to "look ahead" to following statements to determine if the joint compilation of two statements would eliminate redundant coding. A LØAD instruction is sometimes compiled even though the desired quantity would be located in the accumulator from an earlier operation. Second, tricks that might occur to the hand coder do not "occur"

---

* A complete program for the evaluation of r would consider the sign of the radicand and the magnitude of a. The routine has been simplified for illustrative purposes.

to the compiler.   In the routine we have given, for example, time would be saved if the second multiplication and division instructions were replaced by accumulator left and right shifts of 2 and 1 positions, respectively (in a binary machine). Third, since the compiler must be general enough to allow for many situations, it generates extra instructions under some circumstances.   One example is the generation of index register *save* and *restore* instructions surrounding a subroutine call; this is done because that index register might be used for other purposes in the area.

14.2   FORTRAN

The Language

The most widely used compiler is FORTRAN (formula translator).   Written originally by IBM for their 704 computer, it has been modified for their more recent 709 and 7090 computers.   At least a dozen other versions have been written for other computers; some of these compilers have their own names.[2] All the versions are very similar, agreeing in fundamental respects and disagreeing primarily where computer differences exist.

The word FORTRAN is used to refer both to the compiler and to the language. To a programmer they are almost synonomous.   He may, in fact, consider FORTRAN as an extension of the computer, writing in a special language acceptable by the machine.   Many machine characteristics, such as the accumulator, index registers, and sequential addresses, are of no concern.   The programmer needs to know little of computer structure to code in FORTRAN (or any algebraic language); he need only have a knowledge of the compiler language.

In the following paragraphs a summary of the FORTRAN language structure is presented.   This material is not intended to serve as a manual or primer of the language, but rather to serve as an introduction to it.

Constants.   Fixed-point and floating-point numbers may be used; the latter are designated with decimal points.   The distinction made between integers and fixed-point numbers in some versions of FORTRAN will not be made here.   Constants are written as numbers, which refer to the numbers themselves, not to their addresses.   Negative numbers must be signed.   Numbers may be written in exponential form: 6.0135E-6; the base 10 is understood.

Variables.   Symbols are used as names of variables.   They consist of from 1 to 6 characters, each of which is a letter or digit; the first character must be a letter, and the last character may not be F.*   Fixed-point-variable symbols must begin

---

* In some versions of FORTRAN symbols are limited to 5 characters.   The restriction on a terminal F applies because symbols ending with F refer to functions.

with one of the letters I, J, K, L, M, or N. Examples of fixed-point variables are: J, IJK, M1234, and LINEAR. Examples of floating-point variables are: A, Q23, ARRAY, and X2Y2Z3.

Subscripted variables are indicated by placing the subscripts in parentheses. Thus a one-dimensional array of numbers

$$x_1, x_2, x_3, \ldots, x_{10}$$

is indicated as

X(1), X(2), X(3), ..., X(10)

Subscripted symbols refer to consecutive locations in memory (when the compiled object program is placed in memory). The subscripts must be integers. The 6-character limit on symbol lengths does not include the extra length due to the parenthesized subscripts.

It is also possible to refer to two- and three-dimensional arrays. Consider the array

$$a_{1,1} \quad a_{1,2} \quad a_{1,3}$$

$$a_{2,1} \quad a_{2,2} \quad a_{2,3}$$

$$a_{3,1} \quad a_{3,2} \quad a_{3,3}$$

These elements are referred to as

A(1,1), A(1,2), A(1,3), ..., A(3,3)

This sequencing implies storage by row; elements are sometimes stored by column.

Operations and expressions. Five operators may be used to form algebraic expressions: $+$, $-$, $*$ (multiplication), $/$, and $**$ (exponentiation). Certain other operations may be indicated functionally; to indicate $\sqrt{x + y}$, we write

SQRTF(X + Y)

The SQRTF function is one of several functions that are defined in FORTRAN; others that a programmer wishes to use he must define (see discussion of functions to follow).

Expressions, consisting of constants, variables, operators, parentheses, and commas, must obey the rules of FORTRAN given in this section and must be mathematically meaningful. Exponentiation is performed before the other operations; the usual rules of arithmetic apply to the latter and to parentheses. Fixed-point and floating-point quantities may not be "mixed" in an expression, except that fixed-point quantities may be used as exponents of floating-point expressions. Floating-point quantities, however, may not be used as exponents of fixed-point expressions. Some examples of FORTRAN expressions are given in Table 14.1.

TABLE 14.1 EXPRESSIONS

Mathematical Expression	FORTRAN Expression
$x + 5$	X + 5.
xy	X * Y
$x(-y)$	X * (-Y)
$(x + y)^3$	(X + Y)**3
$x^{a+3}y^{b+4}$	X**(A+3.) * Y**(B+4.)
$\left(\dfrac{x + y}{a + b}\right)^{i+2}$	((X+Y)/(A+B))**(I+2)
$x\sqrt{x^2 + y^2}$	X * SQRTF(X**2 + Y**2)

The periods that appear in some expressions are required by the rule that forbids mixing fixed- and floating-point quantities. The expression "A + 3" is mixed, whereas "A + 3." is not.

Statement numbers. Statement numbers are decimal integers used to identify statements. They are used in an arbitrary manner; the integers used bear no relation to one another unless the programmer so desires. Statements are usually placed one to a card; if statements are too long for one card they may be placed on consecutive cards. Blank spaces in statements are ignored.

Arithmetic statements. These are written in the form

$$b = a$$

where *b* is a single symbol whose value is to be set equal to the value of the expression *a*. The symbol *b* or any of the symbols in *a* may be subscripted. An example of an arithmetic statement is the following:

$$X = Y + Z$$

which means "replace the present value of X with the sum of the values of Y and Z."

Statements are *not* equations but rather indicate that new values are to be substituted for old ones. The statement

$$I = I + 1$$

means that the value of I is to be increased by 1.*

---

* An important difference between the significance of an arithmetic expression in a symbolic language and that of one in an algebraic language should be noted. Consider I + 1. An assembler interprets this as the *address* I + 1, that is, the address 1 greater than the address named I. A compiler interprets this as C(I) + 1, that is, 1 greater than the contents of the address named I. Furthermore, the assembler itself performs the addition. The compiler generates coding that, at execution, performs the addition.

Functions. FORTRAN contains several subroutines that the programmer may call on as though they were machine operations. These include square root (SQRTF), exponential (EXPF), natural logarithm (LØGF), sine (SINF), cosine (CØSF), and others. Their use is illustrated by the following: to indicate the logarithm of the sum of the squares of X, Y, and Z, we write

$$\texttt{WWW = LØGF(X**2 + Y**2 + Z**2)}$$

Functions may be defined in the manner of macro-instructions and may be used later in the program. For example, if the function WWW is to be used later, we write

$$\texttt{WWWF(X,Y,Z) = LØGF(X**2 + Y**2 + Z**2)}$$

Functions so defined must have names ending in F. Subsequently, the following statement may be written.

$$\texttt{VALUE = WWWF(A,B,SUM) + SINF(B)}$$

This means that the values of A, B, and SUM are substituted in the function WWWF and the result is added to sin B.

Functions may be used as arguments of other functions. For $\cos (\log x + e^y)$ we write

$$\texttt{R = CØSF(LØGF(X) + EXPF(Y))}$$

Unconditional jump. To indicate an unconditional transfer of control, a statement of the form

$$\texttt{GØ TØ N}$$

is used. N is a statement number.

Conditional jump. To indicate a conditional transfer of control, the IF statement is most commonly used; it is of the form

$$\texttt{IF (E) N1,N2,N3}$$

where E is an expression and the Ni are statement numbers. The function of the statement is as follows: if the value of E is negative, zero, or positive, the statement numbered N1, N2, or N3, respectively, is the next one executed. Two of the statement numbers may be the same; they would be, for example, if the conditions $E > 0$ and $E = 0$ were treated the same.

The following simple FORTRAN program embodies several of these concepts.

Example 14.1 Write a program that sums 100 numbers.

This problem was last coded in Example 8.2 (page 146), and a flowchart appears in Fig. 14.1. Statement numbers appear in the flowchart.

Statement No.	Statement
	$\texttt{SUM = 0.}$

(Continued)

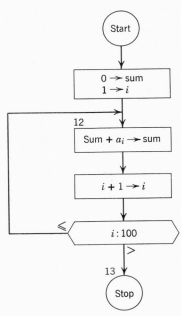

Fig. 14.1.   Flowchart for summation of 100 numbers (Example 14.1).

Statement No.	Statement
	I = 1
12	SUM = SUM + A(I)
	I = I + 1
	IF (I - 100) 12,12,13
13	STØP

The STØP statement indicates when the program is to stop being executed.

Dimension statements.   In order to indicate the size of each set of data, which might be one-, two-, or three-dimensional, DIMENSIØN statements are used:

$$\text{DIMENSIØN A(50), B(20,10), C(5,10,30)}$$

which indicates that A, B, and C, have one, two, and three subscripts, respectively, and that the maximum array sizes are 50, 200, and 1500. Blocks of these sizes are set aside for these variables. Note also that the maximum values of the individual subscripts are also indicated. A DIMENSIØN statement must be used whenever subscripted variables are used.

Loops.   A more convenient way to set up loops than by using the IF statement is by using the DØ statement. It is of the form

$$\text{DØ N I = A,B,C}$$

where N is a statement number, I is a fixed-point variable, and A, B, and C are positive fixed-point constants or variables. The statements following the DØ, through and including statement N, are executed repeatedly, with I successively equal to A, A+C, A+2C, A+3C, ..., until I equals the largest value not exceeding B. The quantity C may be omitted and is then taken to be 1. The set of statements executed repeatedly is called the *range* of the DØ loop. Several rules apply to DØ statements, one of which is that the last statement in a DØ range may not cause a transfer of control.

Example 14.2   Recode the program in Example 14.1 using a DØ loop.

```
        DIMENSIØN X(100)
        SUM = 0.
        DØ 12 I = 1,100
   12   SUM = SUM + X(I)
```

DØ loops may be nested, but the range of an inner loop may not extend beyond the range of an outer loop. As an example of a problem with nested loops, consider the following.

Example 14.3   Write a program to find the sum of the tenth powers of eighty numbers. This problem was coded in Example 8.5 (page 149) and flowcharted in Fig. 2.10 (page 38).

```
        DIMENSIØN X(80)
        SUM = 0.
        DØ 50 I = 1,80
        PØWER = 1.
        DØ 60 J = 1,10
   60   PØWER = PØWER * X(I)
   50   SUM = SUM + PØWER
```

Note that the index J does not appear in the inner DØ loop; the effect then is to repeat statement 60 ten times identically, thus computing the tenth power of X(I) for the current value of I.

Continue statements.   These are dummy statements that cause no operation when the object program is executed. They are used to satisfy the rule that the last statement in a DØ loop cannot be one that transfers control. Later examples illustrate its use.

Subroutines.   It is possible to write closed subroutines which can be compiled separately and called in the manner of symbolic-program subroutines. These are of two types, designated FUNCTIØN and SUBROUTINE.

In the case of FUNCTIØN, the subroutine begins with a statement of the form

FUNCTIØN NAME(A,B,C,...)

where NAME is the name of the subroutine and A, B, C, ... are its dummy arguments. The subroutine is written as a standard program but must contain at least one RETURN statement, the purpose of which is to return control to the main program. Linkages are established automatically by FORTRAN. | To call on a FUNCTIØN subroutine and establish the main-program linkage, we write a statement in the main program of the form

$$RESULT = NAME(ALPHA, BETA, GAMMA, \dots)$$

which states that the result is to be placed in RESULT. The arguments to be processed are located in ALPHA, BETA, GAMMA, . . . , which are placed in appropriate places within the subroutine. Note that one and only one value is computed as the result. The call in the main program is identical to that for the arithmetic statement function; the main difference between the two is that the FUNCTION subroutine may comprise any number of statements, whereas the statement function is limited to one.

SUBRØUTINE is very similar to FUNCTION; it begins with a statement of the form

$$SUBRØUTINE \quad NAME(A, B, C, \dots)$$

It differs, however, in two important respects. First, its call in the main program is of the form

$$CALL \quad NAME \quad (ALPHA, BETA, GAMMA, \dots)$$

and cannot be placed within an expression, as can the FUNCTIØN call. Second, any number of quantities may be computed, whereas the FUNCTIØN subroutine is limited to one. If the corresponding subroutines are properly written, the following two sequences in the main program accomplish the same thing:

(1)

$$ANSWER = SUM(AX, BX, XX) + X**3 + Y**3$$

(2)

$$CALL \quad SUM(AX, BX, XX, RESULT)$$
$$ANSWER = RESULT + X**3 + Y**3$$

The extra argument (RESULT) in the CALL statement indicates where the result of the SUBRØUTINE calculation is to be placed; this result is then used in the following statement. This feature is a requirement with a SUBRØUTINE call; the locations for all results must be given as arguments in CALL.

The sequence of arguments in calls for the FUNCTIØN and SUBRØUTINE programs must of course match the sequence within the subroutine, if locations of arguments and results are not to be confused. The FORTRAN compiler produces a calling sequence of the form described in Section 10.3, provided the associated computer uses that form of linkage.

Input-output. Data are read into the computer by the execution of READ statements. In these statements are lists of the variables for which values are to be read; the items of data correspond in sequence to the lists.* Each READ state-

---

* Data are matched to the list sequences as with input-output subroutines; refer to Section 11.2.

ment reads the contents of one card (or the equivalent). The READ statement
is of the form

$$\text{READ N,A,B,C}$$

where N is the statement number of a FØRMAT statement, and A, B, C, . . .
are the names of variables in the program. The corresponding FØRMAT statement is of the form

$$\text{N} \qquad \text{FØRMAT (. . . . .)}$$

where the contents of the parentheses are similar to the format structure described in Section 11.2.

As an example, if a card has five 10-character octal numbers and three
7-character floating-point numbers (with three digits to the right of the decimal
point) punched on it, the statements

$$\text{READ 32,X,Y,Z,A(1),A(2),A(3),X,Y}$$
$$\text{32} \qquad \text{FØRMAT (5Ø10,3F7.3)}$$

would read this card and assign the 8 numbers read to the variables X, Y, Z,
A(1), . . . , Y. If these variables have other values prior to the execution of the
READ statement, they will be changed to the new values.

For added flexibility in reading data, indexing is possible in a READ statement. For example, the statement

$$\text{READ 88,(X(I), I=1,10)}$$

will read ten items of data from a card and store them in sequence in X(1),
X(2), . . . , X(10). Double and triple subscripting are also allowed, as is the
nesting of indexing in the manner of nested DØ loops.

Output statements are PUNCH and PRINT, which are used analogously to
READ. PUNCH causes a card to be punched, and PRINT causes one line of
printing. Formats are used as with READ statements.

If a monitor system is used, the READ and PRINT statements generally refer
to the input and output tapes, respectively. Variations in these statements
among the several versions of FORTRAN make us unable to list all possibilities.
FORTRAN has other tape operation statements available also.

End. Every FORTRAN program must end with a card that reads END. This indicates the end of the source program to the compiler.

Further Examples of Programs

A series of examples is given here, to illustrate the use of FORTRAN and the
structure of programs.

Example 14.4 Write a program to evaluate the expression

$$f = 4.5 \times 10^5 + e^{x^2}(1 - \log y)$$

for ten pairs of values of x and y. The numbers are punched one pair to a card with field specification 2F12.5. The values of f are to be printed, one to a line.

A simple loop is set up to cycle ten times. The READ and PRINT statements must be included in the loop.

```
        DØ 6 I = 1,10
        READ 5,X,Y
        F = 4.5E5 + EXPF(X**2) * (1. - LØGF(Y))
6       PRINT 7,F
        STØP
5       FØRMAT (2F12.5)
7       FØRMAT (F20.5)
        END
```

This program prints each result in a twenty-character field; the extra space is added for clarity (although it is not needed when only one number appears on a line). If it is preferable to print the input data with each result, the print and format statements would be written

```
6       PRINT 7,X,Y,F
        ....
7       FØRMAT (3F20.5)
```

Example 14.5 Write a program to determine the square root of A, using an iterative approach.

This problem was last analyzed in Section 3.4 and flowcharted in Fig. 3.5 (page 62). The computation will be stopped when it is true that

$$|A - e^2| < \epsilon$$

Since the number of loop cycles is indefinite, an IF statement is more conveniently used than a DØ loop. A DØ loop requires an explicit number of cycles to be stated either in the program or with the data.* An initial estimate (EST) is given with the data. ABSF is the "absolute value of" operator.

```
        READ 66,A,EST,EPSILN
55      EST = 0.5 * (EST + A/EST)
        IF (ABSF(A - EST**2) - EPSILN) 56,55,55
56      PRINT 77,A,EST
        STØP
66      FØRMAT (3F12.4)
77      FØRMAT (2F20.4)
        END
```

Example 14.6 Given two matrices, **A** with m rows and n columns and **B** with n rows and p columns, determine the matrix product

$$C = AB$$

The elements of **C** are given by

$$c_{ik} = \sum_{j=1}^{n} a_{ij} b_{jk}, \qquad 1 \leqslant i \leqslant m, \qquad 1 \leqslant k \leqslant p$$

* A DØ statement may be written in the form
  DØ N I = 1, J
  If then the value of J is supplied with the data, the number of loop cycles is "variable."

where a_{ij} and b_{jk} are the elements of **A** and **B**, respectively. A flowchart of the problem, drawn in Fig. 14.2, shows three nested loops. The loops are indexed by i, k, and j. The innermost loop computes one value of c_{ik}.

For simplicity it is assumed that the elements of the m rows of **A** and the n rows of **B** are on $m + n$ successive cards, one row to a card. Preceding each matrix is a card with the number of rows and columns in that matrix. In the following routine there are three steps, reading cards, computing results, and printing results. Matrices as large as 20×20 are allowed. It is assumed that the elements in **A** and **B** are four-digit integers. A check is made (at statement 4) to see whether multiplication of the matrices is possible, that is, whether the number of columns in **A** equals the number of rows in **B**. This is done by storing the number of columns in **A** temporarily in N1 and comparing that number to the number N subsequently. If they are unequal, a comment is printed; the H control character used in the format statement (999) is discussed in Section 11.2.

To conform to FORTRAN requirements on floating-point variables, the letter L is prefixed to appropriate symbols.

```
        DIMENSIØN A(20,20), B(20,20), C(20,20)
        READ 33,M,N
        DØ 5 I = 1,M
5       READ 34, (LA(I,J), J=1,N)
        N1 = N
        READ 33,N,LP
4       IF (N - N1) 99,6,99
6       DØ 7 J = 1,N
7       READ 34, (LB(J,K), K=1,LP)
        DØ 10 I = 1,M
        DØ 10 K = 1,LP
        LC(I,K) = 0.
        DØ 10 J = 1,N
10      LC(I,K) = LC(I,K) + LA(I,J)*LB(J,K)
        DØ 11 I = 1,M
11      PRINT 35, (LC(I,K), K=1,LP)
        STØP
99      PRINT 999
        STØP
33      FØRMAT (2N5)
34      FØRMAT (20N4)
35      FØRMAT (20N6)
999     FØRMAT (13H ERRØR IN DATA)
        END
```

Example 14.7 Write a program to solve the following cubic equation for its three roots.

$$y^3 + py^2 + qy + r = 0$$

This problem was analyzed in Section 2.1. A flowchart appears in Fig. 14.3. We assume that a subroutine is available to compute the arccosine of a variable. If it is not, it must also be coded. In the flowchart two auxiliary functions, g and h, are computed; their values are used later. This is done to shorten the object program in both space and time. The quantities A and B are also computed separately. The complex expressions for the x_i are written with real and imaginary parts explicitly stated, since those parts must be separately computed.

In the following program AA and BB are used to represent the quantities A and B in

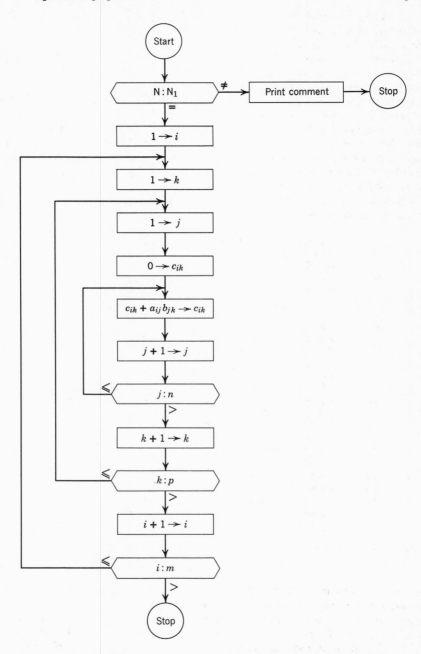

Fig. 14.2.   Flowchart for matrix multiplication (Example 14.6).

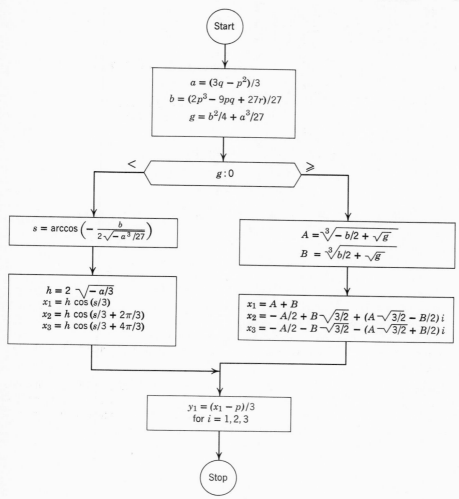

Fig. 14.3. Flowchart of solution of cubic equation (Example 14.7).

the flowchart; A and B in the program represent a and b in the flowchart. $X(1)$, $X(2)$, and $X(3)$ are the real parts of the x_i; $X(4)$, $X(5)$, and $X(6)$ are the complex parts. No input-output operations are shown.

In order to simplify some expressions, two constants are defined at the start; these are set equal to $\sqrt{3}/2$ and π.

A few words of caution are necessary here. This program is only illustrative. In many situations, depending on the coefficients of the cubic equation, this method may be inappropriate, and produce inaccurate results. This is of no concern to us now, however; only coding techniques are being emphasized.

```
          DIMENSIØN X(6), Y(6)
          RAD = SQRTF(3.)/2.
          PI = 3.1415927
          A = (3.*Q - P**2)/3.
          B = (2.*P**3 - 9.*P*Q + 27.*R)/27.
          G = B**2/4. + A**3/27.
          IF (G) 20,10,10
   10     AA = (-B/2. + SQRTF(G))**(1./3.)
          BB = (B/2. + SQRTF(G))**(1./3.)
          X(1) = AA + BB
          X(4) = 0.
          X(2) = -AA/2. + BB*RAD
          X(5) = AA*RAD - BB/2.
          X(3) = -AA/2. - BB*RAD
          X(6) = -AA*RAD - BB/2.
          GØ TØ 40
   20     S = ARCCØSF(-B/(2.*SQRTF(-AA**3/27.)))
          H = 2.*SQRTF(-A/3.)
          X(1) = H*CØSF(S/3.)
          X(4) = 0.
          X(2) = H*CØSF(S/3. + 2.*PI/3.)
          X(5) = 0.
          X(3) = H*CØSF(S/3. + 4.*PI/3.)
          X(6) = 0.
   40     DØ 50 I = 1,6
   50     Y(I) = (X(I) - P)/3.
```

The three roots have the real and complex parts given by Y(1), Y(2), and Y(3) and Y(4), Y(5), and Y(6), respectively.

Example 14.8 Write a program to solve a set of simultaneous, linear, algebraic equations. The Gauss-Seidel iterative method is used.* The set of n given equations is rewritten so that in each one unknown is expressed in terms of the others. The equations may be written in general terms, as follows; all a_{ij} are assumed nonzero:

$$\sum_{j=1}^{n} a_{ij}x_j = b_i, \qquad 1 \leqslant i,j \leqslant n$$

If these are solved for individual unknowns, we have

$$x_i = \left(b_i - \sum_{\substack{j=1 \\ i \neq j}}^{n} a_{ij}x_j \right) \Big/ a_{ii}, \qquad 1 \leqslant i \leqslant n$$

If we let the $(k+1)$th estimates be $x_i^{(k+1)}$, with initial guesses being $x_i^{(1)}$, these equations can be rewritten slightly:

$$x_i^{(k+1)} = \left(b_i - \sum_{\substack{j=1 \\ i \neq j}}^{n} a_{ij}x_j^{(k)} \right) \Big/ a_{ii}, \qquad 1 \leqslant i \leqslant n$$

* In solving a set of algebraic equations we must consider the choice of method carefully. In many situations this method is inappropriate; convergence may not occur. The Gauss-Seidel method applies when the main diagonal coefficient in each row dominates the other coefficients in the row. The method serves, however, to illustrate an approach to the problem.[3]

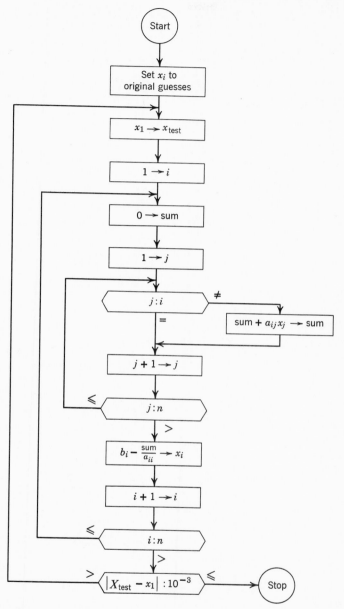

Fig. 14.4. Flowchart for iterative solution of linear algebraic equations (Example 14.8).

For simplicity let the iteration stop as soon as x_1 changes from one step to the next by an amount less than 0.001. The flowchart for this method appears in Fig. 14.4.

It is assumed that the original estimates of the x_i are located in $X(1), X(2), \ldots$ at the start. At each loop cycle the latest value of $X(1)$ is stored in XTEST for later testing. Since only the latest values of the x_i need be saved, new estimates replace old estimates. At statement 77 a test is made to see if $i = j$; if so, the summation (statement 5) is skipped. The program is written to handle twenty equations.

```
        DIMENSIØN A(20,20), B(20), X(20)
70      XTEST = X(1)
        DØ 20 I = 1,N
        SUM = 0.
        DØ 10 J = 1,N
77      IF (J - I) 5,10,5
5       SUM = SUM + A(I,J) * X(J)
10      CØNTINUE
20      X(I) = (B(I) - SUM)/A(I,I)
        IF (ABSF(XTEST - X(1)) - .001) 30,30,70
30      STØP
```

14.3 ALGOL

The Language

ALGOL, an algorithmic language, has been developed as an international algebraic language for writing algorithms. It is suitable for use on any computer, provided the computer has a compiler to effect a translation to machine language. An original version of ALGOL was developed at an international meeting in Zurich, Switzerland, in 1958. A newer version, ALGOL 60, was written two years later. The language is still in the process of development, and the description given here (of ALGOL 60) can be considered only as indicative of the latest form of the language; the process of development seems to be stabilizing, however.[4]

There are several *languages* for writing ALGOL; they differ only in notation. A *publication language,* used for communicating between people (as in papers published on ALGOL programs), allows much freedom in writing; Greek letters may be used, for example. A *reference language* uses convenient mathematical notation, such as "$<$" for "less than," but requires modification before it can be accepted by computing equipment. A *hardware language* uses notation directly acceptable by equipment; for example, only capital letters are used and a special notation is required for "less than," such as "LT." In the other languages both small and capital letters are permitted. The language used in this section is the reference language.

In the following paragraphs a summary of the ALGOL language structure is presented. As with FORTRAN, this material is not intended to serve as more than an introduction to the language.

Numbers. Numbers in integer and floating-point form are allowed; the latter are also called *real* numbers. Examples of numbers are

9,   345901425,   .0015, $4.667_{10}3 (= 4.667 \times 10^3)$, $7.1_{10} - 4$, $_{10}-2$

Superscripts are not allowed; the base 10 is written as a subscript.

Variables. ALGOL variables are quantities referred to by name, as are the variables in algebra. *Variable identifiers* are the symbols used for variables; they are composed of strings of small or capital letters and digits, the first of which is a letter. There is no limit on the size of the symbol.* Examples are

b,   *LIST*,   *start*, $A1234567$,   *GAMMAsquare*

Certain words in ALGOL are reserved for special purposes; they are printed in boldface. Some examples are **go to, if, then, else, for, comment, begin,** and **end.**

Subscripted variables are indicated by placing the subscripts in square brackets. The elements of a two-dimensional array might be written as follows:

$$a[1,1], a[1,2], a[1,3], \ldots , a[3,3]$$

Operations and expressions. Five operations may be used to form algebraic expressions: $+, -, \times, /,$ and $\uparrow$ (exponentiation). Arrows are used to identify quantities that are normally superscripts; x^2 is written as

$$x \uparrow 2$$

Certain other operations may be indicated functionally; to indicate $\sqrt{x + y}$, we write

$$sqrt\ (x + y)$$

Expressions consist of numbers, symbols, operators, parentheses, and commas. Exponentiation is performed before the other operations; otherwise, the usual rules of arithmetic apply. Real and integer quantities may be mixed in expressions. As an example, the expression

$$\frac{-b + \sqrt{b^2 - 4ac}}{2a}$$

is written as follows:

$$(-b + sqrt\ (b \uparrow 2 - 4 \times a \times c))/(2 \times a)$$

Functions. ALGOL contains a number of special functions that the programmer may use as though they were operations. These include square root (*sqrt*), exponential (*exp*), natural logarithm (*ln*), sine (*sin*), cosine (*cos*), and absolute value (*abs*).

Functions may be defined early in a program and used later; this technique is described in the section on subroutines.

Statements. A statement is a generalized instruction for the performance of an

---

* In the hardware language there is a limit on symbol size that depends on the computer and compiler in question.

operation. In a program statements are separated by semicolons. A statement may be assigned a *label* for reference purposes; a label is similar to a symbolic address and may consist of an integer or a symbol. If a label L is assigned to a statement S, it is separated from the statement by a colon:

$$L:S$$

Several statements may be combined to form a *compound* statement, which is delimited by **begin** and **end:**

$$\textbf{begin } S1;\ S2;\ S3;\ S4\ \textbf{end}$$

Assignment statements. These are used to assign values to variables; they are written in the form

$$b := a$$

where b is a symbol whose value is to be set equal to the value of the expression a. For example,

$$x := sum - 1.005$$

means "replace the present value of x with the value of 'sum' decreased by 1.005." As another example, if the value of g is given by

$$g = Ay^2 + By + C$$

and $A = 1.4, B = -3.5, C = 9.9$, and $y = -0.13$, the following compound statement evaluates g:

$$\textbf{begin } A := 1.4;\quad B := -3.5;\quad C := 9.9;\quad y := -0.13;$$
$$g := A \times y{\uparrow}2 + B \times y + C\ \textbf{end}$$

Blank spaces may be inserted freely for ease of reading. Frequently line indentation is used for the same purpose. Neither action has any effect on the compilation process.

Unconditional jump. To indicate an unconditional transfer of control the following statement is used:

$$\textbf{go to } L$$

where L is a label.

Conditional jump. To indicate a conditional transfer of control the **if** statement is used. Consider the statement

$$\textbf{if } R \textbf{ then } S$$

Here R is a *relational* expression that may be true or false, such as $A = B$ or $i = 3n + 2$.* If the expression is true, the statement S following **then** is ex-

---

* Note the difference between the connectives $:=$ and $=$. The former implies assignment of a value; the latter indicates a proposition that may be true or false.

ecuted; if the expression is false, control is passed to the next statement in sequence after S. The statement S can be of any type except another **if** statement. Frequently S is a **go to** statement:

$$\text{if } R \text{ then go to } P$$

Here, if R is true, control will go to P; otherwise, control will go in sequence after the **go to** statement.

Example 14.9   Write a program that sums 100 numbers.   This problem was coded in FORTRAN in Example 14.1 (page 271) and flowcharted in Fig. 14.1.

$$sum := 0; \quad i := 1;$$
$$M: sum := sum + a[i]; \quad i := i + 1;$$
$$\text{if } i \leqslant 100 \text{ then go to } M$$

Another version of the **if** statement is used if two specific, different actions are to be taken for the cases where the expression is true and false.   It is of the form

$$\text{if } R \text{ then } S1 \text{ else } S2$$

If R is true, statement S1 is executed and statement S2 is skipped; if R is false, S1 is skipped and S2 is executed.   In either case, control then passes to the next statement in sequence after S2, unless S1 or S2 causes a transfer of control.   The statement S2 can be of any type, including another **if** statement.

Example 14.10   The value of one of two quantities, a and b, is to be assigned to Z, depending on these conditions:

> If a is positive and b is zero, set Z = a;
> if a is positive and b is nonzero, set Z = b;
> if a is negative and b is zero, set Z = b;
> if a is negative and b is nonzero, set Z = a.

The problem was coded in Example 5.9 (page 95) and flowcharted in Fig. 5.5.

$$\text{if } a < 0 \text{ then go to } R \text{ else if } b = 0 \text{ then } Z := a \text{ else}$$
$$\text{begin } Z := b; \quad \text{go to } Q \text{ end}$$
$$R: \text{if } b = 0 \text{ then } Z := b \text{ else } Z := a;$$
$$Q: \ldots$$

The general rule for nested **if** statements is that the statement following the first relation that is true is executed and the rest of the complete **if** statement is skipped; if all the relations are false, the statement after the last **else** is executed.

It is possible to build up more complex conditional relations (*compound conditionals*) by combining simple relations.   For example, we may state that a particular action is to occur if *either* relation R1 *or* relation R2 is true.   The symbol ∨ (read "or") is used, as in

$$R1 \lor R2$$

Thus we may write

$$\textbf{if } R1 \lor R2 \textbf{ then } S1 \textbf{ else } S2$$

If either $R1$ or $R2$ is true, $S1$ is executed and $S2$ is skipped; if the opposite is true (that is, if both $R1$ and $R2$ are false), $S1$ is skipped and $S2$ is executed. Subsequently control passes as previously.

The symbol $\lor$ is called a *Boolean* operator.* There are four other Boolean operators; two of these are $\lor$ ("and") and $\neg$ ("not"). Using these, we may express relations such as "if both $R1$ and $R2$ are true" and "if either $R1$ is true or $R2$ is false"; more complicated relations are also possible. The other two Boolean operators are beyond the scope of this introduction to ALGOL.†

Loops. Loops are most easily written using a **for** statement, which is of the form

$$\textbf{for } v := FL \textbf{ do } S$$

where v is a variable, FL is a *for-list,* and S is a statement which may be compound. The statement S is executed a number of times, with the variable v (the *control* variable) taking on the values specified in FL. There are three basic forms to the **for** statement.

1. One form, which might be called the "step-until" form, permits stepping of the control variable over a finite range in equal increments. The statement is written‡

$$\textbf{for } v := a \textbf{ step } c \textbf{ until } b \textbf{ do } S$$

where a, b, and c are arithmetic expressions. The statement S is executed repeatedly with the variable v equal successively to a, $a + c$, $a + 2c$, $a + 3c$, until v equals the largest value not exceeding b. Most commonly, a, b, and c are positive or negative integers.§

Example 14.11 Write a program that sums 100 numbers. This problem was coded in ALGOL in Example 14.9, using an **if** statement.

$$sum := 0; \quad \textbf{for } i := 1 \textbf{ step } 1 \textbf{ until } 100 \textbf{ do } sum := sum + a[i]$$

2. A second form uses a list of arithmetic expressions, each entry of which in turn is to be assigned to the control variable for the execution of S. The statement is written

$$\textbf{for } v := E1, E2, \ldots \textbf{ do } S$$

where $E1$, $E2$, ... are arithmetic expressions.

---

* Boolean operators are discussed further in Section 15.1.

† Refer to the cited references on ALGOL for details.

‡ Because of the similarity of this form of the **for** statement to the DØ statement of FORTRAN, the notation of the latter (page 272) has been used here.

§ If c is negative, the previous sentence should end ". . . . the smallest value not less than b."

Example 14.12   Evaluate the formula

$$g = Ay^2 + By + C$$

for each of the values $y = 0.13$, -0.17, 0.45, -1.6, and 2.7, while $A = 1.4$, $B = -3.5$, and $C = 9.9$.

> **for** $y := 0.13, -0.17, 0.45, -1.6, 2.7$ **do**
>> **begin** $A := 1.4;$ $B := -3.5;$ $C := 9.9;$
>> $g := A \times y{\uparrow}2 + B \times y + C$ **end**

The statement that is repeated is bracketed by **begin** and **end,** since that statement is compound.

3. The third form permits repeated execution of a statement as long as a conditional relation is true.   The form is

for $v := E$ **while** B **do** S

where E is an arithmetic expression or a list of arithmetic expressions and B is a Boolean relation.   Sometimes E is the initial value of v, and subsequent values are computed by the statement S.

Example 14.13   Write a program to compute the square root of A, using an iterative approach.

This problem was coded in FORTRAN in Example 14.5.   It is assumed here that an original estimate of $\sqrt{A}$ is given as *initial*, and that *est* is the current estimate.   The quantity ϵ, used to stop the iteration, is called *epsilon*.

> **for** $est := initial$ **while** $abs(A - est{\uparrow}2) < epsilon$
> **do** $est := 0.5 \times (est + A/est)$

Loops may be nested in ALGOL, as in the following example.

Example 14.14   Write a program to find the sum of the tenth powers of eighty numbers. This problem was coded in FORTRAN in Example 14.3.

> $sum := 0;$ **for** $i := 1$ **step** 1 **until** 80 **do**
>> **begin for** $j := 1$ **step** 1 **until** 10 **do**
>>> **begin** $power := 1;$ $power := power \times x[i]$ **end**
>>
>> $sum := sum + power$
>
> **end**

In this program there are two sets of **begin-end** pairs; one is nested within the other.   For reading ease in matching such pairs, these are usually aligned in the program, either vertically or horizontally, as we have shown them.

Array declarations.   An *array declaration* indicates how many numbers are present in an array in each dimension.   It is written in the form

array $subsv[l_1: u_1, l_2:u_2, \ldots]$

where *subsv* is a subscripted variable, and the l_i and u_i are the lower and upper bounds of the subscripts of the *subsv* for the several dimensions. For example, the 3×3 array on page 269 would be written as

$$\textbf{array } a[1:1, 3:3]$$

Several variables may be listed within one array declaration:

$$\textbf{array } a[-4:6, 4:9], b[4:5, 6:20]$$

The subscripts may be negative, but they must be integers. Subscript values refer to successive locations in memory (when the program is translated to machine language). The last array declaration indicates that the *a*-array is 11×6 or 66 in size, and that the *b*-array is 2×15 or 30 in size.

If subscripted variables appear in a program, as they do in Examples 14.9 and 14.14, an array declaration is required. Array declarations, like all declarations, are not executable; they merely provide information to the compiler. The elements of an array must all be of one type, real, integer, or Boolean. The type must be specified, as in **integer array**. The word **array** means **real array**.

Switches. A switch is used to provide a conditional transfer of control to a number of different statements, depending on the value of a stated variable. First, a switch is established by a *switch declaration:*

$$\textbf{switch } s := L1, L2, L3, \ldots$$

where *s* is a variable and *L*1, *L*2, *L*3, . . . are statement labels. The following statement will transfer control to the statement *Li* when the value of *s* is *i* at the time the statement is executed:

$$\textbf{go to } s[i]$$

Subroutines. *Procedures* in ALGOL are equivalent to subroutines. A *procedure declaration* is used to define the subroutine:

$$\textbf{procedure } subrte(P1, P2, \ldots)$$

where *subrte* is the name of the subroutine and *P*1, *P*2, . . . are the parameters. Included among the parameters are both the input and the output variables. The subroutine is later called as follows,

$$subrte(V1, V2, \ldots)$$

with particular values of the parameters given as *V*1, *V*2, ...

Example 14.15   Write a subroutine which accepts three quantities *a*, *b*, and *c*, and conditionally computes the sum of the squares and the sum of the cubes of the quantities:

$$f = a^2 + b^2 + c^2$$
$$g = a^3 + b^3 + c^3$$

If any of the three parameters is negative, the quantity *g* is set equal to -1.

procedure *sumsqcube* (a, b, c, f, g)

    begin $f := a{\uparrow}2 + b{\uparrow}2 + c{\uparrow}2;$

    if $a < 0 \lor b < 0 \lor c < 0$

    then $g := -1$

    else $g := a{\uparrow}3 + b{\uparrow}3 + c{\uparrow}3$

    end

To call on the subroutine to compute the functions for particular values of the parameters, calling the results F and G, *sums* and *cubes,* and *function1* and *function2,* we write

    sumsqcube $(3, 4, 2, F, G)$

    sumsqcube $(0, 1, 5, sums, cubes)$

    sumsqcube $(-3, 4, 8, function1, function2)$

for which the computed answers would be

    $F = 29, \quad G = 99$

    $sums = 16, \quad cubes = 26$

    $function1 = 89, \quad function2 = -1$

Functions are considered to be a special case of procedures, namely, those procedures where the result is a single value. The function is used in a statement by calling it in the manner of a procedure, but the name of the function is considered to be a variable.

In the procedure declaration for a function, the word **procedure** is preceded by a *type* word (**real, integer,** or **Boolean**) to identify the variable. The variable is assigned a value in the body of the procedure.

Example 14.16 Write a function which computes the value of f, as defined in Example 14.15, given a, b, and c. The function is real (that is, it is a floating-point number).

    real procedure *sumsquare*(a, b, c)

    sumsquarefn $:= a{\uparrow}2 + b{\uparrow}2 + c{\uparrow}2$

A function may be used in an expression as if it were a variable. To add the sum of the squares of *little, medium,* and *big* to the fourth power of *result,* to yield the value of *newresult,* we write

    newresult $:= sumsquarefn$ $(little, medium, big) + result{\uparrow}4$

Input-output. Input-output operations are of no concern in this introduction to ALGOL. Statements called *read, print, punch,* etc., are sometimes used in the literature by way of example. ALGOL was designed, however, to be a language as independent as possible of computer characteristics. Input-output operations were therefore omitted from the formal structure of the language. If a compiler is written for a particular computer, its programmer must include his own input-output procedures.

There are a number of other features of ALGOL that have not been described; they may be found in the cited references, where the reader will also find many other examples of ALGOL coding.

Further Examples of Programs[5]

Example 14.17   Given a set of n numbers, count the number of negative numbers present. This problem was coded in Example 8.4 (page 148) and flowcharted in Fig. 8.2.

$$j := 0$$
$$\textbf{for } i := 1 \textbf{ step } 1 \textbf{ until } n \textbf{ do}$$
$$\textbf{if } a[i] < 0 \textbf{ then } j := j + 1 \textbf{ else } j := j$$

Example 14.18   Given two matrices, **A** with m rows and n columns and **B** with n rows and p columns, determine the matrix product

$$c_{ik} = \sum_{j=1}^{n} a_{ij}b_{jk}, \qquad 1 \leqslant i \leqslant m, \quad 1 \leqslant k \leqslant p$$

where a_{ij} and b_{jk} are the elements of **A** and **B**, respectively.

This problem was coded in FORTRAN in Example 14.6 and flowcharted in Fig. 14.2.   It is coded here without input-output operations.

$$\textbf{for } i := 1 \textbf{ step } 1 \textbf{ until } m$$
$$\textbf{begin for } k := 1 \textbf{ step } 1 \textbf{ until } p; \quad c[i,k] := 0$$
$$\textbf{begin for } j := 1 \textbf{ step } 1 \textbf{ until } n$$
$$c[i,k] := c[i,k] + a[i,j] \times b[j,k]$$
$$\textbf{end}$$
$$\textbf{end}$$

Example 14.19   Write a program to solve a set of linear algebraic equations, using the Gauss-Seidel method.

The problem was analyzed and coded in FORTRAN in Example 14.8 and flowcharted in Fig. 14.4.   Here twenty equations are permitted.

$$START: xtest := x[1];$$
$$\textbf{for } i := 1 \textbf{ step } 1 \textbf{ until } n \textbf{ do}$$
$$\textbf{begin sum} := 0; \quad \textbf{for } j := 1 \textbf{ step } 1 \textbf{ until } n \textbf{ do}$$
$$\textbf{begin if } j = i \textbf{ then go to } Q \textbf{ else}$$
$$sum := sum + a[i,j] \times x[j]; \quad Q:$$
$$\textbf{end; } x[i] := (b[i] - sum)/a[i,i]$$
$$\textbf{end; if } abs(xtest - x[1]) > .001 \textbf{ then go to } START$$

Summary

Algebraic languages are convenient for coding problems that can be expressed as sequences of formulas to be evaluated.   The structure of these languages permits the programmer to code without considering the structure or organization of a computer.   The languages resemble the nature of the problems to a large degree.

An algebraic program consists of a sequence of statements which can be classified as executable and nonexecutable.   Executable statements indicate operations to be performed; nonexecutable statements provide information to the compiler and resemble pseudo-operations.   The concepts of indexing, looping, branching, and forming subroutines are all available in flexible form in compiler languages.

During the compilation process the statements are translated into machine language and are then executed in an object program.

Notes

1. Information about compilers is available from the Association for Computing Machinery (New York).   Material is published on the development of new compilers in their monthly *Communications*.   The entire January 1961 issue was devoted to the subject of compilers.

2. The following book provides an introduction to the structure and use of FORTRAN.

> D. D. McCracken, *A Guide to FORTRAN Programming*, Wiley, 1961.

The following manual is useful as a reference on FORTRAN.

> IBM Corporation, *General Information Manual*, 1961, Form F28-8074-1.

The following paper offers a formal description of FORTRAN.

> I. N. Rabinowitz, "Report on the Algorithmic Language FORTRAN II," *Comm. Assoc. Computing Machinery*, **5** (June 1962), pp. 327–337.

3. The Gauss-Seidel method is described in

> R. G. Stanton, *Numerical Methods for Science and Engineering*, Prentice-Hall, 1961, p. 199.

4. The following references offer detailed information on ALGOL. This is the original ALGOL report:

> A. J. Perlis and K. Samelson, "Preliminary Report—International Algebraic Language," *Comm. Assoc. Computing Machinery*, **1**, No. 12 (1958), pp. 8–22.

This gives a formal description of the language:

> P. Naur (ed.), "Report on the Algorithmic Language ALGOL 60," *Comm. Assoc. Computing Machinery*, **3** (May 1960), pp. 299–314.

This paper elaborates on the Naur paper, and it is pedagogical in approach:

> H. Bottenbruch, "Structure and Use of ALGOL 60," *J. Assoc. Computing Machinery*, **9** (April 1962), pp. 161–221.

This is a text on the subject:

> D. D. McCracken, *An Introduction to ALGOL Programming*, Wiley, 1962.

5. A number of algorithms appear monthly in the *Comm. Assoc. Computing Machinery*.   They offer many examples of ALGOL coding.

PROBLEMS

Section 14.1

14.1. Consider what complications are introduced into the compilation process by the presence of parentheses. Develop an algorithm for matching parentheses in an algebraic expression, as in the following:

$$F = h + (a + b \times (c - d)/(c + e))$$

The algorithm must be a rule that the program can use to match each left parenthesis with its right parenthesis. In addition, the order in which the parenthesized subexpressions are to be evaluated must be determined.

14.2. Draw a flowchart of a program to analyze an algebraic expression with parentheses. Operations such as the following must be shown: subroutines for generating coding sequences; tests for operators, parentheses and variables; parentheses matching; setting up of loops; etc.

Section 14.2

14.3. Write FORTRAN programs to solve the following problems. DIMENSION statements should be included where needed.

(a) Evaluate F_j for $j = 1, 2, \ldots, 50$:

$$F_j = a_j b_j + \sin a_j x_j$$

(b) Evaluate F_j for $j = 1, 2, \ldots, 100$:

$$F_j = \sum_{i=1}^{25} (a_{ij} + b_{ij})$$

(c) Evaluate e^x by a power series, in the two forms of Problem 8.7.

(d) Solve the mesh problem of Problem 8.8.

(e) Evaluate 1000 values of f_{ijk}:

$$f_{ijk} = a_i b_j c_k$$

All three subscripts run from 1 through 10 inclusively.

(f) Solve a quadratic equation by the quadratic formula, taking all possible coefficient values into account.

(g) Sort the 100 numbers $a_i (i = 1, \ldots, 100)$ and place the sorted numbers, referred to as the b_i, in a new list.

(h) Evaluate an integral approximately, through the use of Simpson's rule:

$$\int_a^{a+2nh} f(x)\, dx \approx \frac{h}{3} (f_0 + 4f_1 + 2f_2 + 4f_4 + \cdots + 4f_{n-1} + f_n)$$

Here h is the interval between values of x for which $f(x)$ is known. The f_i are these known values.

(i) Given the elements of a 3×3 determinant, evaluate the determinant. Use double-subscript notation.

(j) Given the elements of a 4 × 4 determinant, evaluate the determinant. Use double-subscript notation.

(k) Determine the sum of the elements above the main diagonal in a matrix of order $n \times n$.

(l) Given three ordered lists N, P, and Q, each having 20 numbers, form a single ordered list R of 60 numbers.

(m) Write expressions for performing complex arithmetic in terms of real arithmetic operations. Do this for addition, subtraction, multiplication, and division.

(n) Given the following lists of matrix elements, develop an algorithm for determining i and j for the kth entry in the list, where k is any integer.

1. $a_{11}, a_{12}, a_{13}, a_{14}, \ldots, a_{1n}, a_{21}, a_{22}, \ldots, a_{nn}$.
2. $a_{12}, a_{13}, a_{14}, \ldots, a_{1n}, a_{23}, a_{24}, \ldots, a_{n-1,n}$.
   (These are the elements above the main diagonal.)
3. $a_{11}, a_{12}, a_{21}, a_{13}, a_{22}, a_{31}, \ldots, a_{nn}$.
   (These are ordered by the sum of their subscripts.)

(o) Compute the product of three matrices, of the following orders: C of order $m \times n$, B of order $n \times p$, and A of order $p \times q$:

$$d_{ij} = \sum_{h=1}^{n} \sum_{k=1}^{p} c_{ih} b_{hk} a_{kj}$$

D, the product matrix, is of order $m \times q$.

(p) Evaluate the formula

$$q = \sin (x + y) + \ln \cos (y + 2z^2)$$

for all combinations of these values:

$$x = 0.1, 0.2, \ldots, 2.2$$
$$y = 0.10, 0.11, \ldots, 0.22$$
$$z = 0.05, 0.07, \ldots, 0.17$$

There are 2002 values for the formula.

Section 14.3

14.4. Write ALGOL programs to solve the problems in Problem 14.3. Use **array** statements as needed.

15

NONNUMERICAL PROBLEMS

In a nonnumerical problem the contents of words in memory are not treated as though they contained numbers (although in fact they do). Rather, the contents treated as alphanumeric strings of characters or symbols. For example, they might be algebraic expressions, coded information, or English words. For this reason the term *symbol manipulation* is used to characterize the procedures used.

A fairly common characteristic of a nonnumerical problem is that there is no algorithm or standard procedure for solving it. More precisely, the algorithms needed for solution are very complex—if they are known to exist at all.

The following list of problems, considered in this chapter, serve to illustrate the types of problem usually categorized as nonnumerical: the analysis of a symbolic expression, the packing and coding of alphanumeric information, the proving of geometry theorems, and the playing of the game of Nim.

15.1 NONNUMERICAL CONCEPTS

Nonnumbers from Numbers

Since we know that most computers operate only on numbers, we may wonder how problems without numbers can be programmed. By means of BCD codes, described in Section 11.2, it can be done. In that section we saw that a sequence of bits (comprising a *bite*) is used in a binary machine to represent each of approximately 48 different alphanumeric characters.*   In decimal machines, letters of the alphabet are coded in other fashions.

Consider three types of alphanumeric information that might be supplied as data to three different programs: (1) a symbolic expression for an assembly program, (2) a pattern of 0's and 1's for a binary machine processor, and (3) a statement about geometry for a theorem-proving program.   We are interested here in the data only, not in the programs to which they are supplied.

The three sets of data might be:

    (A)   NAME-WØRD+34

    (B)   110100010001100000

    (C)   TRIANGLE ABC WITH RIGHT ANGLE C

Coded as BCD, these strings become†

(A)   452144254066 465124200304

(B)   010100010000 000100000001 010000000000

(C)   635131214527 432560212223 606631633060 513127306360 ...

When these numbers are stored within the computer, they are simply 12-digit octal numbers and are treated as such or, equivalently, as 36-bit binary numbers.‡ These numbers may be added, subtracted, or multiplied, but most likely they will be shifted, masked, or packed.

Logical Operations

The concepts of shifting and masking for the purposes of packing and unpacking information were introduced in Section 12.4.   The term *logical*, used in reference to the shift and mask instructions, comes from the area of logic, often used to describe relationships among computer circuits and functional units.[1] The term is also applied to the operators used to connect algebraic quantities in logical expressions.   The connectives are frequently known as *and, or,* and *not;* symbolically they may be written as $\cdot$, $+$, and $'$, respectively.   The elementary rules of Boolean algebra, applied to a binary number system, are

$$
\begin{array}{cc}
0 + 0 = 0 & 0 \cdot 0 = 0 \\
0 + 1 = 1 & 0 \cdot 1 = 0 \\
1 + 0 = 1 & 1 \cdot 0 = 0 \\
1 + 1 = 1 & 1 \cdot 1 = 1 \\
0' = 1 & 1' = 1
\end{array}
$$

---

* In some computers all 64 distinct 6-bit bites are used to represent characters.

† Refer to page 209 for a list of the BCD codes.

‡ In a computer with a different word structure than the DELTA 63, the form of the internal number is, of course, different.

A number of binary computers have instructions that parallel the three connectives of Boolean algebra. The rules of the algebra are applied to individual
bits within words, but the words are considered as sets or collections of bits. The
results are "logical or," "logical and," and "logical not (complement)" instructions. For example, the "logical or" of these two 15-bit words

010011000010100

100111100100001

is the word

110111100110101

Wherever there is a 1 in either of the original words, there is a 1 in the resultant
word. The "logical not" of the word

000110110001101

is the word

111001001110010

Wherever there is a 1 in the original, there is a 0 in the resultant word, and vice
versa. The "logical and" operation is illustrated by the use of the DELTA 63 mask
register.

To illustrate further the use of logical instructions, we imagine what might be
done with the three sets of data given earlier. As noted, the details of the associated programs are not of interest. All the alphanumeric information, however, must be processed in some manner before it is useful within the main body
of the programs. Such processing is considered for each case in turn; the format of the DELTA 63 words is assumed in these discussions.

Analysis of Symbolic Expressions

A symbolic expression, such as

NAME-WØRD+34

must be analyzed into its component parts before it can be assembled by the
assembler. Assume that the first step, then, is to list these parts, one to a word:

NAME
—
WØRD
+
34

This is an unpacking problem; unpacking was considered in Example 12.5
(page 247). This unpacking problem is different, however, because each item

to be unpacked is of variable length. If, for example, the expression had been written with six spaces allotted per item, as in Fig. 15.1, then unpacking would be little problem, since each six spaces automatically fills one word.

If five spaces were allotted per item, the unpacking process would also be relatively simple. Because the length of each item is fixed (at five), there is no need to test each character to determine where each item ends. Coding the problem may be accomplished as follows.

1. Unpack the complete string, putting one character in a word, as in Example 12.5.
2. Pack five characters at a time into one word.

Returning to our original problem, we note that the analysis is more complex than in the cases just considered. Each item may be one to six characters long, and a test of each character is required. An analysis is described in the following example.

Example 15.1   Write a routine that will analyze a symbolic expression, placing each symbol and each operator in sequence in a list, one to a word. Only expressions involving symbols and the operators $+$ and $-$ need be considered.

The problem is flowcharted in Fig. 15.2. After the string is unpacked and stored in LIST, one character at a time is brought into the AC (at the right). The character is examined; if it is an operator ($+$ or $-$), then a symbol has just ended; that symbol is to be stored in NEWLST. At that point, the operator can also be stored in NEWLST. If the character examined is a letter, it is packed into the MR by shifting. In this way letters within one symbol are packed in the MR, as in Example 12.4 (page 245). When a blank is encountered, the process stops, after the last symbol is stored.

Each character is examined to see if it is (1) a letter, (2) an operator, or (3) a blank. The last two possibilities are checked by testing for (2) BCD 20 ($-$) or 40 ($+$) and (3) BCD 60 (blank). Any other possibility is treated as a letter. In the program that follows the unpacking is assumed completed, with characters individually stored at the right in LIST (see Example 12.5). A pointer (XR2) is used to indicate the next available space in NEWLST.

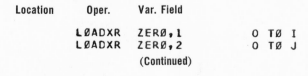

Location	Oper.	Var. Field			
	LØADXR	ZERØ,1	0	TØ	I
	LØADXR	ZERØ,2	0	TØ	J
		(Continued)			

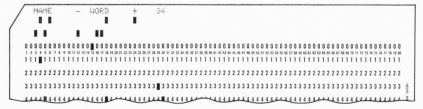

Fig. 15.1.   Data card.

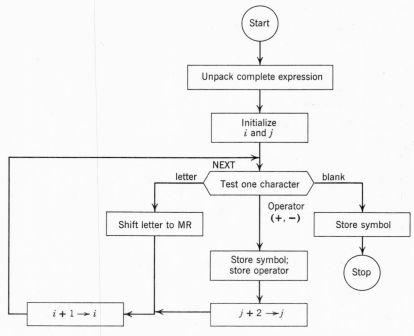

Fig. 15.2.   Flowchart of symbolic expression analysis (Example 15.1).

```
          LØADM    ZERØ          CLEAR MR
NEXT      LØAD     LIST,1        FETCH 1 CHARACTER
          CØMPAR   BLANKT        TEST FØR BLANK
          JUMP     *+2             NØ
          JUMP     BLANK           YES
          CØMPAR   PLUS          TEST FØR "+"
          JUMP     *+2             NØ
          JUMP     ØPER            YES
          CØMPAR   MINUS         TEST FØR "-"
          JUMP     *+2             NØ
          JUMP     ØPER            YES
          LSHIFT   30            HERE IF LETTER...SHIFT
          RØTATE   6                TØ RIGHT ØF MR
          INCRXM   1,1           I+1 TØ I
          JUMP     NEXT
ØPER      STØREM   NEWLST,2      STØRE SYMBØL
          STØRE    NEWLST+1,2    STØRE ØPERATØR
          INCRXM   2,2           J+2 TØ J
          INCRXM   1,1           I+1 TØ I
          JUMP     NEXT-1
BLANK     STØREM   NEWLST,2      STØRE SYMBØL
          HALT

ZERØ      DECML    0
BLANKT    ØCTAL    60
PLUS      ØCTAL    20
MINUS     ØCTAL    40
```

A few more comments are appropriate on the two means of supplying the symbolic data—with a constant space allotment and with a more compact, variable space allotment. When information is supplied to a program in a fixed manner, a *fixed format* is said to be used; otherwise, a *variable format* is used. These terms describe the two formats of the symbolic expression discussed. Numerical data that are supplied to a program are invariably given with a fixed format. Symbolic instruction cards are a combination of the two types, since each field on the card generally must begin in specified columns, but the lengths of the fields may vary. A program that accepts variable-format information is more complex. In general, the more variable the data, the more complicated the coding.

Packing Binary Information

The binary string of information

$$\textbf{110100010001100000}$$

fills three words if stored in BCD fashion. Since the information is binary, it is highly wasteful to store it in BCD form, since 6 bits are then used for each bit of data. The 5 leftmost zeros in each 6-bit bite can be removed. They are redundant.

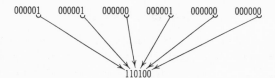

36 bits: 000001   000001   000000   000001   000000   000000

6 bits: 110100

To effect this packing, each word is placed in the AC and the following two instructions are executed as a pair six times:

Oper. Var. Field

LSHIFT   5
RØTATE   1

If this is done with the given string, the right part of the MR will look as follows (in binary):

$$\bullet\bullet\bullet\textbf{000000000000110100}$$

Example 15.2   The following program takes 6 words of BCD 0's and 1's (in BITS to BITS+5) and packs them into one word, BITPAK.

```
Location    Oper.      Var. Field

            SETXRI    6,2
NEWWRD      LØAD      BITS,2          NEXT WØRD TØ AC
            SETXRI    6,1
NWCHAR      LSHIFT    5               NEXT CHARACTER TØ MR
            RØTATE    1
```

(Continued)

```
INCRXM    1,1
XJUMP     NWCHAR,1
INCRXM    1,2
XJUMP     NEWWRD,2
STØREM    BITPAK
HALT
```

Coding Alphanumeric Information

The statement

TRIANGLE ABC WITH RIGHT ANGLE C

is highly redundant. For example, suppose a series of geometric statements is to be processed. The vocabulary of those statements is limited; it might consist, for example, of words such as

TRIANGLE	RIGHT ANGLE	CØNGRUENT
SQUARE	ACUTE ANGLE	ANGLE
RECTANGLE	ØBTUSE ANGLE	SIDE
PARALLELØGRAM	EXTERIØR ANGLE	SIMILAR

With a limited vocabulary, any statement will contain redundant information. For example, the statement we gave might be coded as*

TR ABC, RTA C

Statements are punched on cards in the uncoded form because they strongly resemble English. This is highly advantageous, because any abbreviated language is harder to learn: full English words are easier to remember than abbreviations, since the latter are not standardized. For this reason, algebraic languages use English words, even though abbreviated forms are less redundant.

The use of English words, however, puts a burden on the program, which must condense, abbreviate, or otherwise code the English into a more manageable form. The coded form we have given (TR ABC, RTA C) may itself be too unwieldy. An even more compact form might be developed by a set of rules of the following structure:

Each 36-bit word contains one statement. Bits S and 1–5 indicate the type of figure, bits 6–12 indicate the vertices of interest, bits 13–20 indicate special conditions (such as right angles), ...

In any case, before any coding can occur, the words in the statement must be identified. The words or phrases are long, however; in our list they run to 13 letters, too many to fit into one word (in BCD). If the vocabulary consists entirely of words or phrases that are unique in their first 6 letters (including blanks),

* The term *codify* is sometimes used for *code* in this application, to distinguish it from *code* as defined in Section 1.1.

then only that much of each word or phrase serves to identify each. The list
we gave becomes, in effect, the following:

TRIANG	RIGHT	CØNGRU
SQUARE	ACUTE	ANGLE
RECTAN	ØBTUSE	SIDE
PARALL	EXTERI	SIMILA

Then, after each term is isolated, the first 6 characters must be compared to
the entries in a table, and so a search is made.

Example 15.3 The following program codes the C(TERM) and puts the code in
CØDTRM. If the C(TERM) is not found in the list, control will pass to ERRØR.

Location	Oper.	Var. Field	
	SETXRI	160,1	TABLE HAS 160 ENTRIES
	LØAD	TERM	
AGAIN	CØMPAR	TABLE,1	CØMPAR WITH I-TH ENTRY
	JUMP	*+2	NØ
	JUMP	FØUND	YES
	INCRXM	1,1	
	XJUMP	AGAIN,1	
	JUMP	ERRØR	NØT IN TABLE
FØUND	LØAD	CØDTBL,1	FETCH I-TH CØDE NUMBER
	STØRE	CØDTRM	
	• • •	• • • • •	
TABLE	BCD	1,TRIANG	
	BCD	1,SQUARE	
	BCD	1,RECTAN	
	BCD	1,PARALL	
	• • •	• • • • •	
CØDTBL	ØCTAL	20	
	ØCTAL	21	
	ØCTAL	23	
	ØCTAL	30	

Here the code for TRIANG is 20, the code for SQUARE is 21, etc.

To code a set of quantities into another set, it is necessary in general that two
lists appear in the program: a list of the quantities being coded, in their exact
form, and a list of the codes. If the simple search coded in this example is used,
the two lists are "parallel" in storage, that is, the matching pairs occupy
the same relative positions with respect to the heads of the lists. When that is
true, an index register can pick up the code in the manner of the example.

One important application of the coding of symbols into numbers is in the
assembly of symbolic expressions. Each symbol must be converted to its equivalence, that is, to the address at which the symbol is defined. For this purpose
the symbol table, described in Section 6.3, is used.

The inclusion of an error exit, as in Example 15.3, is important. If some data
are mispunched, it is possible that a term on the card (or its first 6 characters)
does not appear in the list. In that event, it is often desirable that no further

processing be performed and that the programmer be informed by a printed comment.

15.2 EXAMPLES OF NONNUMERICAL PROBLEMS

Theorem Proving

Every branch of mathematics has its set of theorems requiring proof. The theorems of plane Euclidean geometry are perhaps the best known; proofs of dozens of theorems appear in many high school texts on the subject. It is interesting to consider how a theorem might be proved on a computer.[2] First, however, let us consider how a geometric proof might be constructed.

Every statement in a geometric proof requires a "reason." The reason must be an axiom, a postulate, or a previously proven statement. If a hypothesis is given and it is to be proven, it is necessary to select from a list of already proven statements several that will provide reasons within the proof. In other words, we must select statements which can be used as reasons for subsequent statements in the proof. The selected statements are general: "parallel lines have equal alternate interior angles." They are used, however, in a specific situation: "angle BCD equals angle CDF." Stated differently, a statement in a proof is a specific example of the statement given as its "reason." This method of proof is *deductive reasoning.*

A given statement may be a specific example of a number of general statements. For example, any of the following general statements has, as a specific statement, "angle ABC equals DEF":

1. "Corresponding angles of congruent triangles are equal."
2. "Vertical angles of intersecting lines are equal."
3. "Opposite angles of a parallelogram are equal."

Thus a tree-like structure can be drawn, as in Fig. 15.3. There the box at the head of an arrow represents a specific instance of the statement represented by the box at the tail of that arrow. Thus P is a specific case of statements $P1$, $P2$, and $P3$; in other words, $P1$, $P2$, and $P3$ may act as reasons for P in a proof.

In the same way, $P2$ can be justified by one of the statements $P21$, $P22$, $P23$, or $P24$. The complete tree would very probably have many branches. Some of these branches could be combined, since some statements offer reasons for more than one other statement.

A written proof must start at the top of the picture in Fig. 15.3, at one of the many boxes at that level. A valid proof follows a path from the top to the bottom, along paths consisting of arrows and boxes; an example is the path (shown in the figure) through boxes $P232142$, $P23214$, . . . , $P2$, P. In selecting a method for proof, however, we proceed from the bottom upwards, thereby selecting in turn reasons for our final statement, reasons for those reasons, and so on. In

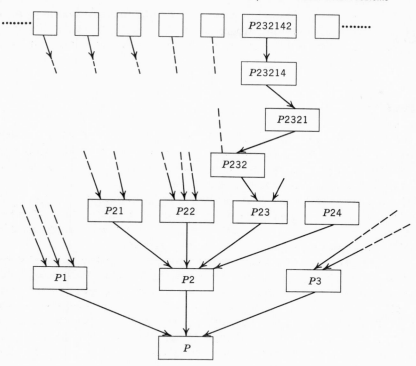

Fig. 15.3. Statements as reasons for other statements.

proceeding from the bottom, we are *analyzing* the problem and write no formal proof; later, in proceeding from the top, we are *synthesizing* and write down the steps of the proof. This is one method of proving geometric theorems or hypotheses.

The computer, in providing a proof for a given proposed theorem, begins searching at the bottom of the tree and traces paths backward from heads to tails of arrows through sequences of boxes. When a box is encountered that requires two or more reasons, all the associated paths must be traced. A proof is found when paths are traced from the bottom to boxes at the top all of which represent given facts (the hypotheses). Each path encountered must terminate at a hypothesis if it is to comprise part or all of the proof.

The program, then, must have the ability to follow arrows backward from box to box. A computer word may contain (1) a statement (coded in numerical terms) and (2) the one or more prior boxes (indicated by addresses or equivalent information). In general, all the possible paths would be traced until matching hypotheses are found.

A complete analysis of the type described would undoubtedly be very slow and cumbersome. Part of the complex problem breakdown would be a study of how steps might be shortened. For example, if the hypotheses were examined originally, certain paths in the tree might be "cut off," since following them would lead to dead ends without matching hypotheses. At the very least, the programming job is complex, and the execution of the program is lengthy and involves many decisions.

Game Playing

Every game of skill is ideally played according to a set of rules. Players use strategy to guide their choices of moves or actions; the strategy depends on the conditions existing at a given time. Because of the discrete nature of most games, a computer can be programmed to play them.

The difficulty in computer game playing is programming the computer to play well, that is, to use a good strategy. Games that have simple theories and strategies, such as Tic-Tac-Toe and Nim, can be programmed without much trouble. A program for Nim is given in this section.

Chess strategy is so complex, if played optimally or nearly so, that computers that play it require large storage and a great deal of time. Each board situation has at least one optimal move (a move that maximizes the chance of winning for a player). At the same time, there are billions of board situations. Since it is impossible to learn all the optimum moves, a player classifies situations in some manner and attempts to optimize his move for each class. To do this, he looks ahead several moves and notes other moves and countermoves and their consequences.[3]

Computer programs generally follow this strategy. They look ahead a few moves (from two to four, usually) and evaluate each possible sequence of moves. A tree-like structure is built up, as in the theorem-proving problem. Since branching is so broad, even three moves may yield thousands of paths. From the possible paths the best is chosen. There are other considerations also: all pieces in danger must be moved, and if a chance occurs to capture an opponent's piece safely, it must be considered.

Because the possibilities for moves are numerous, it is important that some branching be rejected before all its paths are traced. An experienced player does this; he rejects some moves because they seem intuitively bad. It is difficult to state in precise terms the reasoning behind the rejection or acceptance of moves; for that reason, programming a good chess strategy is a formidable task.

Nim

The game of Nim is played as follows. Any number of groups of coins (or other objects), with any number of coins in each group, comprise the starting situation. Two players alternate taking turns; in each turn any number of coins may be removed from one group and one group only. The player who removes

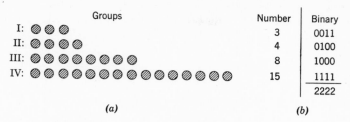

	Groups	Number	Binary
I:		3	0011
II:		4	0100
III:		8	1000
IV:		15	1111
			2222

(a)   (b)

Fig. 15.4.   A Nim position.

the last coin wins.   (The opposite game may be played: the player who removes
the last coin loses.)

Every position (specific distribution of coins in groups) can be called "odd"
or "even."   If a player, after making a move, leaves an even position, he is
guaranteed a win if he makes no errors, no matter what his opponent does.

A given position can be easily checked for evenness or oddness if the binary
number system is used.   The number of coins in each group is written in binary
form, and each column is considered separately.   If there is an even number of
1's in *each* column (zero is counted as even), the position is even.   If there is at
least one column with an odd number of 1's, the position is odd.[4]   The groups
in Fig. 15.4a are counted in binary form in Fig. 15.4b, and the column counts
show that the position is even.

If a player is faced with an odd position, he can always create an even position (and so is assured a win).   If a player is faced with an even position, he is
forced into creating an odd position by his move, and must rely on a slip by his
opponent, if he is to win.   The player's only choice is to make a "random"
move.   The situation is flowcharted in Fig. 15.5.

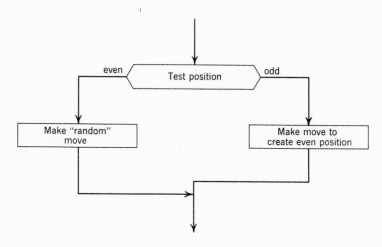

Fig. 15.5.   Flowchart of a move in Nim.

Consider the position in Fig. 15.4, with counts of 3, 4, 8, and 15. Assume play starts with A and proceeds as shown in Table 15.1. Each move by A is countered by one for B that creates a new even position. By writing out each position in binary form, the reader can check the moves.

TABLE 15.1 NIM MOVES

Player A	Player B	Position after B Moves
6 from group III	10 from group IV	3, 4, 2, 5
3 from group II	5 from group IV	3, 1, 2, 0
1 from group I	1 from group II	2, 0, 2, 0
2 from group I	2 from group III	0, 0, 0, 0

The rule for making a move to create a new even position from an odd position is the following. Determine those columns (when the counts are in binary form) that have odd numbers of 1's; they require change. All changes in columns must occur within one row, since only one group of coins can be changed. Therefore a row must be altered by changing the bits in the designated columns: 0's must be changed to 1's, and 1's must be changed to 0's. Only those rows having a 1 in the leftmost column requiring change can be altered.*

Consider the situations in Fig. 15.6, which illustrates proper moves. In position I the two rightmost columns require change. Only the fifth row, with a count of 14, has a 1 in the second column from the right. In position II two columns require change. Three rows have 1's in the leftmost of these columns,

```
Position I:  │ Move │ Result
   1   0001   │      │  0001
   4   0100   │      │  0100
   5   0101   │      │  0101
  13   1101   │      │  1101
  14   1110   │  -1  │  1101
       ────   │      │  ────
       2413   │      │  2404
        ↑↑
```

```
Position II:  │ Move │ Result │ Move │ Result │ Move │ Result
              │  A   │        │  B   │        │  C   │
   1   0001   │      │  0001  │      │  0001  │      │  0001
   4   0100   │  -3  │  0001  │      │  0100  │      │  0100
   7   0111   │      │  0111  │  -5  │  0010  │      │  0111
   9   1001   │      │  1001  │      │  1001  │      │  1001
  14   1110   │      │  1110  │      │  1110  │  -3  │  1011
       ────   │      │  ────  │      │  ────  │      │  ────
       2323   │      │  2224  │      │  2222  │      │  2224
        ↑ ↑
```

Fig. 15.6. Moves in Nim.

---

* The proof is left to the reader; see Problem 15.6.

the third column from the right. The three possible moves (A, B, and C) are shown.

What about the number of coins to be removed from the selected group? To determine the new count in that group, write down the original count in binary. Change the bits in the columns requiring changing (that is, change the 0's to 1's, and vice versa). The modified number is the new count. The difference between the old and new counts is the number of coins to be removed. As an example, consider position II in Fig 15.6. The second row is

$$0 \quad 1 \quad 0 \quad 0$$

Since the first and third columns from the right are to be changed, these bits are altered to produce the following new count:

$$0 \quad 0 \quad 0 \quad 1$$

This number, 1, when subtracted from the original count, 4, yields 3, the number to be removed.

To illustrate additional nonnumerical coding techniques a move in Nim is coded. An analysis of one move was made already, and is summarized here.

1. Add the 1's in each column of the binary counts of the rows.
2. Determine which columns have an odd number of 1's.
3. Determine those rows having 1's in the leftmost column requiring change.
4. Determine the new count by modifying the bits in those columns requiring change.

To simplify the coding, the first row tested that meets the requirement in step 3 will be altered.

A logical instruction that is useful here is described. In Section 15.1 the "logical not" instruction was mentioned; it is now introduced as a DELTA 63 instruction.

COMPLEMENT ACCUMULATOR (CØMPL) (40). Every bit of the accumulator that is 1 is changed to 0, and every bit that is 0 is changed to 1. The sign is also changed.

Example 15.4* Write a program to make a Nim move; if the position presented is even, make a "random" move by removing one coin from the first nonzero group; if the position presented is odd, make a move to create an even position.

A large range of positions will be accepted; up to 35 bits may be present in each count (that is, $2^{35} - 1$ is the maximum count), and up to 1000 groups of coins may be present. Although these limits are extraordinarily high, coding this case is no more difficult than coding a 5-group game with count limits of 20.

The counts are present in the block starting at CØUNTS; the number of groups (n) is located in GRPNUM. The counts are stored internally in binary form, which makes a good deal of the coding simple. CØLUMN is used to indicate the columns requiring

---

* The reader may skip the coding of this problem with no loss in continuity.

change; each bit position corresponds to one column, and 1 indicates a change. LEFCØL is used to indicate the leftmost column requiring change.

The program is coded in several stages. In the first stage steps 1 and 2 (listed earlier) are coded. To add the 1's in each column, a list is required of the counts with all bits masked out execpt the column of interest. That list is added and an odd count indicates the column requires change.

The first stage is flowcharted in Fig. 15.7. There are two inner loops within an outer loop, although only one inner loop is drawn. The first inner loop forms the masked list; index j refers to the group number. For a given column, all the entries in that column of all the rows are stored in the block at MCØUNT. There are n rows. The second inner loop sums the entries in MCØUNT and thereby determines the number of 1's in the ith column.

After the number of 1's is determined, it is necessary to determine whether it is odd or even. This is most easily done by shifting the number 35 bit positions to the left, placing the bit in position 35 in the sign of the AC. If the number is odd, the AC sign becomes negative; if the number is even, the AC sign remains positive. The JUMPPL instruction is used to separate the cases. If the number is odd, a 1 is stored in the proper bit position in CØLUMN. For this stage, a table of 35 words (BITS1), each containing a 1-bit in a different position, is used. In the flowchart, m_i is the ith mask (a single 1 bit), and c_j is the jth masked count.

Location	Oper.	Var. Field	
	SETXRI	35,2	1 TØ I
NEXCØL	CLEARS	CØLUMN	
	LØADMK	BITS1,2	M(1) TØ MASK REGISTER
	SETXR	GRPNUM,1	1 TØ J
NEXRØW	LØAD$	CØUNTS,1	C(J) TØ MCØUNT(J)
	STØRE	MCØUNT,1	
	INCRXM	1,1	J+1 TØ J
	XJUMP	NEXRØW,1	
	SETXRI	GRPNUM,1	FØRM SUM ØF "1"S IN
	LØAD	ZERØ	1-TH CØL.
	ADD	MCØUNT,1	
	INCRXM	1,1	
	XJUMP	*-2,1	
	LSHIFT	35	SHIFT BIT 35 TØ SIGN
	JUMPPL	EVEN	JUMP IF EVEN NUMBER
	LØAD	BITS1,2	
	ADD	CØLUMN	M(1) ADDED TØ "CØLUMN"
	STØRE	CØLUMN	
EVEN	INCRXM	1,2	
	XJUMP	NEXCØL,2	I+1 TØ I
	•••	•••••	
BITS1	ØCTAL	000000000001	"1" IN BIT 35
	ØCTAL	000000000002	"1" IN BIT 34
	ØCTAL	000000000004	"1" IN BIT 33
	ØCTAL	000000000010	"1" IN BIT 32
	•••	•••••	

At the end of the first stage, the columns requiring changing are indicated by 1's in CØLUMN. The second stage consists of the coding for step 3 and contains two parts—3a: determination of the leftmost column to be changed, and 3b: determination

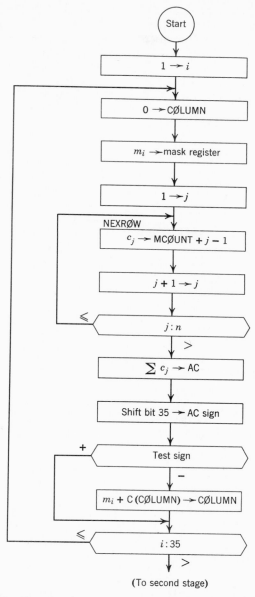

Fig. 15.7. Flowchart of first stage of Nim problem (Example 15.4).

of the first row with a 1 in that column. To code 3a, the C(CØLUMN) are placed in the AC and are shifted left 1 bit position at a time, until the sign of the AC becomes minus. At that point, a 1 has been shifted into it. XR1 is used for loop control and the $C(XR1)_m$ at the time the AC first becomes negative "points" to the leftmost column. If

the pointer is then used to select a word with a 1-bit in the proper position, that column
can be identified in LEFCØL. For example, if the AC changes sign after 20 shifts, the
leftmost 1 must have originally been located in bit 20. The table of single 1-bits required
is located in the block at BITS2. Step 3a is coded here; step 3b is coded below.

Provision is made here for the even position possibility shown in Fig. 15.4; if the loop
is cycled 35 times and the AC sign is never set minus, then no 1's are present and
no columns require change.

Location	Oper.	Var. Field	
	SETXRI	35,1	
	LØAD	CØLUMN	
SHIFT	LSHIFT	1	SHIFT 1 BIT PØSITIØN
	JUMPMI	LEFTC	JUMP AT LEFTMØST "1"
	INCRXM	1,1	
	XJUMP	SHIFT,1	
	JUMP	EVEN	NØ CØLUMNS NEED CHANGING
LEFTC	LØAD	BITS2,1	FETCH PRØPER BIT
	STØRE	LEFCØL	
	• • •	• • • • •	
BITS2	ØCTAL	200000000000	"1" IN BIT 1
	ØCTAL	100000000000	"1" IN BIT 2
	ØCTAL	040000000000	"1" IN BIT 3
	• • •	• • • • •	

To code step 3b, each row count is checked to see if it has a 1 in the bit identified in
LEFCØL. This is done by loading each count into the AC with the C(LEFCØL) in the
mask register. When a nonzero word is first placed in the AC, the first such row count
has been identified. Again, the index register "points" to the particular row count.

Location	Oper.	Var. Field	
	SETXR	GRPNUM,1	
	LØADMK	LEFCØL	PUT "LEFCØL" BIT IN MASK REG.
GETBIT	LØAD$	CØUNTS,1	CHECK ØNE BIT ØF EACH CØUNT
	JUMPNZ	FØUND	
	INCRXM	1,1	
	XJUMP	GETBIT,1	
FØUND	• • •	• • • • •	XR1 STILL PØINTS TØ CØUNT
			TØ BE MØDIFIED

In the third stage step 4 is coded. Here the number of coins to be removed from the
selected row must be determined. This involves a sequence of operations on the bits of
CØLUMN (containing 1's where columns are to be changed) and a word from the
CØUNTS block, selected by the XR1 pointer.

Oper.	Var. Field
LØADMK	CØLUMN
LØAD	CØUNTS,1
CØMPL	

(Continued)

```
STØRE$    TEMP
LØADMK    CØUNTS,1
LØAD      CØLUMN
CØMPL
STØRE$    TEMP+1
LØAD      TEMP
ACD       TEMP+1
STØ       CØUNTS,1
JUMP      PRINT
```

PRINT is a routine that prints the counts after the program has calculated the move. If the computer is to play against a man, it must inform him of its move. Somehow, then, the man must inform the computer of his move. This might be done by feeding in new data cards each time with the new counts; these counts would then be stored in the block at CØUNTS and control would go to the start of the program.

One other routine is needed; in the event that the program finds an even position, it is to make a "random" move: remove one coin from the first nonzero group.

Location	Oper.	Var. Field		
EVEN	SETXR	GRPNUM,1		
	LØAD	CØUNTS,1	TEST 1 CØUNT	
	JUMPNZ	EVEN1	JUMP AT 1ST NØNZERØ CØUNT	
	INCRXM	1,1		
	XJUMP	EVEN+1,1		
	JUMP	ALLDØN	JUMP IF ALL ARE 0, GAME ØVER	
EVEN1	SUBT	ØNE	SUBT ØNE FRØM CØUNT	
	STØRE	CØUNTS,1		
	JUMP	PRINT		
	•••	•••••		
ØNE	DECML	1		

ALLDØN is a routine that prints an appropriate comment.

Other Areas of Interest

An area that has received a great deal of attention and programming effort is the translation of languages by the computer.[5] At least one compiler language has been written for this purpose and has received wide recognition. The language is COMIT, written at M.I.T.; it is useful in symbol manipulation problems in general, although a number of its characteristics are well suited for language translation problems.

The recognition of patterns by computers is also being studied intensively.[6] At present, digits and letters written by hand can be identified by a computer. The computer traces the shapes, noting loops, cross points, curves, etc., and examines an internal listing of features of all characters. It is hoped that this work will lead to ready identification of fingerprints and photographs.

15.3 LISTS

What Are Lists?

Computer memory is usually numbered serially, starting with 0. Both program execution and the indexing of quantities proceed in sequence through memory in a random-access computer. As a result, it is frequently convenient to think of memory as a linear tabulation of instructions, constants, and data.

The structure of a number of problems, however, does not follow this linear format. For this reason, methods that utilize storage in a nonlinear manner have been developed; memory is considered to be structured either in a multi-dimensional or in a tree-like form.

The following example illustrates the difficulties of a linear memory. Consider the evaluation of a string of symbols and arithmetic operators:

$$\texttt{(NAME-LIST/WØRD)+ABC}$$

The evaluation might be performed by first unpacking the individual parts of the expression, as in Example 15.1. The individual parts, the symbols and the operators, are called *tokens;* in this expression there are nine tokens: (, NAME, −, . . . , and ABC. By the rules of arithmetic the division operation is to be performed first. Next, the subexpression LIST/WØRD must be replaced by its equivalence. If the nine tokens were originally stored in successive words in memory, it then becomes necessary to move part of the list up so that the tokens remaining are in sequence in adjacent locations.

Nonnumerical problems generally have complex structures with widely varying storage requirements. A method of dynamic storage allocation is needed to provide space for computation as it is needed during the execution of the program.

Lists (or *list structures*) have been developed to solve the problems created by trying to fit a complex structure into a linear memory. A list may be defined as an ordered set of tokens, connected in a structure such that at least one successor to each token can be identified. In some list structures predecessors of tokens can be similarly identified. A simple example of a list is an ordered set of integers. The successor of one integer is the "next larger" integer. A more complex example is offered by the tree drawn in Fig. 15.3, showing interrelation between geometric statements.

Example of a List

Coding languages have been developed for the convenient use of lists.[7] In these languages specialized list structures are used. A list is considered to be a set of memory words, interconnected in some manner. For example, the ad-

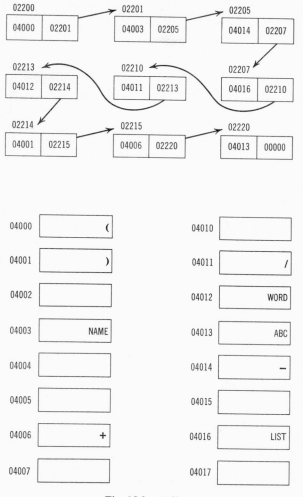

Fig. 15.8.   A list.

dress of each word may be stored in the word that precedes it in the list.   Each word in the list may contain two addresses; one is the address of the item that belongs at that point, and the other is the address of the next word in the list. The latter address is a *pointer* address.   Figure 15.8 illustrates the structure.   The numbers outside the boxes are location addresses for the boxes.   The list tokens indicated comprise the symbolic expression given earlier.   Note that the order of the tokens is given by the pointer addresses; the tokens need not be listed in memory in sequence.   The pointer address 00000 signals the end of the list.

With a list structure, the insertion or deletion of tokens is relatively simple. For example, to insert the subexpression +DIGIT immediately after NAME in

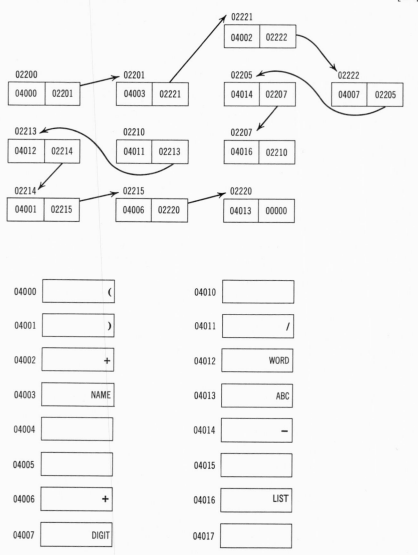

Fig. 15.9.   Modified list.

the expression in Fig. 15.8, the pointers are modified as shown in Fig. 15.9. Two words were added to the list; only one pointer already in the list was changed (from 02205 to 02221), and everything else in the list was unchanged. Two tokens were added to the block at 04000.   Deletion of tokens is also simple; pointers are modified, and nothing else is done.   There will be extraneous information in words that were once part of the list, but since pointers bypass those words, no reference is made to them.

As lists are processed, many are replaced by others or are for some reason of no further use. If the space taken by such lists is never again used, the available space within the computer may eventually be depleted. The words no longer needed are scattered all over memory, and a means is required for determining where they are. This is accomplished by forming a list of available space. In this list each word points to a successor and to an available word. This list has the same structure as the list described. If the scheme is to function properly, each list operation must supply to the available-space list those words made free by the operation. Thus at any time all free space is linked into one list. The programmer is free of worry over the space.

Other Types of Lists

A more complex list structure is illustrated by the symbolic expression

$$((NAME-LIST/WØRD)+ABC)*(X1*X2+X3/X4)$$

A special type of list, drawn in Fig. 15.10, is developed for algebraic expressions. There are two types of list words. One type contains three items: two pointers, each to other words in the list, and an operation code. Thus each word provides a binary branching of the list, so that a tree can be built up. The

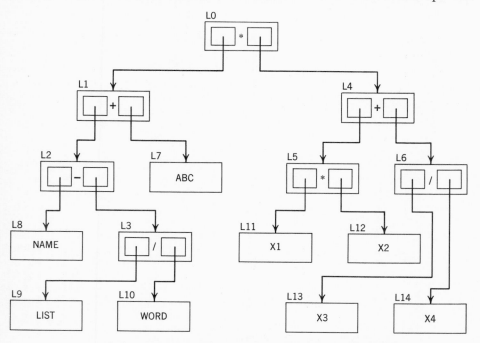

Fig. 15.10. Special list structure for algebraic expressions.

other type contains a token. Token words have special marks for identification.
A coding sequence to establish the list structure in memory is given in the next
example. A convention in symbolic language is described first.

If the operation field in a symbolic instruction is left *blank* and three subfields are
given in the variable field, the contents of the assembled word is apportioned as follows:

Subfield	Machine Word Portion
Address	Bits 21–35
Tag	Bits 18–20
Third field	Bits S, 1–14

This convention permits a 15-bit field to be assembled in the leftmost portion of a word.
Compare this convention to that described in Section 8.1; in that one the third variable-
field subfield assembled into only 6 bits. As examples, consider the following:

Machine Word	Symbolic Instruction	
0 01 0001 22236	LØAD	A,1
0 57 1000 01135	READC	NUMBER,,8
22103 04 22133		LIST,4,NAME

The spacing of the machine word in the last case is slightly different to reflect the inclusion of two 15-bit fields.

Example 15.5 Develop a list structure for Fig. 15.10. The following conventions are
used with list words.

1. In list words with three fields, the leftmost and rightmost 15-bit fields will each contain a pointer to two words; these words are the operands of an operator. The tag will
be used to contain the associated operator, as follows:

Operation	Tag
Addition	1
Subtraction	2
Multiplication	3
Division	4

2. In token words the tag 7 will be used. The address field will be used to contain the
equivalence of the token.

The tree structure shown in Fig. 15.10 makes parentheses unnecessary; none is stored
as a token in the list. The following listing is labeled to match Fig. 15.10. Equivalences
are assumed for each of the symbols: NAME, LIST, WØRD, ABC, X1, X2, X3, and X4.

Location	Contents	Location	Oper.	Var. Field
01000	01004 03 01001	L0		L1,3,L4
01001	01007 01 01002	L1		L2,1,L7

(Continued)

```
01002   01003 02 01010        L2          L8,2,L3
01003   01012 04 01011        L3          L9,4,L10
01004   01006 01 01005        L4          L5,1,L6
01005   01014 03 01013        L5          L11,3,L12
01006   01016 04 01015        L6          L13,4,L14
01007   00000 07 00115        L7          ABC,7
01010   00000 07 00400        L8          NAME,7
01011   00000 07 42000        L9          LIST,7
01012   00000 07 00221        L10         WØRD,7
01013   00000 07 03300        L11         X1,7
01014   0C000 07 03301        L12         X2,7
01015   00000 07 03305        L13         X3,7
01016   00000 07 03310        L14         X4,7
```

In this list structure it should be noted that the actual locations of the several words are irrelevant, as long as the pointers are correct in order to link the words. Any available locations in memory may be used for the pointers and the operands, as long as the structure is as indicated in Fig. 15.10, where no reference is made to memory words. The list-processing program that will analyze this list likewise must be coded to be independent of memory locations. All that the program must have as information is the start of the list, location L0.

Although a structure of the type in Example 15.5 lends itself to ready analysis, it has a decided disadvantage in that this list must be created from the original expression. A synthesis procedure is therefore also required. The synthesis approach is time consuming and wasteful, unless it is feasible to provide the data to the program in the form that appears in that example. That form, however, is so dissimilar to the original-expression form that it is unreasonable to supply it in that manner.

One other list structure will be considered. In this structure the expression to be evaluated may be placed in its original form in memory. With each token in this list structure is associated a pair of pointers, a "backward" and a "forward" pointer. These point, respectively, to the preceding and following tokens. Figure 15.11 shows the structure for the expression considered earlier:

$$(NAME-LIST/WØRD)+ABC$$

As the expression is evaluated in the usual manner, the division subexpression (LIST/WØRD) is replaced by its equivalence. The resulting structure is shown in Fig. 15.12; X represents the equivalence of the triplet. In order to

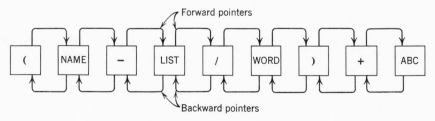

Fig. 15.11. Double-pointer list structure.

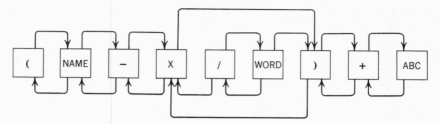

Fig. 15.12.   List structure with a deletion.

effect this change, it is necessary only to modify two pointers after making the substitution.   Here the substitution is made by replacing the first token of the triplet with the triplet equivalence.

With the changes shown, the token following X is).   The fact that tokens intervene physically is irrelevant since the following token is *defined* as the one pointed to by the forward pointer; the preceding token is similarly defined.   The pointers from the deleted tokens (/ and WORD) are ignored, since the program will never refer to them once the change is accomplished.   Succeeding operations are performed in a similar manner, and the expression is thus evaluated.

In processing a list it is necessary to be able to sequence from one token to the next.   In the examples studied in earlier chapters, processing of data generally proceeded in a sequential manner and was a simple matter.   In the list structures described here, processing proceeds by means of pointers in a manner that is generally not sequential.

In processing lists several operations that are frequently performed can be identified.   A *sublist* is a useful concept in this context; it is a contiguous portion of a list or a separate list that is to become part of another list.   The following operations can be identified.

1. *Deleting a sublist within a list.*   Examples of deletions have been given.

2. *Inserting a sublist.*   It is possible to replace a single token with a sublist. Alternately, a sublist may be inserted between two tokens in the list.

3. *Branching of a list.*   Although branching within a list has not been discussed, it is nonetheless a useful operation.   Often a list branches at a point (as in Fig. 15.10), and operations to effect the branching are required.

4. *Searching for a token.*   This operation consists of searching through a list for a specified token and noting the address of the token.   Alternately, the addresses of *all* appearances of the token might be required.

5. *Substituting for a token.*   This operation consists of substituting a given sublist for all appearances of a specified token.

15.4 TABLE-LOOK-AT TECHNIQUES

The Method

The table-look-at technique is described briefly in Section 8.3, where it is described as a nonloop use of index registers. Now it is studied further and considered as a technique in the manipulation of data.

A fairly common problem in programming is the *mapping* of one set of integers into another set. Mapping can be considered as the evaluation of an integer function, that is, a function whose arguments and values are integers. The table-look-at technique effects a mapping in a simple and rapid manner, involving a single reference or "look" at a table. Mapping is said to occur *from* an integer, termed the *argument, to* an integer, termed the *image*. The sets of arguments and images are termed the *domain* and the *range,* respectively. If the process is viewed as function evaluation, the image is the value of the function for a given argument.

The basis of the table-look-at procedure consists of two operations:

1. Placement of the argument into an index register.
2. Operation on the contents of the effective address, determined by that index register.

The direct address of the instruction is the start of a table, the entries of which represent the range of images. We may consider the mapping as an evaluation of an integer function:

$$y = f(x_0 + x)$$

Here x is the argument, x_0 is the direct address, and y is the image.

The integer function which is evaluated need not be analytic. It need only be representable as an ordered list of numbers, one number stored per memory word. Because the list of arguments is stored in this manner, the table-look-at method is limited to those mappings where the argument domain does not exceed memory size. For example, it may not exceed 32768 in the DELTA 63. Actually, the limit is lower than this, because some memory space is required for the program and, possibly, for the monitor.

Integer Conversion

A common problem is that of converting each integer of a given set into another integer, either in a one-to-one or a many-to-one transformation. Two examples are (1) the classification of integers by the assignment of class numbers to each, and (2) the evaluation of a nonanalytic function, a function that is not expressable as a formula. These examples are considered in turn.

Example 15.6   Let a block of integers n_i ($1 \leqslant n_i \leqslant N_0$ for $i = 1, 2, 3, \ldots, k$) be located starting at BLØCK. It is desired to classify them by assigning a class number c_i to each. To perform this classification, the integer n_i (the argument) is placed in XR2 and the number c_i, located in the n_ith word from TABLE, is fetched. This number is stored in the n_ith position of a parallel table, CLASS.*

Location	Oper.	Var. Field	
	SETXR	K,1	
ARG	LØAD	BLØCK,1	ØBTAIN ARGUMENT
	PADDXM	0,2	PLACE IN XR2
	LØAD	TABLE,2	FETCH CLASS NUMBER
	STØRE	CLASS,1	STØRE IN NEW TABLE
	LØØPXR	ARG,1,1	

In this problem the argument domain is N_0 in size and a table (TABLE) of that size contains the numbers c_i. These numbers cover the image range. A limitation to this method is the maximum size of N_0 permitted, since a table of that size is required.

Pattern Detection

The problem of detecting and counting all appearances of a specified set of bit patterns in a block of words is considered here. For example, suppose each word contains nine 4-bit bites, packed so that they occupy contiguous positions. It might be necessary to count all appearances of bites 1011 and 0110 in the words. Or perhaps all strings of 1-bits at least thirteen long have to be counted, where the strings are considered to run from word to word. Many of these jobs can be quickly accomplished using the table-look-at technique.

Example 15.7   Count all appearances of bites 1011 and 0110 in the block of k words starting at PATTRN, and place these counts in CNTR1 and CNTR2, respectively. Consider each word to consist of nine 4-bit bites.

The arguments are numbers from 0 to 15 inclusive; these are the decimal numbers represented by the 16 possible bites. A transfer of control is made to one address in a 16-word table, depending on the argument. In all but two of these locations, a jump is made immediately back to the main routine. In the other two, jumps are made to counting routines, after the execution of which control is returned to the main routine.

Location	Oper.	Var. Field	
	SETXR	K,1	
LØØP1	LØADM	PATTRN,1	PUT A WØRD IN MR
		(Continued)	

* LØØPXR is a macro-instruction, defined in Section 17.2 (page 365). It is used here because of its utility in loop control. It combines the functions of the INCRXM and XJUMP instructions.

```
              SETXRI   9,2
      LØØP2   LØAD     ZERØ                CLEAR AC
              RØTATE   4                   PUT 1 BITE IN AC, XR3
              PADDXM   0,3
              JUMP     TABLE,3
      ØUT     LØØPXR   LØØP2,2,1
              LØØPXR   LØØP1,1,1
```

Fourteen of the 16 instructions in the block at TABLE are:

```
      JUMP       ØUT
```

These correspond to the 14 bites that are not processed. The other two instructions are

```
      JUMP     CØUNT1
```

```
      JUMP     CØUNT2
```

which occupy the seventh and twelfth words in the block, corresponding to the two patterns to be processed.

The routine at CØUNT1 is

```
CØUNT1   LØAD     CNTR1              ADD 1 TØ CØUNT
         ADD      ØNE
         STØRE    CNTR1
         JUMP     ØUT
```

The routine at COUNT2 is similar.

If we wish to speed up the bite-counting process, we can do so, at the expense of space. In Example 15.7, for instance, two bites at a time can be processed. The 8-bit bite

$$10110110$$

can cause a jump to a routine that increases both counters by 1, and the bite

$$01100110$$

can cause a jump to a routine that increases the second counter by 2. The technique is the same, except that a table of 256 words is required. The time to process a given number of words is half the time needed in Example 15.7. This is another example of the space-time balance in coding.

Another example of the last-mentioned approach is provided by the problem of counting the number of 1-bits in a word. Bites of 2, 3, 4, 6, or 9 bits may be processed simultaneously, with a single counter used. The mapping here is from the integer represented by the bite to the integer that is the number of 1-bits present in the bite. For example, if the bite is 110010, the count is 3. Tables that are 4, 8, 16, 64, and 512 words in size respectively are needed for the bite sizes indicated. The speed of processing is inversely proportional to the bite size.

Ordering Integers

A method for ordering (sorting) a set of integers into ascending sequence is described here. The method has limited application because a block whose size is equal to the range is required, and duplicated integers are not taken into account.

Example 15.8   A block of integers n_i ($1 \leqslant n_i \leqslant N$ for $i = 1, 2, \ldots, k$), located in a block starting at NUMBRS, is to be ordered and placed in another block starting at LIST. This is done by "reserving" in the latter a location for each integer, the location being located n_i words from LIST. Storage of an integer in LIST is effected by a STØRE instruction whose effective address is determined by the integer itself. If the block LIST is initially cleared, the k numbers will be ordered with empty words interspersed according to nonexisting values. A routine for "squeezing out" the zeros is then required.

Location	Oper.	Var. Field	
	SETXR	K,1	
LØØP1	LØAD	BLØCK,1	FETCH INTEGER
	PADDXM	0,2	STØRE IN XR2
	STØRE	LIST,2	STØRE IN "LIST"
	LØØPXR	LØØP1,1,1	

This loop constitutes the integer-ordering process. Note, for instance, that the number 45 is stored in LIST+45, 873 in LIST+873, etc. The zero-removing routine is the following:

Location	Oper.	Var. Field	
	SETXR	N,1	
	SETXR	N,2	
LØØP2	LØAD	LIST,1	FETCH NUMBER
	JUMPZE	*+3	
	STØRE	LIST,2	MØVE IT IF NØNZERØ
	INCRXM	1,2	
	LØØPXR	LØØP2,1,1	

The two XR's act as pointers here; XR1 also serves for loop control. XR1 points to the number being tested; XR2 points to the next available location for its final position. The presence of a zero (indicating a missing value) leaves XR2 unchanged, so that each nonzero number is stored in a successive position in the list. A count of the number of entries in LIST is given at the end by the $C(XR2)_m$.

A few comments on the time of this routine are appropriate. Approximately $7k + 4N_0$ instructions are executed. If the integers are sparsely distributed over the range, the process is slower (per integer to be ordered) than if they are densely distributed. This is true because time is wasted processing zeros. If the "density" is defined as k/N_0, the time per integer (in number of instructions) is given in this table.

Density (k/N_0)	1.0	0.5	0.25	0.1	0.05
Instrs./integer	11	15	23	47	87

It should be noted that the time per integer is independent of the number of integers, for a given integer density.

The sorting method described here is much faster than standard techniques (described in Section 16.2). It has the limitation mentioned earlier, however, that the range of integers cannot exceed memory size.

General Remarks

The table-look-at technique is useful when speed is the most important factor and the required room can be spared. The programmer, in determining the size of the tables he has room for, must strike a compromise in the time-space balance.

Summary

Nonnumerical problems require a wide variety of operations to be performed in their solution. This requirement is due primarily to the complex algorithms that must be developed for their solution. Among the operations studied in this chapter are analyzing a variable format structure, searching a table in order to code symbols into numbers, masking a portion of a word, determining the leftmost 1-bit of the accumulator, classifying integers, and detecting specified bit patterns. The variety of these operations characterizes the nature of nonnumerical problems. It serves to explain why writing down a sequence of formulas does not usually help in the solution of these problems.[8]

In order to realize these operations, some specialized techniques have been developed. Two of these, list structures and processing and table-look-at techniques, have been described. Lists find widespread use in many areas, such as language translation. Table-look-at techniques provide rapid processing of special operations.

Notes

1. The following book contains a chapter on logic and Boolean algebra as applied to computers.

I. Flores, *Computer Logic: the Functional Design of Digital Computers,* Prentice-Hall, 1960, Chapter 9.

2. The following paper describes a geometry-theorem-proving program.

H. Gelernter, J. R. Hansen, and D. W. Coveland, "Empirical Explorations of the Geometry Theorem Machine," *Proc. Western Joint Computer Conference,* May 1960, pp. 143–150.

3. The following papers describe chess playing by computers.

C. E. Shannon, "Programming a Computer for Playing Chess," *Phil. Mag.,* **41** (1950), pp. 256–275.

A. L. Samuel, "Programming Computers to Play Games," in *Advances in Computers,* Vol. 1 (ed. by F. Alt), Academic Press, 1960, pp. 165–192.

4. A proof of the binary method for Nim is given in

C. L. Bouton, "Nim, a Game with a Complete Mathematical Strategy," *Ann. Math.,* series 2, **3** (1901–2), pp. 35–39.

5. The following paper discusses computer language translation.

Y. Bar-Hillel, "The Present Status of Automatic Translation of Languages," in *Advances in Computers,* Vol. 1 (ed. by F. Alt), Academic Press, 1960, pp. 91–163.

6. A recent paper on pattern recognition is the following.

W. H. Highleyman, "Linear Decision Functions, with Application to Pattern Recognition," *Proc. IRE,* **50** (1962), pp. 1501–1514.

7. The following references describe languages developed for list processing; the second reference includes an extensive introduction to lists.

J. McCarthy, "Recursive Functions of Symbolic Expressions and their Computations by Machine, Part I," *Comm. Assoc. Computing Machinery,* **4** (April 1960), pp. 184–195.
A. Newell (ed.), *Information Processing Language—V,* Prentice-Hall, 1961.

8. A paper on languages used for nonnumerical problems is the following.

B. F. Green, Jr., "Computer Languages for Symbol Manipulation," *Trans, IRE,* **EC-10** (1961), pp. 729–735.

The following issue is devoted to symbol manipulation problems.

Comm. Assoc. Computing Machinery, April 1960.

PROBLEMS

Section 15.1

15.1.   Write a program to realize the parentheses algorithm of Problem 14.1.   The program should match and sort parentheses pairs.   Include a check for the erroneous use of parentheses, such as an unequal number of left and right parentheses or more right parentheses than left parentheses up to a given point, as in the following: $((\dots) \dots) \dots) \dots$

15.2.   Write a program for a compiler that checks algebraic expressions to see if they are mathematically meaningful.   Restrict expressions analyzed to 12 characters or less, and limit variables (symbols) to 1 character each.   Consider such errors as improper use of parentheses (see Problem 15.1), adjacent operators, and unfinished expressions.   Examples of legal expressions:

$$A + (B*C/D) \qquad (A+2)/(A-2)$$

Examples of illegal expressions:

$$A*/B+2 \qquad B-C-D-$$

15.3.   The odd-numbered bits in the 100-word block at BITS are to be packed into the 50-word block at PACKED in the following way: the odd bits from BITS through BITS + 49 are to be squeezed to the right to fill bits 18–35 of PACKED through

PACKED + 49; the odd bits from BITS + 50 through BITS + 99 are to be squeezed left to fill bits S and 1–17 of PACKED through PACKED + 49. Write a program to accomplish this process.

15.4.   The DELTA 63 monitor requires a scanning program to analyze format statements in order to provide the proper output on tape. Write a program to accomplish this, using the format conventions of Section 11.2 and the instructions and conventions of Section 7.2.

Section 15.2

15.5.   Write a program that, given a Tic-Tac-Toe "board situation," makes an optimum move, one that will not lead to a loss.

15.6.   Prove the statement in the text (page 306) concerning the game of Nim.

15.7.   A square is drawn and its corners are labeled, in sequence around the perimeter, 1, 2, 3, and 4. Its two diagonals are drawn and their intersection is labeled 5. Write a program that will determine whether a given ordered set of 3 integers from the total set (1, 2, 3, 4, 5) forms a connected path in the figure without passing through unnamed points. For example, 1-2-5 represents a connected path, but 1-3-4 does not.

15.8.   A regular hexagon is drawn and its vertices are labeled, in sequence around the perimeter, 1, 2, 3, 4, 5, and 6. Its 3 diagonals are drawn and their intersection is labeled 7. Write a program that will determine whether a given ordered set of 3 or 4 integers from the total set forms a connected path without passing through unnamed points.

15.9.   Flowchart a checkers-playing program.

15.10. Flowchart a bridge-bidding program. The "input" to the program is one hand of 13 cards and the sequence of bids up to the computer's hand. After each bid by the computer, the other 3 bids are to be made, also by the computer, on a random basis that is consistent with the computer's hand and previous bidding.

15.11. Program a Chinese-checkers game player.

15.12. Given 2 English words, each containing no repeated letters and each having any number of letters up to and including 12, determine how many letters in any positions they have in common. Write a program for this purpose. The words, which may fill two adjacent computer words each, are stored so that they are pushed to the left of the "leftmost" word; unused bits are filled with alphanumeric blanks.

15.13. Given 5000 English words, stored in 10,000 computer words in sequence starting at WØRDS, write a routine to determine

(a) the number of English words with exactly one or two vowels;

(b) the number ending in E;

(c) the number having at least one repeated letter; and

(d) The number of 7-letter words.

Words are stored in a pair of computer words each, in the manner of the words of Problem 15.12.

Section 15.3

15.14. Discuss the several list structures described in the text. Under what circumstances might each be useful? In what types of programs would they each be used? Suggest other list structures.

Section 15.4

15.15. Using the table-look-at technique, write routines to

(*a*) count the number of 1's in a specified block of words;

(*b*) count the appearance of 4 consecutive 1's in a block of words, considering any bite of 4 bits;

(*c*) determine whether a computer word contains an even or an odd number of 1's;

(*d*) compute the function cos (cos *x*) using a single table.

16

DATA PROCESSING

The term *data processing* is used here to refer to problems that involve a great many data but relatively little processing per item of data. Most business problems and a number of scientific problems have these characteristics.

The emphasis in this chapter is on the operations, primarily on large files of data, that are performed in data-processing problems. Of particular interest are the operations of sorting numbers, merging lists of numbers, and searching through lists of numbers. Business and scientific problems are frequently similar in structure; however, in business problems, the major effort is on input-output operations and operations on tape files. By contrast, the major effort in scientific problems is on computation.

16.1 DATA-PROCESSING PROBLEMS

What Is Data Processing?

Data processing is considered here to refer to computation involving few operations on large amounts of data. Nevertheless, the term is used also in both a more restricted and a far broader sense. In the restricted sense, data processing refers to the gathering, recording, filing, and documenting of numbers and names associated with the task of managing a business organization. In the broad sense, it refers to all the collecting and processing of data done by people or computers.

The first definition is used in preference to the more restricted one because, from the programmer's point of view, programming techniques are more dependent on the nature of the problem—the amount of processing per number, for example—than they are on the application. There are many "scientific" problems that involve little computation per item of data.

Examples of scientific data-processing problems are the ordering of numbers, the calculation of a histogram, and the evaluation of a series of polynomials. Examples of business data-processing problems are the calculation of the payroll for a group of employees, the analysis of an inventory, and the updating of a number of charge accounts.

Business Data Processing[1]

Computers were used to help solve business problems almost from their earliest stages of development. Interest in this application was strong enough to influence computer design; today there are many large-scale computers designed for business purposes.

A business man views a computer not as a separate entity but as one of a collection of integrated units. The purpose of the whole is to permit the efficient operation of a company. The jobs of payroll, inventory, record keeping, purchasing, report preparing, advertising, selling, and billing might constitute the set of business operations in a company. The role of the computer varies among companies, but in general it serves as the central computational and storage facility. In all these operations people play the vital roles, but the computer serves to link their jobs together.

Among the operations that computers perform in business applications are the following.

1. *Recording of information.* Information may be received in many forms. To be available for machine computation, it must be uniformly stored. The information must be properly identified, it must be checked for accuracy and redundancy, and it must be coded for rapid processing by the computer.*

2. *Processing of information.* Arithmetic operations must be performed, as on a payroll, where taxes, other deductions, and take-home pay must be computed. Sorting operations must be performed so that records may be kept in some desired sequence. Updating operations must be performed so that accounts, purchases, and billing operations may be current.

3. *Preparation of reports.* The output phase of business data processing usually involves the preparation of printed reports. The term *reports* is used in a very general sense; reports may include the status of an inventory, statement of

---

* *Coding* in this chapter refers to the transformation of general information into machine numbers, not to the writing of computer instructions.

a charge or bank account, bills for services or materials, checks in payment of expenses or salaries (the latter accompanied by a statement of deductions), and lists of purchases to be made at a given time.

The three categories of operations may readily be compared with these operations: (1) reading of data, (2) computation, and (3) printing of results. These are the basic jobs of any computer problem; we have been concerned primarily with step (2), which, from a programmer's point of view, is the most important and most complex operation of the three. In business applications, however, input-output operations are probably even more important. Calculations, as we have noted, are relatively few in number. The use of intermediate tapes is also a vital phase of business data processing; it is also primarily an input-output operation.

Files[2]

A company must keep records of its various operations. Records are usually organized as *files*, which are simply ordered collections of information. They must be ordered for information to be efficiently extracted for use; without ordering, a lengthy search for particular information would be necessary.

A set of files is generally organized into *master files* and *temporary files*. Master files contain information of a permanent nature, such as names and addresses of customers or employees, policy, account, or Social Security numbers, and rates of pay. Temporary files contain information that is less permanent, such as current business transactions, new information to be filed, and hours worked by employees during the current week.

The units of information storage are the *field*, the *entry*, the *record*, and the *file*. A *field* is a group of alphanumeric characters that form one item of information, such as a name, address, an amount of money, or an account number. An *entry* is a group of related fields, such as the information on one employee for payroll purposes, a business transaction, or a set of related numbers. A *record* is a group of entries that is moved as a whole, as from tape to internal memory. This is done to minimize input-output read and write times. Finally, a *file* is a complete set of records.* Several files may be stored on one tape, but sometimes a long file is stored on two or more tapes.

General files may be classified into two general types, which correspond to internal computer memory and external tape memory: these are *random-access* and *sequential* files.

Sequential general files are more common; for this purpose, magnetic tapes are used almost exclusively. The information is stored linearly, that is, each

---

* There is ambiguity here. The word *file* refers to both a collection of records and to a collection of information in general. The latter definition is the broader one. The collection will be referred to as a *general file*.

item follows the previous one and the tape reading head must skip past all the information not to be processed. Very often information in a sequential file is ordered numerically or alphabetically, and a search for a particular record must be made.

Random-access general files have the advantage that any item can be as quickly obtained for processing as any other. It is not necessary to pass over information intervening between entries that are to be read. If information is to be added to a general file, it is easier to add it to a random-access file. It is necessary to go clear to the end of a sequential file to add new information, unless the file is reorganized.

The existence of general files in business data-processing problems serves to distinguish them from scientific data-processing problems. We have noted the overall similarity between the two areas: both involve input, computation, output, and additional storage. In scientific problems the additional storage is almost always transient; there is little need to save intermediate results, aside from debugging needs, possibly. On the other hand, the storage of information in general files in business problems is of vital importance; no business could function properly without records.

16.2 DATA-PROCESSING OPERATIONS[3]

Most operations in business data processing are concerned with general-file maintenance, the job of keeping files up to date. An operation associated with maintenance is the extraction of information as required. The list that follows summarizes some of the nonarithmetic operations involved in file maintenance and removal of file information. Scientific data processing usually is concerned with only a few of these items. The operations are:

1. *auditing* information to determine accuracy and consistency on receipt;
2. *editing* information to remove extraneous items or to modify the form for output purposes;
3. *coding* information so that it can be more readily processed by the computer;
4. *recording* information for processing or storage;
5. *verifying* a procedure for accuracy;
6. *transmitting* data from one medium to another;
7. *converting* data from one form to another;
8. *transcribing* data, transforming their medium of storage;
9. *ordering* data, arranging them in some specified sequence, such as numerically or alphabetically;*
10. *sorting* data, grouping them into separate lists, according to some characteristic;

* The term *sorting* is generally used in this sense.

11. *merging* ordered files, combining them into one file when their records have identical structures;

12. *collating* files, combining them into one file when their records have different structures;

13. *searching* files for specified entries or for entries with specified characteristics;

14. *adding* records to files;

15. *deleting* records from files;

16. *modifying* information on files;

17. *checking* information in files.

In many situations not all these operations are unique; possibly, several are combined into one or some are identical to others. In some cases, several of the operations do not even exist. In this section a few of the operations are examined, and some coding techniques useful in a few of them are given.

Editing

Editing takes two general forms. First, it involves the removal of extraneous information from records on receipt in order that the information may be stored more efficiently. For example, three money items might be received as

$$\$45.75 \quad \$180.20 \quad \$2,200$$

The dollar signs, the decimal points, and the comma are redundant. Furthermore, for consistency, the last figure should have a cents field added. The edited information might be in this form:

$$4575 \quad 18020 \quad 220000$$

Second, editing involves the reverse process, modifying information for the purpose of printing. Punctuation often has to be supplied, and alphanumeric information might be required. As an example, the last three integers given might have to be printed in the form

$$TOTALS \ldots \quad DAY \quad \$45.75 \quad WEEK \quad \$180.20 \quad MONTH \quad \$2,200.00$$

The editing job involves supplying the punctuation, the spacing, and the alphanumeric words.

Conversion

Data conversion is concerned with changing data from one form to another: analog data to digital data, data in one code to data in another code, or data in one number system to data in another number system.

Conversion between the decimal system and the binary or octal system is described in Section 4.1. Another useful set of conversions is that between BCD code and the number systems. Three programs for performing data conversions between BCD and number systems are given.

Example 16.1   Write a routine to convert alphanumeric octal information to binary form.

Alphanumeric information may include numbers in octal or decimal form (among other forms). Here we assume the information is octal. For example, the octal number 651772 is, in BCD code, the number

$$060501070702_8$$

To convert this to binary form, all that is required is that the 3 0-bits in the left half of each 6-bit BCD bite be deleted. This problem is almost the same as the problem of packing binary information, programmed in Example 15.2. A loop to convert one BCD word (36 bits) into one binary number (18 bits) is the following (the number to be converted is initially in the AC):

Location	Oper.	Var. Field
	SETXRI	6,1
LØØP	LSHIFT	3
	RØTATE	3
	INCRXM	1,1
	XJUMP	LØØP,1

Example 16.2   Write a routine to convert alphanumeric decimal information to binary form.

To obtain the binary equivalent of an alphanumeric decimal number, we need only determine the numerical value of the alphanumeric number and store it in a binary computer. For example, the number 456, stored in BCD as

$$000100000101000110_2$$

consists of three integers, 000100_2, 000101_2, and 000110_2. If we call these A, B, and C, respectively, the value of the number is

$$A \times 10^2 + B \times 10 + C$$

When the value is computed in a binary computer, it will be stored as a binary number.

The evaluation of the number is most easily performed by initially unpacking individual characters, as in Example 12.5 (page 247). Assuming this has been done, and the 6 characters are stored in DIGITS to DIGITS + 5, a routine is needed to multiply each digit by an appropriate power of 10. In the flowchart of Fig. 16.1, the digits are d_i and the powers of 10 are p_i.

Location	Oper.	Var. Field	
	SETXRI	6,1	
	CLEARS	SUM	
NEXDIG	LØAD	DIGITS,1	D(I)*P(I)
	MULT	PØWERS,1	

(Continued)

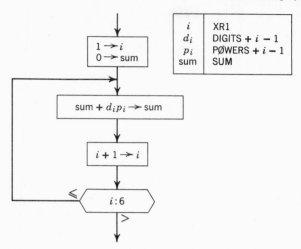

Fig. 16.1.   BCD-to-binary conversion (Example 16.2).

```
            ADD       SUM                    ACCUMULATE SUM
            STØRE     SUM
            INCRXM    1,1
            XJUMP     NEXDIG,1
            •••       •••••
 DIGITS     BLØCK     6
 PØWERS     DECML     100000,10000,1000,100,10,1
 SUM
```

Example 16.3   Write a routine to convert binary numbers to alphanumeric decimal form.

This is the reverse of the process of Example 16.2, but it is not possible to program the problem in the opposite manner.   Instead, a simple approach is obtained by using the repeated division process described in Section 4.2.   Arithmetic must be done in binary; in a binary machine this is done automatically.   The remainders are saved in binary, which happens to be their BCD form, since the remainders are all single digits.   The number to be converted is located in NUMBER.   A 35-bit number may contain as many as 11 decimal digits, when converted.

```
Location     Oper.     Var. Field
             SETXRI    11,1
             LØAD      NUMBER
 MØRE        DIV       TEN
             STØREM    LIST,1            STØRE REMAINDER (IN M.R.)
             INCRXM    1,1
             XJUMP     MØRE,1
```

After execution of this routine, the 11 digits are stored in sequence in the block at LIST. A packing routine can place them in 2 words; they will then be in BCD form.

By using these routines, the one in Example 15.2 (packing binary information, or alphanumeric binary to machine binary conversion), and two others that convert binary to alphanumeric binary and octal, the computer can be used to convert between the number systems. The conversion will, of course, be between two number systems in external form. Within the computer, if it is a binary machine, numbers must of course be stored in binary form.

Sorting (Ordering)*4

A file of records is more easily searched for particular entries if the records are arranged in numerical or alphabetical sequence. The operation of taking an arbitrarily ordered sequence and arranging it in sequence is called *sorting* or *ordering*. Alphabetic information is stored in most computers in numerical form, so that these considerations of numerical sorting of integers apply generally to alphabetic sorting.

Sometimes information of a general nature is to be sorted. Then a numerical *key* is very often assigned to each item, and the sorting is done on the keys. In the following discussion numbers will be sorted; whether they are keys or not is irrelevant.

There are three main types of sorting: *radix* sorting, *merge* sorting, and *interchange* sorting. Each is considered in turn.

Radix sorting (or *digit* sorting) is used quite frequently for the sorting of punched cards; it is usually done by machine. Radix sorting is accomplished in several passes; the number of passes is equal to the number of digits in the largest number. In the first pass all numbers with the same last (rightmost) digit are grouped; if decimal integers are being sorted, 10 groups are required. If the grouping is done by machine, 10 storage bins, numbered 0, 1, 2, . . . , 9 are used. Consider the numbers at the left in Table 16.1; after one pass they are grouped as shown.

After this is accomplished, the 10 groups are placed together in one list, with 0's first, 1's next, etc. In the second pass the process is repeated, grouping being done by the second digit from the right. Table 16.2 shows the situation after the second pass is completed. The last digits within each new group are in ascending order. Since the second digits are the same in each group, the last two-digit pairs in each group are in ascending order.

A third pass groups the numbers by the third digit from the right, after all the groups have been placed together as just prior to the second pass. In Table 16.3 the situation after the third pass is completed is shown; this is the final pass because these numbers have three digits. Reasoning as before, we see that now

---

* *Sorting* is used overwhelmingly in the literature in preference to *ordering* for the arranging of items in sequence. Here, *ordering* was used to distinguish this process from item classification. However, to follow the trend, we use *sorting*.

TABLE 16.1 FIRST PASS IN RADIX SORTING

Original List	0	1	2	3	4	5	6	7	8	9
401	610	401	222	333	104		666	667	228	329
329	550	991			984			207		489
667		451			224					129
104		331								
222										
984										
228										
991										
451										
333										
610										
331										
489										
666										
224										
550										
129										
207										

TABLE 16.2 SECOND PASS IN RADIX SORTING

First-Pass List	0	1	2	3	4	5	6	7	8	9
610	401	610	222	331		550	666		984	991
550	104		224	333		451	667		489	
401	207		228							
991			329							
451			129							
331										
222										
333										
104										
984										
224										
666										
667										
207										
228										
329										
489										
129										

the rightmost three-digit triplets must be in sequence (that is, the entire numbers are in sequence), because at the start of the third pass two-digit pairs at
the right were in ascending order. If the 10 groups are now put together in one
list, with 0's first, 1's next, and so on, a single ordered list is obtained.

TABLE 16.3 THIRD PASS IN RADIX SORTING

| Second-Pass | | | | | Groups | | | | | |
List	0	1	2	3	4	5	6	7	8	9
401		104	207	329	401	550	610			984
104		129	222	331	451		666			991
207			224	333	489		667			
610			228							
222										
224										
228										
329										
129										
331										
333										
550										
451										
666										
667										
984										
489										
991										

Merge sorting (or *collative* sorting) is very useful when numbers on a tape
are to be ordered. There are many variations; the simplest version of the technique is examined. The variations lead to increased speed of sorting.

In merge sorting, a list of numbers (assumed to be on a tape) is split into
two equal lists, one on each of two tapes. Table 16.4 shows an original list of
16 numbers; the numbers are placed alternately on tapes $A1$ and $B1$. (The
number 16 is chosen for convenience and simplicity in this explanation.)

TABLE 16.4 FIRST STAGE OF MERGE SORTING

Original Tape:

56 88 21 10 55 20 96 74 27 19 35 89 44 11 77 42

Tape $A1$:   Tape $B1$:
56 21 55 96 27 35 44 77   88 10 20 74 19 89 11 42

In the second stage the first numbers on each tape are compared. They are stored on another tape ($A2$) in order, with the higher number second. Then the second numbers on each tape are compared and stored in order on another tape ($B2$). The third numbers are stored (ordered) on $A2$. The process continues, the ordered pairs being placed on $A2$ and $B2$, alternately. At the end of the second stage, the situation is as shown in Table 16.5. The ordered pairs are bracketed.

TABLE 16.5   SECOND STAGE OF MERGE SORTING

Tape $A2$:   Tape $B2$:

|56 88| |20 55| |19 27| |11 44| |10 21| |74 96| |35 89| |42 77|

In the third stage an ordered pair is read from each of tapes $A2$ and $B2$ and *merged* to form one ordered sequence of 4 numbers. (Merging, the process of combining ordered lists into one list, is considered later in this section.) This sequence is put out on tape $A1$. The second ordered pairs from $A2$ and $B2$ are merged to form another sequence of 4 ordered numbers, put on tape $B1$. This process is continued, sequences of 4 ordered numbers being put alternately on $A1$ and $B1$. Here, with only 16 numbers, there are only 4 such sequences. At the end of the third stage, the situation is as shown in Table 16.6.

TABLE 16.6   THIRD STAGE OF MERGE SORTING

Tape $A1$:   Tape $B1$:

|10 21 56 88| |19 27 35 89| |20 55 74 96| |11 42 44 77|

In succeeding stages the process continues. Each stage merges sequences of ordered numbers to form sequences twice as large. Table 16.7 shows the tapes after the fourth stage. The two final sequences are merged into one sequence, shown in Table 16.8.

TABLE 16.7   FOURTH STAGE OF MERGE SORTING

Tape $A2$:   Tape $B2$:

|10 20 21 55 56 74 88 96| |11 19 27 35 42 44 77 89|

In one variation of this sorting method the lengths of ordered sequences are not fixed, but are permitted to vary. There may happen to be some ordering in the original list by chance, or some additional ordering may result from the merging process. This is taken into account in *variable-length* merge sorting.

TABLE 16.8 FINAL STAGE OF MERGE SORTING

Final Tape:
    10 11 19 20 21 27 35 42 44 55 56 74 77 88 89 96

Interchange sorting (or *exchange* or *internal* sorting) is useful if all numbers are stored in internal memory. It is accomplished by comparing adjacent numbers in a list and interchanging them if they are unordered. The first and second numbers are compared, and the smaller is placed first. Then the second and third are compared, and the smaller is placed in the earlier (second) position. This process continues until the last two numbers are compared and possibly interchanged. This series of comparisons constitutes the first pass, at the end of which the largest number in the list is last.

During succeeding passes, those known to be in order need not be checked. Thus in the second pass, the largest number is known to be last and need not be checked. The process is illustrated in Table 16.9, which shows the ordering after each pass.

TABLE 16.9 PASSES IN INTERCHANGE SORTING

Original:	56	88	21	10	55	20	96	74	27	19	35	89	44	11	77	42
Pass 1:	56	21	10	55	20	88	74	27	19	35	89	44	11	77	42	96
Pass 2:	21	10	55	20	56	74	27	19	35	88	44	11	77	42	89	96
Pass 3:	10	21	20	55	56	27	19	35	74	44	11	77	42	88	89	96
Pass 4:	10	20	21	55	27	19	35	56	44	11	74	42	77	88	89	96
Pass 5:	10	20	21	27	19	35	55	44	11	56	42	74	77	88	89	96
Pass 6:	10	20	21	19	27	35	44	11	55	42	56	74	77	88	89	96
Pass 7:	10	20	19	21	27	35	11	44	42	55	56	74	77	88	89	96
Pass 8:	10	19	20	21	27	11	35	42	44	55	56	74	77	88	89	96
Pass 9:	10	19	20	21	11	27	35	42	44	55	56	74	77	88	89	96
Pass 10:	10	19	20	11	21	27	35	42	44	55	56	74	77	88	89	96
Pass 11:	10	19	11	20	21	27	35	42	44	55	56	74	77	88	89	96
Pass 12:	10	11	19	20	21	27	35	42	44	55	56	74	77	88	89	96

Example 16.4 Write a routine to perform an interchange sort of 100 numbers, located in NUMBRS.

Let l_i be the ith location in the list. During the first pass, the first comparison made is between the $C(l_1)$ and the $C(l_2)$, and the last comparison made is between the $C(l_{99})$ and the $C(l_{100})$. The ith comparison is made between the $C(l_i)$ and the $C(l_{i+1})$; i runs from 1 to 99. On each succeeding pass, i runs from 1 to one lower number. In the flowchart in Fig. 16.2, i runs from 1 to p; p is initially 99 and runs down to 1. In order to realize the backward indexing of p, a counter (PCNTR) is used.

The AC and MR are used to effect an exchange if required; one number is stored temporarily in each. To end the process a check against the $C(PCNTR)$ is made; when that reaches zero, the process ends, since modification of that counter is made after a pass is completed.

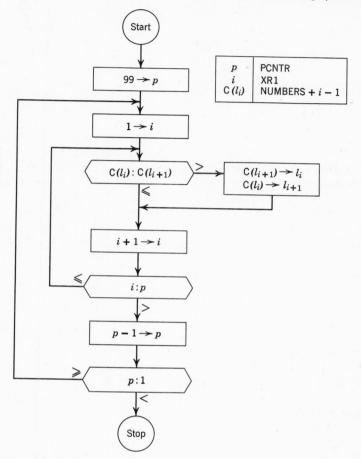

Fig. 16.2.   Flowchart for interchange sort (Example 16.4).

Location	Oper.	Var. Field	
	LØAD	**Q99**	**99 TØ P**
	STØRE	**PCNTR**	
NEWPAS	**SETXR**	**PCNTR,1**	
NEWNUM	**LØAD**	**NUMBRS,1**	**L(I) TØ AC**
	CØMPAR	**NUMBRS+1,1**	**CØMPARE TØ L(I+1)**
	JUMP	**NØ**	
	JUMP	**NØ**	
	LØADM	**NUMBRS+1,1**	**L(I+1) GREATER**
	STØREM	**NUMBRS,1**	
	STØRE	**NUMBRS+1,1**	
NØ	**INCRXM**	**1,1**	
	XJUMP	**NEWNUM,1**	

(Continued)

```
          LØAD     PCNTR              P-1  TØ  P
          SUBT     ØNE
          STØRE    PCNTR
          JUMPNZ   NEWPAS
          HALT

Q99       DECML    99
ØNE       DECML    1
PCNTR
```

There are more efficient ways to code the interchange sorting procedure. For example, generally several passes before the $(n-1)$th pass (if there are n numbers in the list), the ordering is complete; Table 16.9 shows that only 12 passes are required to order the 16 numbers. A test can be built into the program to see if ordering is complete before the $(n-1)$th pass. If a pass occurs without interchanges, ordering is complete. An indicator, set to zero prior to each pass, can be used for this purpose. In the program equivalent of the right branch of the flowchart in Fig. 16.2, where the interchange is effected, a single instruction can be inserted:

CLEAR   INDIC

If, prior to each pass, INDIC is set to nonzero, this instruction will cause INDIC to be zero if and only if an interchange occurred. A test (JUMPNZ) after each pass can terminate the program when no interchange has occurred.

Another way to speed up the process is to alternate the directions in which passes are made. This tends to decrease the number of passes required. A few trials will indicate this fact to the reader.

The three sorting methods described are generally used in different situations, as we pointed out: radix sorting for sorting cards, merge sorting for sorting data on tapes, and interchange sorting for numbers in memory.* As a result, a valid comparison of sorting speeds is difficult. A program to perform radix sorting in memory would sort by binary digits in a binary machine and by decimal digits in a decimal machine. The time to sort by this method is approximately proportional to n, where n is the number of items. The time for merge sorting is proportional to $n \log n$; the time for interchange sorting is proportional to n^2. The choice of methods depends in part on the number of items to be sorted; it depends more on the medium in which the items are stored. Within a given medium, another consideration is the amount of space available; some sorting methods require additional space for intermediate usage.

Merging

If two lists or files are each ordered, the process of combining them into a single ordered list or file is called merging. To effect the merge all that is nec-

---

* A radix method, *radix exchange,* is very common for internal sorting.

essary is that, at any point in the process, the two numbers that currently head the unmerged portions be compared; the smaller is stored in the new, merged list. A computer program to perform the merging of two lists stored in memory follows.

Example 16.5   Write a routine to merge the lists in the blocks at LIST1 and LIST2, of sizes m and n respectively, forming a single ordered list, NEWLST.   The original lists have no more than 1000 numbers each.

The flowchart in Fig. 16.3 shows the process.   The entries in LIST1 are a_i; the entries in LIST2 are b_j; the locations in NEWLST are l_k.   XR1 and XR2 act as pointers to the two original lists; XR3 acts as a pointer to NEWLST.

In order to insure that trouble does not occur when either list is exhausted, an extra number is assumed present at the end of each list.   This number is larger than any number in the list and is not counted (in the counts m and n).   When $m + n$ numbers are merged and the process stops, these numbers are ignored.   At the end of the merging process, a dummy number (in LARGE) must be attached to the end of NEWLST.*

Location	Oper.	Var. Field	
	LØAD	M	FØRM M + N
	ADD	N	
	STØRE	MN	
	SETXR	MN,3	
	LØADXR	ZERØ,1	
	LØADXR	ZERØ,2	
NEXT	LØAD	LIST1,1	CØMPARE A(I) TØ B(J)
	CØMPAR	LIST2,2	
	JUMP	SMALL2	B(J) SMALLER
	JUMP	SMALL2	EQUAL
SMALL1	STØRE	NEWLST,3	A(I) SMALLER, TØ L(K)
	INCRXM	1,1	I+1 TØ I
	JUMP	MØDK	
SMALL2	LØAD	LIST2,2	
	STØRE	NEWLST,3	B(J) TØ L(K)
	INCRXM	1,2	J+1 TØ J
MØDK	INCRXM	1,3	K+1 TØ K
	XJUMP	NEXT,3	
	LØAD	LARGE	STØRE LARGE NUMBER
	STØRE	NEWLST+1,3	AT END ØF "NEWLST"
	HALT		
M			
N			
MN			
ZERØ	DECML	0	
LIST1	BLØCK	1001	
LIST2	BLØCK	1001	
NEWLST	BLØCK	2001	

---

* The reader is cautioned once more of the discrepancy between computer indexing and arithmetic indexing.   When the $C(XR1)_m$ is set to 0 in this program, this corresponds to setting index i (which XR1 represents) to 1.   The same is true of the other XR's.

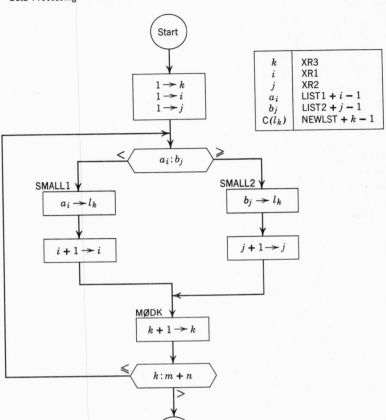

Fig. 16.3. Flowchart of merging process (Example 16.5).

Searching

A list or file of records is searched for a number of reasons: to retrieve, to delete, to add, or to modify information. The search may occur in several ways. If the list is unordered, the search begins at the start of the list and involves examination of every item until the match is found. A duplicate of the item must be "on hand" to be matched to all items in the list. When a match is found, the search is at an end. A method was given in Example 15.3 (page 301) for this type of search.

If the list is ordered, as in a telephone directory, it can be searched in *batches*. A batch is a group of records, fixed in size for a given application. The first entry in each batch is examined until a batch is identified as the one containing the entry sought. If, for example, there are 500 records per batch, every 500th record is examined. Later, when the right batch is identified, every record in that batch is examined. Analogously, we may search through a telephone directory by reading the top line of every tenth page until a name is found that is past the name sought. Then we may examine every name in the previous batch until the name is found.

Batch searching is reasonable for a computer, particularly for tape files, but not for a person. We do not look for names in the manner described. Instead, using our knowledge of how names are distributed in the alphabet, we open the book immediately to approximately the place where we expect the name to be. Then, we flip pages back or forth, examining perhaps the top name on each page or every other page. Finally, we look on the right page and scan it as the book as a whole was scanned.

There is a manner of searching an ordered list that is similar to the telephone search just described. It is easily programmed because the sequence in which items are examined is precisely stated. This contrasts with the human scan of the telephone directory, which follows no explicit rules.

The scheme is the *binary search;* it works as follows. A list is assumed sorted in increasing order. The list (whose size is known) is considered divided into two equal parts, and the middle entry is examined. If the sought item is larger, the upper half is divided and its middle entry is examined; if the sought item is smaller, the lower half is divided. This process continues. At every stage, it is possible to identify a sequence approximately half as long as one previously identified, as the one containing the item. An example illustrates the method.

Consider the following ordered list of 15 numbers:

$$10 \quad 11 \quad 13 \quad 17 \quad 22 \quad 29 \quad 30 \quad 31 \quad 44 \quad 49 \quad 60 \quad 63 \quad 68 \quad 71 \quad 76$$

The number at hand is 30, and we wish to find it in the list. The middle entry is the eighth, 31. This is greater than 30, so we next examine the middle entry in the lower half of the total list, the sequence of first to seventh numbers; this is the fourth, 17. This is smaller than 30, so we next examine the middle entry of the upper half of the list just divided, the sequence of fifth to seventh numbers; this is the sixth, 29. This is smaller than 30, so we next examine the middle entry of the upper half of the list just divided, the sequence consisting of just the seventh number; this is the number sought.

In this list of 15 numbers no more than 4 numbers need be examined; on the average, less than 3 numbers need be examined. This is true if each examination answers the three-way question: "greater than, equal to, or less than?" In general, if a list contains n numbers, $[\log_2 n]$ numbers must be examined; the square brackets mean "the largest integer in."

The binary search is very fast, provided all the entries in the list are readily available, as in a random-access general file or in memory. One application of the search is in the assembly of a symbolic program. During pass 2 of the assembly process, the symbol table must be searched whenever a symbolic address appears in the variable field of a card. Since this is done so often during the pass, the table is sorted at the end of pass 1, when all its entries have been collected.

16.3 COBOL

A compiler has been written to handle business data processing problems. It is called COBOL (common business-oriented language). Its structure is very similar to ALGOL, particularly with respect to statements. COBOL has a number of features designed to be particularly useful to business problems. The language had its beginnings in 1959; by 1961, a language was produced.[5]

Statements are written almost in the form of English sentences, except that the vocabulary and syntax are more restrictive. Certain words are *reserved* and may be used only in specific situations; *verbs* denote specific actions; *nouns* are the names given to quantities of interest in the program. These three categories are grouped under the heading of *words.*

Following are some examples of statements in COBOL; they are preceded by their ALGOL equivalents.

1. *result* : = (*sum* − 20)/7
   SUBTRACT 20 FROM SUM GIVING TEMP; DIVIDE 7 INTO TEMP
   GIVING RESULT

2. *grosspay* : = *rate* × *hours* + 0.5 × *overtime* − *deduc*
   COMPUTE GROSSPAY = RATE * HOURS + 0.5 * OVERTIME
   − DEDUC

3. **if** *sum* > 100 **then go to** *tabroutine* **else** *newsum* : = *sum* × 2
   IF SUM IS GREATER THAN 100 THEN GO TO TAB-ROUTINE;
   OTHERWISE MULTIPLY SUM BY 2 GIVING NEWSUM

Expressions to be evaluated may either be written as English sentences (example 1) or as formulas (example 2). In the latter case, the formulas are almost identical to ALGOL formulas; operators are different, and the word COMPUTE is required in COBOL. Conditional statements are possible, as shown in example 3. Compound and nested conditionals may also be used, in a manner similar to those in ALGOL (see Section 14.3).

A COBOL program is organized into four divisions—procedure, data, environment, and identification. The *procedure division* specifies the steps in the problem to be solved; it corresponds to the executable portion of a symbolic program. This division is essentially independent of particular computers. The *data division* is used to describe the files of data that the program is to process. The individual records of data are also described. Among the types of information that may be given are type of data (for example, alphanumeric), size of data (in number of characters), picture of data (that is, appearance when printed out, for editing process; for example, "$XXXX.XX"), and range of data. Space for calculations and constants are also handled in the data division.

The *environment division* specifies the equipment being used. It contains descriptions of the computer to be used; memory size, number of tape units, and console switches may be stated, for example. This division is completely dependent on a particular computer. The *identification division* identifies the source program and compilation outputs. Any desired information may be included for identification purposes.

If an object program is too large to fit entirely within memory, COBOL permits the segmentation of the program. Several parts are loaded separately into memory for execution; the compiler provides for automatic loading where necessary. Data may not be segmented, however. Several types of segmentation may be specified.

Summary

Data-processing problems are those requiring only relatively few calculations to be performed on large amounts of data. This is a characteristic of most business problems, but it is also true of some scientific problems. The three phases of computer solution of problems are: input, computation, and output. Most of the operations in business problems have to do with input-output operations, whereas most of the work in scientific problems is computational. Storage files are characteristic of business problems; the operations associated with maintaining files are characteristic of business data processing.

From a programmer's point of view, the more important file maintenance operations are editing data, converting data, sorting records, merging files, and searching files. Data to be operated on may be in several forms—on punched cards, in tape files, or in memory—and the methods chosen for these operations depend on the particular form present.

Notes

1. The following handbook has a section on business data-processing problems in general, with particular emphasis on sorting techniques.

H. D. Huskey and G. A. Korn (ed.), *Computer Handbook,* McGraw-Hill, 1962, Section 21.2.

2. The following books describe files in some detail.

D. D. McCracken, H. Weiss, and T. H. Lee, *Programming Business Computers,* Wiley, 1959, Chapter 2.

E. W. Martin, Jr., *Electronic Data Processing,* Irwin, 1961, Chapters 11 and 12.

3. The following book has a chapter on data-processing operations.

E. M. Grabbe, S. Ramo, and D. E. Wooldridge (ed.), *Handbook of Automation, Computation, and Control,* vol. 2, Chapter 3.

4. These books have extensive material on sorting (ordering) methods.

D. D. McCracken, H. Weiss, and T. H. Lee, *op. cit.,* Chapter 15.

R. S. Ledley, *Digital Computer and Control Engineering,* McGraw-Hill, 1960, Chapter 7.

5. The following issue is devoted entirely to papers on COBOL.

Comm. Assoc. Computing Machinery, May 1962.

PROBLEMS

Section 16.2

Write programs in HAP or FORTRAN (or both, where feasible) to solve the following problems.

16.1. Input data, punched on cards, are to be edited. The information is in dollars-and-cents form, with the cents portion (.XX) sometimes omitted. The data are placed on the cards with single intervening blanks; 2 blanks or more before column 72 terminate the card. The items are to be stored, in units of cents, 1 to a word in memory, starting at MØNEY. There are 100 items.

16.2. The reverse editing job is to be done, the output containing cents information (.XX) in all cases. Any easily readable output format is acceptable.

16.3. Convert data in floating-point format on cards to floating-point format in memory. On cards, each number is in the form X.XXXXXE±YY; internally, each number is to be in DELTA 63 floating-point format.

16.4. 1000 positive integers are to be sorted in the following ways: (*a*) by radix sorting in a binary system; (*b*) by merge sorting; (*c*) by interchange sorting more efficiently than indicated in the text. In case (*c*), the text method does not allow for a complete ordering before $n - 1$ passes; use a method other than the one suggested.

16.5. 500 items are to be searched by a binary search, the location of the found item being placed in an index register. If the sought item is not in the list, the index register is to be cleared.

The following problems are not to be coded.

16.6. Assembly program symbol tables are usually sorted, as noted in Section 6.3, in order to facilitate the search necessary in pass 2. Consider the cases of 10-, 100-, and 1000-symbol programs and the time required for the retrieval of each symbol once for the cases of sorted and unsorted symbol tables. Take sorting time into account. Assess the desirability of sorting in these cases.

16.7. A two-way merge was considered in the text. Consider three- and four-way merges and develop appropriate techniques using them. Compare the three types of merge.

16.8. Other collection-and-sorting methods have been developed besides the procedure that accumulates all entries and later sorts them. One approach is to accumulate

a relatively few items in a "bucket," sort them, and then merge them with all previously sorted items. A variation involves the subsequent merging of all the
smaller sorted collections. Assuming 1000 items are to be collected and sorted,
consider these alternate approaches for various bucket sizes and develop an
optimum procedure. Flowchart this procedure.

17

MACRO-INSTRUCTIONS

The macro-instruction has been introduced in Chapter 10 and described as one type of open subroutine. This is its simplest form, wherein it serves primarily to save coding effort. In this chapter macro-instructions are reexamined and are seen to provide powerful compiler-like extensions to an assembly language. They permit the symbolic language to be modified in many ways for special purposes, permitting a programmer to create a special-purpose coding language.

For macro-instructions to be able to provide these facilities, a number of pseudo-operations are required. In examining these pseudo-operations and the resulting new coding techniques, we see that it is possible to perform such tasks as developing a coding language for a particular purpose, simulating extra computer features, and easily modifying programs to produce additional information of value.

17.1 MACRO-INSTRUCTION PSEUDO-OPERATIONS

Elementary Macro-instructions

In the elementary use of a macro-instruction, a sequence of coding is defined in skeleton form. The coding is so defined because it will be used several times in a program with variations only in addresses or operations, not in structure. Those parts of the sequence that vary from one usage to another are identified in the skeleton form so that later, when the sequence is used, particular addresses or operations may be substituted. An example, by way of review, follows.

Example 17.1   Define and use a macro-instruction that sums three numbers and stores the result.

The macro-definition is

Location	Oper.	Var. Field
SUM3	MACRØ	A,B,C,S
	LØAD	A
	ADD	B
	ADD	C
	STØRE	S
	MACEND	

This macro-instruction sums the C(A), C(B), and C(C), and stores the sum in S.

Consider the macro-call

SUM3	WØRD,DIGIT,NUMBER,RESULT

This call expands into the sequence

LØAD	WØRD
ADD	DIGIT
ADD	NUMBER
STØRE	RESULT

There is no restriction on the nature of the alphanumeric strings that may be substituted for dummy arguments.   The following indicates some possibilities.

Example 17.1, Continued   Call the SUM3 macro-instruction, using more complex call arguments.

	Oper.	Var. Field
1.	SUM3	WØRD+1,(DIGIT+1,3),NUMBER,RESULT

This call expands into

LØAD	WØRD+1
ADD	DIGIT+1,3
ADD	NUMBER
STØRE	RESULT

2.	SUM3	WØRD+NAME−23,,NUMBER+3,/Ø/44000

This call expands into

LØAD	WØRD+NAME−23
ADD	
ADD	NUMBER+3
STØRE	/Ø/44000

Note that symbolic expressions, blanks, octal addresses, and other alphanumeric strings may be used as call arguments. In order to avoid ambiguity, however, strings containing commas are included within parentheses; the latter are removed as their contents are substituted.

The coding into which a macro-instruction expands is possibly not printed;

the call alone is printed. Thus, a sequence of coding which included a SUM3 call might look as follows; the assembled object program is given at the left.

Location	Contents	Location	Oper.	Var. Field
00100	0 32 0001 00012		SETXRI	10,1
00101	0 01 0000 00223	LØØP	LØAD	X
00102	0 02 0000 00224		STØRE	Y
00103			SUM3	NAME,W,X,Z
00107	0 21 0000 00117		JUMPPL	NEXT
00110	0 33 0001 00002		INCRXM	2,1
•••	••••		•••	••••

Note that the SUM3 expansion spans four instructions, at locations 00103 through 00106; the addresses in the first column indicate this fact.

If it is desired that the expanded coding be printed, a special pseudo-operation is available.

The Assembly of Macro-instructions

When a macro-definition is encountered, the normal assembly process in pass 1 must be suspended. A definition is signaled by a MACRØ pseudo-operation, and the assembler accepts the definition and stores it for future use. Later in pass 1, when a macro-call is encountered, the call arguments given must be substituted for the dummy arguments, and the macro-instruction must be expanded. These processes occur in pass 1 so that, at the end of that pass, the coding of the program appears in precisely the form the programmer would have written it without macro-instructions. Macro-definitions are ignored in pass 2.

The macro-definitions are stored in a table within the assembler in a compact form. In any sequence of coding there is a good deal of redundancy; since space is sometimes in short supply within the assembly program, the macro-definition is stored with a minimum of redundancy. Consider the SUM3 macro-definition in Example 17.1. That definition occupies 6 cards; at 72 usable columns per card, that is 432 characters. In memory, the information can be squeezed into a great deal less space. For example, let us assume these conventions in squeezing the information into less space:

1. The macro-name and number of arguments are listed first.

2. The symbol $ indicates the end of a field on one card; the symbol $$ indicates the end of a card; the symbol $$$ indicates the end of the definition.

3. Dummy arguments are numbered for convenience, using the symbols =1, =2, ...

Then the macro-definition appears within the assembler as follows.

    SUM3$4$$ $LØAD$=1$$ ADD=2$$ ADD=3$ $STØRE$=4$$$

This string occupies only 51 characters.

When a macro-call is encountered, the assembler must search through its list of macro-definitions and, on finding the matching definition, substitute call arguments. The first call argument is substituted for all appearances of $=1$, etc.

Pseudo-operations*

In order to provide for more advanced uses of macro-instructions, a number of special pseudo-operations are available within the HAP assembly language. These permit more powerful coding techniques and, in effect, allow the programmer to communicate more closely with the assembler. As with the pseudo-operations already introduced, these new ones affect the manner of assembly, now in a more subtle manner than previously. Their purpose and use is best indicated by an examination of their properties.

In order to appreciate the reasons for these special pseudo-operations, we consider some of the difficulties imposed by the elementary use of macro-instructions. Assume that a complex expression is to be evaluated using the macro-instruction defined in Example 17.1.

Example 17.2 Compute the value of p:

$$p = (a + b + c)(d + e + f + g + h)/(a + d + h)$$

Use the SUM3 macro-instruction.

Oper.	Var. Field
SUM3	A,B,C,TEMP
SUM3	D,E,F,TEMP+1
SUM3	TEMP+1,G,H,TEMP+1
SUM3	A,D,H,TEMP+2
LØAD	TEMP
MULT	TEMP+1
DIV	TEMP+2
STØRE	P

In this program, to sum five numbers, the SUM3 macro-instruction must be used twice in succession. A temporary location TEMP + 1 is required for the storage of the first sum. The second and third calls should be examined; they expand to the following:

LØAD	D
ADD	E
ADD	F
STØRE	TEMP+1
LØAD	TEMP+1
ADD	G
ADD	H
STØRE	TEMP+1

---

* The pseudo-operations described in this section are available in BE-FAP, the assembler at the Bell Telephone Laboratories. They appear here in slightly different form and use.[1]

It is clear that two instructions are redundant here; it is not necessary to store the contents of the accumulator and immediately reload the accumulator with the same number. It would be very convenient to be able to suppress the assembly of those instructions under such circumstances.

The difference between not assembling instructions and skipping over assembled instructions during program execution must be kept clearly in mind. In the former case, the instructions are not physically a part of the object program. In the latter case, they are present, but are bypassed by an instruction such as JUMP.

Conditional Assembly

If the assembler is able to assemble instructions conditionally, then coding sequences can be suppressed or assembled as desired under certain conditions. This is accomplished by writing the sequences in macro-definitions and causing them to assemble or not, depending on the nature of the call.

The following pseudo-operations in the HAP assembler are used to effect conditional assembly.

```
        Oper.    Var. Field

      IFSAME     S,T

      IFDIFF     S,T
```

The subfields S and T represent alphanumeric strings. The instruction that is next after the IFSAME pseudo-operation is assembled if and only if S and T are identical strings. The instruction that is next after the IFDIFF pseudo-operation is assembled if and only if S and T are different identical strings.

For example, the pseudo-operation

```
      IFSAME    ABC,XYZ
```

will cause suppression of the next instruction; the pseudo-operation

```
      IFSAME    ZZ+1,1+ZZ
```

will also cause suppression, since the strings are not identical. On the other hand, both the following pseudo-operations will cause assembly of the next instruction.

```
      IFSAME    LIST,LIST

      IFDIFF    ZZ+1,1+ZZ
```

Generally, one or both of the strings S and T are dummy arguments in a macro-definition. The nature of the call arguments in the macro-call then determines whether or not the next instruction will be assembled.

This pseudo-operation may be used to suppress the instructions discussed in Example 17.2. For example, if we write

IFDIFF   A,AC

then assembly of the next instruction will occur if and only if A is not AC.

Example 17.3   Revise the SUM3 macro-instruction to suppress AC instructions as indicated. Recode the evaluation of p, given in Example 17.2.

The macro-definition is

Location	Oper.	Var. Field
SUM3	MACRØ	A,B,C,S
	IFDIFF	A,AC
	LØAD	A
	ADD	B
	ADD	C
	IFDIFF	S,AC
	STØRE	S
	MACEND	

Consider the following call and how it will be treated by the assembler.

SUM3   D,E,F,AC

Consider the first IFDIFF. The S and T subfields are different ($S = C$, $T = AC$, on substitution), so that assembly of the next instruction occurs. Next consider the second IFDIFF. The S and T subfields are identical (they are both AC, on substitution), so that the next instruction is not assembled. Therefore this call expands as follows:

Oper.	Var. Field
LØAD	D
ADD	E
ADD	F

By similar reasoning, the call

SUM3   AC,G,H,TEMP+1

expands into

Oper.	Var. Field
ADD	G
ADD	H
STØRE	TEMP+1

The revised coding begins as follows (see Example 17.2):

SUM3	A,B,C,TEMP
SUM3	D,E,F,AC
SUM3	AC,G,H,TEMP+1
SUM3	A,D,H,TEMP+2
• • •	• • • • •

The second and third calls expand into

```
L ØAD     D
ADD       E
ADD       F
ADD       G
ADD       H
STØRE     TEMP+1
```

The redundant coding of Example 17.2 is not assembled.

In this use of the IFSAME pseudo-operation, the symbol AC is used since it is suggestive of the accumulator. Of course, any desired symbol may be used.

A slight variation of the SUM3 macro-instruction is possible, if use is made of a blank call argument. The macro-instruction is rewritten using the convention that an omitted third call argument means that the sum is to be left in the accumulator. Thus the call

```
Oper.        Var. Field

SUM3         WW,XX,ZZ
```

means that the sum is to be placed in ZZ, whereas the call

```
SUM3         WW,XX
```

means that the sum is to be left in the accumulator.

The macro-instruction is

```
SUM3     MACRØ     A,B,C,S
         IFDIFF    A,AC
         LØAD      A
         ADD       B
         ADD       C
         IFDIFF    S
         STØRE     S
         MACEND
```

If a third symbol is omitted in the call for SUM3, S is replaced by a blank, and the two variable-field strings of the second IFDIFF pseudo-operation are then identical (both are blank); the result is no assembly of the STØRE instruction. Only when a symbol is given for S are the two strings different and assembly of STØRE occurs.

An assembler may be written to include an indefinite number of IF-type pseudo-operations that would test various conditions existing at assembly time. Depending on the outcome of these conditions, assembly would be permitted or suppressed. Two other such pseudo-operations are introduced here as illustrations of what can be done; their use is illustrated in Section 17.2. Before they are examined, however, it is necessary to examine assembler arithmetic.

The symbolic expressions that are permissible in a HAP variable field are not limited to sums and differences of symbols. The operations of multiplication and division may also be used. For example, if A is defined at location 00010 (that is, A has the *equivalence* 00010) and B is defined at location 00020, the following expressions have the values or equivalences indicated (in octal):

A/3	00002
A+2*B	00050
5/2*2	00004
A−B	77770

The rules of arithmetic that apply to the evaluation of a symbolic expression are:

1. Multiplication and division are performed first, from left to right.
2. Addition and subtraction are performed next, from left to right.
3. Division is of integers, and fractional remainders are discarded.
4. All arithmetic is performed modulo 2^{15} (100000_8).

It must be recalled that this arithmetic is done by the assembler at assembly time. The result computed is considered to be an operand address of the instruction which is assembled into the address field.

The following conditional pseudo-operations are also available:

Oper. Var. Field

IFZERØ   Q

IFNØNZ   Q

The subfield Q represents a symbolic expression, composed of symbols and arithmetic operators. The instruction that is next after the IFZERØ pseudo-operation is assembled if and only if the equivalence of Q (that is, the arithmetic value of Q) is 0. The instruction that is next after IFNØNZ is assembled if and only if the equivalence of Q is not 0.

As examples of the use of these pseudo-operations, consider the following:

IFNØNZ   Q/5

IFZERØ   Q−Q/2*2

The first pseudo-operation leads to assembly of the next instruction (next in a program) if and only if Q is 5 or greater. (More precisely, assembly occurs if the equivalence of Q is 00005 or greater.) If Q is 4 or less, Q/5 is zero under the rules of assembler arithmetic, so that assembly is suppressed. If Q is 5 or greater, Q/5 is nonzero and assembly occurs. The second pseudo-operation leads to assembly of the next instruction if and only if Q is even. For example, if Q = 1, the expression is $1 - 1/2*2 = 1$, since $1/2 = 0$ by the rules stated. If Q = 2, the expression is $2 - 2/2*2 = 0$. Succeeding integers yield the values 1, 0, 1, 0, ...

Repetition in Coding

Frequently it is necessary to repeat a coding sequence a number of times within a macro-definition. An example is the following problem.

Example 17.4 Write a macro-instruction to determine the sum of the cubes of three quantities and to store the result.

The macro-definition is

Location	Oper.	Var. Field
SUMCUB	MACRØ	A,B,C,S
	CLEARS	TEMP
	LØAD	A
	MULT	A
	MULT	A
	ADD	TEMP
	STØRE	TEMP
	LØAD	B
	MULT	B
	MULT	B
	ADD	TEMP
	STØRE	TEMP
	LØAD	C
	MULT	C
	MULT	C
	ADD	TEMP
	STØRE	S
	MACEND	

Not only is this coding repetitious but the method used does not permit the number of quantities to be cubed to be variable. It is possible to use a loop to avoid both of these difficulties, but for a problem this small the value of a loop is questionable.

The REPEAT pseudo-operation permits the repetition of a sequence without explicit writing of all the coding occurrences. One parameter is permitted to vary in the several occurrences.

Coding delimited by

Oper.	Var. Field
REPEAT	A

at the start and

Oper.
REPEAT

at the end is repeated once for each call argument supplied for the dummy argument A, the coding being assembled with the call arguments substituted for A. The several call arguments for A are placed within parentheses, separated by commas.

Example 17.4, Continued Recode the SUMCUB macro-instruction, using REPEAT.

The new macro-definition:

Location	Oper.	Var. Field
SUMCUB	MACRØ	X,S
	CLEARS	TEMP

(Continued)

```
REPEAT    X
LØAD      X
MULT      X
MULT      X
ADD       TEMP
STØRE     TEMP
REPEAT
STØRE     S
MACEND
```

The call

```
SUMCUB    (X1,X2,X3),RESULT
```

expands into

```
CLEARS    TEMP
LØAD      X1
MULT      X1
MULT      X1
ADD       TEMP
STØRE     TEMP
LØAD      X2
...       ...
```

The sequence is the same as given earlier, except for an extra STØRE instruction near the end of the sequence.

The second macro-definition is shorter than the first and serves for any number of repetitions. Thus the same definition can be called on by the following instructions:

Oper.	Var. Field
SUMCUB	(WØRD1,WØRD2),ANSWER
SUMCUB	(Y1,Z1,X1,A1,B2,C3),SUM

In the first case two parameters are involved; in the second, six parameters are involved. Through the use of the REPEAT pseudo-operation a macro-instruction of variable length may be defined. The length of the expanded coding depends on the manner in which the macro-instruction is called.

Created Symbols

Within a macro-definition, it is sometimes convenient to refer to a symbolic address as in the following example.

Example 17.5 Write a macro-instruction that adds the larger of two numbers to a third, leaving the sum in the accumulator. If the numbers are equal, a jump to EQUAL should occur.

The macro-definition is

Location	Oper.	Var. Field
LARSUM	MACRØ	A,B,C
	LØAD	A
	CØMPAR	B
	JUMP	DD
	JUMP	EQUAL
	LØAD	B
DD	ADD	C
	MACEND	

The symbol DD is used in the location field in order that the first JUMP instruction can have a reference address. If this macro-instruction is called more than once, however, the symbol DD will be multiply defined, since it will appear in the location field once per expanded sequence. It should be noted here that a symbol so appearing in an expanded macro-instruction sequence is defined, even if the sequence is not printed.

To avoid this multiple definition and to permit the programmer to utilize references internal to a macro-instruction, the *created-symbol* feature is used.

Any arguments designated within a macro-definition by a CREATE pseudo-operation are replaced by *created symbols* whenever a call argument is not given for those arguments in a macro-call. The following symbols are created: ..001, ..002, ..003, etc.; they are created in sequence under the conditions stated.

Example 17.5, Continued   Rewrite the macro-instruction LARSUM, permitting a created symbol.

The macro-definition, which has one extra dummy argument, is

Location	Oper.	Var. Field
LARSUM	MACRØ	A,B,C,DD
	CREATE	DD
	LØAD	A
	CØMPAR	B
	JUMP	DD
	JUMP	EQUAL
	LØAD	B
DD	ADD	C
	MACEND	

The call

LARSUM   NUMBR1,NUMBR2,DIGIT

which means "add the larger of the C(NUMBR1) and the C(NUMBR2) to the C(DIGIT), and leave the sum in the AC," expands into

	LØAD	NUMBR1
	CØMPAR	NUMBR2
	JUMP	..001
	JUMP	EQUAL
	LØAD	NUMBR2
..001	ADD	DIGIT

In the call for LARSUM, only three arguments are given, although there are four dummy arguments in the new definition. The assembler supplied the symbol ..001, substituting it for the fourth, DD, designated on the CREATE card. The jump to the ADD instruction is a characteristic of the macro-instruction coding and is of no direct concern to the programmer. Hence it is desirable for a created symbol to be used here. The next time this macro-instruction is called, the symbol ..002 would be substituted for DD (provided there was no intervening use for that symbol).

A somewhat different use of a created symbol is given in the following example.

Example 17.6 Write a macro-instruction that places the larger of two numbers in the accumulator. If the numbers are equal, a jump to EQUAL should occur.

The macro-definition is

Location	Oper.	Var. Field
LARGER	MACRØ	A,B,DD
	CREATE	DD
	LØAD	A
	CØMPAR	B
	JUMP	DD
	JUMP	EQUAL
	LØAD	B
DD	BLØCK	0
	MACEND	

The call

	LARGER	WØRD5,WØRD7

expands into

	LØAD	WØRD5
	CØMPAR	WØRD7
	JUMP	..001
	JUMP	EQUAL
	LØAD	WØRD7
..001	BLØCK	0

The purpose of this macro-instruction is similar to that of the instruction in Example 17.5, except that no action beyond the loading of the larger number in the accumulator is to occur; the ADD instruction is to be omitted. A jump to the instruction after the second LØAD instruction is required, yet in this case the next instruction is "outside" the macro-instruction, that is, it is the instruction immediately after the macro-instruction. To make the reference to coding within the macro-definition, as is necessary, the BLØCK pseudo-operation with a 0 in the variable field is used. In this way, no words are assembled at that point, but ..001 is the symbol assigned to the address of the word following the second LØAD instruction, that is, the instruction immediately following the macro-instruction.

Remote Assembly

A macro-instruction may require constants or temporary storage in its use. Normally these words are placed out of the executable portion of the program, and this may be done for the macro-instruction as well. Nevertheless, constants and storage words may be imbedded within a macro-instruction so that they need no additional attention on the programmer's part. Since macro-instructions are part of the executable sequence of coding, it would be necessary to insert jump instructions so that the extra words can be bypassed.

By using a special pseudo-operation, any symbolic instructions or constants may be *remotely* assembled, that is, assembled at the end of a program, even though they appear physically before the end.

Coding delimited by the card

REMØTE

at the start and at the end is assembled as normally but is not assigned to memory locations until the end of the program.

Example 17.7   Write a macro-instruction to evaluate and store the function

$$f(x) = 5a + bc$$

A constant, 5, and one word of temporary storage are required. In the following macro-instruction, these two words are remotely assembled.

Location	Oper.	Var. Field
FUNCTN	MACRØ	A,B,C,R,FIVE,TEMP
	CREATE	FIVE,TEMP
	LØAD	A
	MULT	FIVE
	STØRE	TEMP
	LØAD	B
	MULT	C
	ADD	TEMP
	STØRE	R
	REMØTE	
FIVE	DECML	5
TEMP		
	REMØTE	
	MACEND	

The call

FUNCTN   XX,YYY,ZZZZ,ANS

expands into

Location	Oper.	Var. Field
	LØAD	XX
	MULT	..001

(Continued)

```
              STØRE      ..002
              LØAD       YYY
              MULT       ZZZZ
              ADD        ..002
              STØRE      ANS
```

while the two words

```
     ..001    DECML      5
     ..002
```

are assembled at the end of the program. Created symbols are used to refer to these two words to avoid multiple definitions as before.

Nested Macro-instructions

We leave temporarily the topic of pseudo-operations to consider a useful coding technique: the nesting of macro-instructions. Example 17.8 illustrates it.

Example 17.8   Write a macro-instruction that computes one of these two functions:

$$f = a + b, \quad \text{if } a \text{ and } b \text{ are both positive;}$$
$$g = a - b, \quad \text{otherwise}$$

Two macro-instructions for addition and subtraction are defined first:

Location	Oper.	Var. Field
ADDMAC	MACRØ	A,B,C
	LØAD	A
	ADD	B
	STØRE	C
	MACEND	
SUBMAC	MACRØ	A,B,C
	LØAD	A
	SUBT	B
	STØRE	C
	MACEND	

The main macro-definition is

CØMPUT	MACRØ	K,L,S,SUB,ØUT
	CREATE	SUB,ØUT
	LØAD	K
	JUMPMI	SUB
	LØAD	L
	JUMPMI	SUB
	ADDMAC	K,L,S
	JUMP	ØUT
SUB	SUBMAC	K,L,S
ØUT	BLØCK	0
	MACEND	

The call

CØMPUT   THIS,THAT,RESULT

expands into the following coding, where $L(a)$ = THIS, $L(b)$ = THAT, and $L(f)$ or $L(g)$ is RESULT.

```
            LØAD      THIS
            JUMPMI    ..001
            LØAD      THAT
            JUMPMI    ..001
            LØAD      THIS      )
            ADD       THAT      ) EXPANSIØN ØF "ADDMAC"
            STØRE     RESULT    )
            JUMP      ..002     )
    ..001   LØAD      THIS      )
            SUBT      THAT      ) EXPANSIØN ØF "SUBMAC"
            STØRE     RESULT    )
    ..002   BLØCK     0
```

There are several things to note here. First, the coding is not optimized. Both time and space could be saved, but this is of no concern here. Second, the inner macro-instructions ADDMAC and SUBMAC are expanded as soon as their calls are encountered within the CØMPUT macro-definition, after which the coding within the latter continues to be assembled. Third, the symbol ..001, assigned to the SUBMAC call, is effectively assigned to the first instruction assembled from that macro-instruction and is shown so assigned.

Another point to note about nested macro-calls is that symbols that are to be substituted only into inner macro-definitions must nonetheless be identified in the outer macro-definition dummy-argument string. An example is the dummy argument S of the CØMPUT definition, used to identify the location where the result is to be stored. Although not used within the outer macro-instruction, this address is used by the inner one and is carried to the latter by substitution within the former.

Setting an Equivalence

The SET pseudo-operation introduced in Section 8.2 is useful with macro-instructions. Its use is given here by way of review.

Consider the pseudo-operation

Location	Oper.	Var. Field
S	SET	T

The assembler assigns the value of the symbolic expression T to the symbol S.

Using SET, we may write, at two points in a program,

Location	Oper.	Var. Field
CØUNT	SET	1
...		.....
CØUNT	SET	CØUNT+1

The second SET assigns the value 2 to CØUNT. If the second operation is encountered a number of times during an assembly, CØUNT is successively set to the integers 1, 2, 3, ... and therefore acts as a counter. The usefulness of this facility is discussed in Section 17.2.

Operation Renaming

It is possible to supply a new name for machine instructions, a technique that is useful with macro-instruction applications.

Consider the following pseudo-operation, where S is a symbol and T is a standard assembler symbolic operation.

Location	Oper.	Var. Field
S	ØPSYN	T

The assembler assigns the symbol S to the machine instruction named by T. For example, if a programmer wishes to use FETCH for LØAD and to use PLACE for STØRE, he writes the following instructions *before* he uses the new names:

FETCH	ØPSYN	LØAD
PLACE	ØPSYN	STØRE

After these assignments, the old names (LØAD, STØRE) retain their former significance. The usefulness of this facility is discussed in Section 17.2.

Assembly Time "Jumps"

Many of the operations that occur at program execution time can be caused to occur at assembly time, if the assembler is appropriately written. For example, the jump operation can be provided during a macro-expansion.

Consider the following pseudo-operation, used to provide an assembly time "jump."

Oper.	Var. Field
TØ	X

If this pseudo-operation is assembled within a macro-instruction, all the instructions following it prior to the instruction labeled X are skipped, that is, not assembled. For this pseudo-operation to be used meaningfully, it must follow a conditional pseudo-operation, such as IFSAME or IFZERØ; in this way the jump becomes conditional. If the jump is unconditional, the intervening coding might just as well be omitted from the macro-definition.

Example 17.9 Write a macro-instruction that is to be used to evaluate one of the two following expressions:

$$f_1 = x^2 + 2xy$$
$$f_2 = x^2$$

The expression f_1 is to be evaluated if two arguments (x,y) are given; f_2 is to be evaluated if only one argument (x) is given. In either case, the sum is to be placed in RESULT.

In the macro-definition that follows, when the second call argument is omitted, the IFSAME pseudo-operation causes assembly of the next instruction (the blank substituted for Y matches the blank already there), which is the TØ pseudo-operation. Then the next four instructions are not assembled, since the fifth is labeled Q; at assembly, Q is replaced by a created symbol.

Location	Oper.	Var. Field
FUNCTN	MACRØ	X,Y,Q
	CREATE	Q
	CLEARS	TEMP
	IFSAME	Y
	TØ	Q
	LØAD	TWØ
	MULT	X
	MULT	Y
	STØRE	TEMP
Q	LØAD	X
	MULT	X
	ADD	TEMP
	STØRE	RESULT
	MACEND	

17.2 SPECIAL USES OF MACRO-INSTRUCTIONS

Some of the uses to which macro-instructions and their pseudo-operations can be put have been examined. In the first section of this chapter we were concerned primarily with the development of coding techniques that utilize the tools described. Four specialized uses of these techniques are now considered: (1) the development of a coding language peculiar to a class of problems at hand; (2) the simulation of special features on a computer, (3) the modification of an existing program for the purpose of providing additional information beyond that produced by the normal execution of the program, and (4) the use of macro-instructions in a recursive or iterative manner.

Language Development

In Chapter 14 we saw that FORTRAN and ALGOL were developed as languages for the coding of problems wherein the major operations were the evaluation of expressions. In the same manner, other problem-oriented languages may be written with other classes of problems in mind. Macro-instructions are well suited to this task, since operations can be written as though they were instructions. Frequently the problem at hand comprises a sequence of operations that can be so coded. By combining normal symbolic coding with macro-instructions, a programmer can create a language to suit his particular needs.

Consider a problem in which blocks of data are processed. Assume that the following operations are frequently used:

1. clearing a block;
2. moving one block so that it is appended to another;
3. duplicating a block, placing the second copy immediately following the first;
4. reading from tape into a block;
5. printing out a block.

Some of these operations are now coded as macro-instructions.

Example 17.10 Write macro-instructions to perform two of the five block operations.

1. *Clearing.* By this is meant placing zeros in every word in the block. The call is to have the form

Location	Oper.	Var. Field
	CLRBLK	BLØCK,N

This means "Clear the block starting at BLØCK of size C(N)"; the number of words in the block is located in N.

For use in this and in following macro-instructions, another macro-instruction is defined:

LØØPXR	MACRØ	W,X,Y
	INCRXM	Y,X
	XJUMP	W,X
	MACEND	

Since the INCRXM-XJUMP pair of instructions is so common at the end of loops, this macro-instruction, combining them, will be used. The call

	LØØPXR	BACK,1,2

is read as "Increase the $C(XR1)_m$ by 2; if the modifier of XR1 is less than its tally, jump to BACK, otherwise continue in sequence."*

The CLRBLK macro-definition is

CLRBLK	MACRØ	A,B,Z
	CREATE	Z
	SETXR	B,5
Z	CLEARS	A,5
	LØØPXR	Z,5,1
	MACEND	

XR5 is used in the block macro-instructions and is therefore to be used outside the macro-instruction with caution. Here Z becomes a created symbol.

2. *Moving.* The call is to have the form

Location	Oper.	Var. Field
	MØVBLK	BLØCK1,N1,BLØCK2,N2

* IBM 7090 users will recognize this macro-call as a slightly revised TIX instruction.

This means "Move the block at BLØCK1 of size C(N1) so that it immediately follows the block at BLØCK2 of size C(N2)."

The macro-definition is

```
MØVBLK  MACRØ    A,B,C,D,Z1,Z2
        CREATE   Z1,Z2
        LØAD     Z1
        ADD      D
        STØRAD   Z2
        SETXR    B,5
        LØAD     A,5
Z2      STØRE    **,5
        LØØPXR   Z2-1,5,1
        REMØTE
Z1               C
        REMØTE
        MACEND
```

The first three instructions place the quantity $C + C(D)$ into the address at Z2; this is the address of the first word following the block at C, which is the block called BLØCK2. If, for example, the second block has 38 words, the address in Z2 becomes BLØCK + 38. The address C is needed in the address field of location Z1, but it must be assembled elsewhere, so it is "remoted." Within the loop, the first word in BLØCK1 goes into the first word *after* BLØCK2, and the process of movement begins.

3–5. These macro-instructions are not coded here but their calls would have the following forms.

Duplicating:

Oper.	Var. Field
DUPBLK	BLØCK,N

"Duplicate the block at BLØCK of size C(N) immediately after itself."

Reading:

READBK	BLØCK,N,TAPE

"Read from tape unit TAPE a record into the block at BLØCK of size C(N)."

Printing:

PRTBLK	BLØCK,N,TAPE

"Print on tape unit TAPE a record from the block at BLØCK of size C(N)."

With macro-instructions of this type, block manipulation becomes a simple task. A routine that processes blocks of data and utilizes these macro-instructions follows.

Example 17.11 Write a program that (1) reads three blocks of data (with no more than 2500 numbers in each) from tape F, placing them in blocks starting at LIST, TABLE, and DIGITS, (2) combines these into one larger block at DIGITS, (3) places in a new block at NUMBRS all positive numbers from this block that are less than 1000, and (4) then prints out the list of such numbers on tape G. The number of words in each of the three records on tape appears in a three-word record at the start of the tape.

After the three blocks are read in, they are combined at DIGITS. In order to add the third block (TABLE) the size of the combined blocks at DIGITS and LIST must be computed. The total size of the combined blocks is needed for the loop within which all positive numbers less than 1000 are stored in NUMBRS. As each number is stored in that block, the $C(XR2)_m$ is increased by 1; XR2 is used as a pointer to the next available location in the block at NUMBRS. Finally, the number of words in NUMBRS is placed in SZ4 and used in the PRTBLK macro-instruction. In the program, note that the three-word record will be read into SZ1 through SZ1+2, that is, into SZ1, SZ2, and SZ3.

The program is

```
        Location        Oper.                           Var. Field

        READTF    SZ1                     READ 3-WØRD RECØRD
        READBK    LIST,SZ1,F
        READBK    TABLE,SZ2,F
        READBK    DIGITS,SZ3,F
        MØVBLK    LIST,SZ1,DIGITS,SZ3
        LØAD      SZ1                     FØRM SIZE ØF 2 BLØCKS
        ADD       SZ3
        STØRE     SUMSZ
        ADD       SZ2                     FØRM SIZE ØF 3 BLØCKS
        STØRE     TØTLSZ
        MØVBLK    TABLE,SZ2,DIGITS,SUMSZ
        SETXRI    0,2
        SETXR     TØTLSZ,1
MØRE    LØAD      DIGITS,1                PLACE PØSITIVE INTEGERS
        JUMPMI    NØLIST                    SMALLER THAN 1000
        CØMPAR    THØUS                     INTØ "NUMBRS" LIST
        JUMP      NØLIST                  JUMP IF GR. THAN 1000
        JUMP      NØLIST                  JUMP IF = 1000
        STØRE     NUMBRS,2
        INCRXM    1,2
NØLIST  LØØPXR    MØRE,1,1
        STØRXR    SZ4,2                   STØRE CØUNT ØF NUMBERS PRINTED
        PRTBLK    NUMBRS,SZ4,G
        HALT

SZ1
SZ2
SZ3
SZ4
SUMSZ
TØTSZ
THØUS   DECML     1000
LIST    BLØCK     2500
TABLE   BLØCK     2500
DIGITS  BLØCK     7500
NUMBRS  BLØCK     7500
```

The block-processing macro-instructions defined here offer one example of the use of macro-instructions to develop a special-purpose "language." Frequently the complete set of macro-instructions required in a language is developed as coding proceeds; it is sometimes difficult to foresee in advance what set of instructions will be required.

Simulation of Special Features

All computers have only a finite number of special registers and have a definite, fixed word structure. Through the use of macro-instructions it is possible to simulate extra computer features. Here two examples are given of this approach: (1) the simulation of additional index registers and (2) the simulation of a three-address machine on a one-address machine.

Most computers have a limited number of index registers. Three is a fairly common number, although some recent computers have six or more, as does the DELTA 63. It might be desirable, in the coding of some problems, to have an indefinite number of index registers. If a programmer writes a program to classify a given list of numbers into 10 different lists in the manner of Example 8.6 (page 149), he needs 11 index registers.* By saving and restoring the contents of the index registers, the limit imposed by three or six such registers is avoided, but this involves a great deal of "bookkeeping." Through the use of macro-instructions, additional index registers can be simulated. In so doing, no memory space or execution time is saved, but a great deal coding effort may be saved.

Example 17.12   Write macro-instructions to simulate 100 index registers, using the LØAD instruction as a specific illustration.

Normal assembler instruction names, for example, LØAD, ADD, SUBT, are to be used by the programmer in the usual manner, but with tags as high as 100. Since an instruction such as

$$\text{LØAD} \qquad \text{LIST,68}$$

would be misinterpreted by the assembler under normal circumstances, the name LØAD must refer to a macro-instruction. This macro-instruction must produce the proper coding for the simulation of XR68.

In order that the assembler operation names be interpreted as macro-instruction names, new names must be assigned for the machine instructions. This may be done by a series of pseudo-operations as follows:

Location	Oper.	Var. Field
LØADZ	ØPSYN	LØAD
ADDZ	ØPSYN	ADD
SUBTZ	ØPSYN	SUBT
• • •	• • •	• • • •

Now the original names (in the variable field) may be used as macro-instruction names.

Since the DELTA 63 has 7 index registers, 93 must be simulated; XR8 through XR100 will be simulated by 93 words in memory, in a block starting at SIMXR. Thus, XRJ, $J = 8, 9, \ldots, 100$, will be simulated by location

$$\text{SIMXR+J-8}$$

* In that example, a list of numbers was sorted into two lists, one consisting of the negative numbers and one consisting of the positive numbers.

Consider the simulation of the LØAD instruction. One of three coding sequences must be assembled, conditional on the tag: (1) an untagged LØAD instruction is required if no tag is present; (2) a normal, tagged LØAD instruction is required if a tag from 1 to 7 is given; and (3) a coding sequence as follows is required if a tag from 8 to 100 is given: the instructions assembled must, when they are executed later, modify the LØAD operand address by the contents of the *simulated* XR. These conditions are depicted in Fig. 17.1.

Conditional-assembly techniques are required. Two decisions must be made. The test for a tag can be made with the IFSAME and IFDIFF pseudo-operations, each having one blank string in the variable field; this technique was used in the last macro-definition of Example 17.3. The test for the "size" of the tag can be made with the same pseudo-operations, in the manner of the examples given in the last section (page 355). Because these pseudo-operations affect only the next instruction, it is necessary that a macro-call be given within an outer macro-definition.

The instructions assembled in the event that a tag from 8 through 100 is given provide for saving and restoring XR1, which is used as the *actual* index register, for executing the LØAD instruction, and for loading XR1 with the $C(SIMXR + J - 8)$.

The macro-definitions are

Location	Oper.	Var. Field	
LØAD	**MACRØ**	**A,T**	
	IFSAME	**T**	
	LØADZ	**A**	ASSEMBLE IF NØ TAG
	IFDIFF	**T**	
	LØAD1	**A,T**	ASSEMBLE IF TAG
	MACEND		
LØAD1	**MACRØ**	**A,T**	
	IFZERØ	**T/8**	ASSEMBLE IF TAG IS 7 ØR LESS

(Continued)

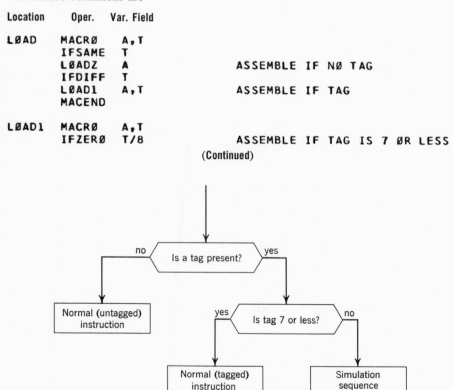

Fig. 17.1.   Conditional assembly of instruction (Example 17.12).

```
                    LØADZ    A,T
                    IFNØNZ   T/8                ASSEMBLE IF TAG
                    LØAD2    A,T                       EXCEEDS 7
                    MACEND

          LØAD2     MACRØ    A,T
                    STRXRZ   SAVX1,1            ("STØRXRZ")
                    LØDXRZ   SIMXR+T-8,1        ("LØADXRZ")
                    LØADZ    A,1
                    LØDXRZ   SAVX1,1
                    MACEND
```

The use of a normal machine operation name as a macro-instruction name re-assigns that name to the latter function and deletes its use as a machine operation for that assembly. Thus LØAD now refers only to the macro-instruction.

Note that instruction names ending in Z are used when a machine instruction is to be assembled. The following three macro-calls lead to the accompanying expansions:

	Oper.	Var. Field	
1.	LØAD	SWITCH	CALL
	LØADZ	SWITCH	EXPANSIØN
2.	LØAD	LIST,5	CALL
	LØADZ	LIST,5	EXPANSIØN
3.	LØAD	NAME,32	CALL
	STRXRZ	SAVX1,1	EXPANSIØN
	LØDXRZ	SIMXR+32-8,1	
	LØADZ	NAME,1	
	LØDXRZ	SAVX1,1	

Other machine instructions are similarly simulated, but a different coding structure is needed for some instructions, such as LØADXR, INCRXM, and XJUMP. To simulate LØADXR, for example, we need only place a number in the proper SIMXR word (if the tag is 8 or more); it is not necessary to use a real index register in the process. Similarly, to simulate INCRXM, we need only increase the proper SIMXR word.

Through the use of macro-instructions it is possible to simulate multi-address computers on a single-address computer such as the DELTA 63. To illustrate the technique, a simple three-address computer will be simulated.

The simulated computer, known as the DELTASIM 73, has the following set of instructions.

HALT		Stop.
ADD	A, B, C	Add the C(A) to the C(B); store the sum in C.
SUBT	A, B, C	Subtract the C(B) from the C(A); store the difference in C.
MULT	A, B, C	Multiply the C(A) by the C(B); store the product in C.
DIV	A, B, C	Divide the C(A) by the C(B); store the quotient in C.

MOVE   A, B, C   Move the block of words from A to B inclusive to the block
                        from C to C+B−A.
JUMP   A   Send control unconditionally to A.
JUMPPM   A, B, C   Send control to B is the C(A) is positive; send control to C
                        otherwise.

The 73 has no accumulator or multiply register; it has three index registers. For
simplicity, all arithmetic is done by integer operations.
    These instructions are simulated with the following macro-definitions.

HALT. This is the same as the DELTA 63 instruction, and the latter may be used.

ADD   Location   Oper.   Var. Field

                        ADDZ   ØPSYN   ADD
                        ADD   MACRØ   A,B,C
                                  LØAD   A
                                  ADDZ   B
                                  STØRE   C
                                  MACEND

SUBT. The macro-instruction is similar to the ADD macro-instruction.

MULT   MULTZ   ØPSYN   MULT
                        MULT   MACRØ   A,B,C
                                  LØAD   A
                                  MULTZ   B
                                  STØRE   C
                                  MACEND

DIV. The macro-instruction is similar to the MULT macro-instruction.

MOVE*   MØVE   MACRØ   A,B,C,Z
                                  CREATE   Z
                                  SETXRI   B−A+1,5
                        Z   LØAD   A,5
                                  STØRE   C,5
                                  LØØPXR   Z,5,1
                                  MACEND

The size of the block to be moved is B − A + 1; this value is placed in XR5.

JUMP. This is the same as the DELTA 63 instruction.

JUMPPM   JUMPPM   MACRØ   A,B,C
                                  LØAD   A
                                  JUMPPL   B
                                  JUMPMI   C
                                  MACEND

To indicate the use of an index register (1, 2, or 3), the tagged address
replaces the dummy argument, except on MØVE. For example,

                        ADD   (LIST,1),(TABLE,1),(SUM,1)

_____

* There is a difference between the structure of this MØVE macro-instruction and that of the
MØVBLK macro-instruction defined earlier (page 366).

Through the use of macro-instructions we may also simulate additional accumulators, index registers that modify addresses by subtraction rather than by addition, shift registers that automatically shift words as they enter the accumulator, etc. These features are available on some computers.

Providing Additional Information

A program normally supplies a certain amount of information: the printed results. A programmer may wish to have additional information supplied to him; an example is information on the status of the program during its execution, as for debugging. Through the use of macro-instructions this can be relatively simply obtained. The extra information can be provided in one of two ways: (1) macro-calls for routines that supply this information can be inserted into the program at desired points; (2) the machine instruction operation names can be redefined as in Example 17.12 to be macro-instructions that provide the information and execute the instruction. In either case, reassembly is necessary.

Example 17.13 The first technique might use a macro-instruction as follows; this provides a printout of the contents of several words in memory:

Location	Oper.	Var. Field
PRINT	MACRØ	X
	JUMPSX	ØUTPUT,7
		FMT
	REPEAT	X
	ZERØ	X
	REPEAT	
	MZERØ	
	MACEND	

The format FMT must be supplied. Consider the following coding sequence:

LØAD	TR4
ADD	TR6
SUBT	SEVEN
STØRE	NUMBR
PRINT	(NUMBR,WØRD,WØRD+3,XYZ)

This causes printing of the contents of NUMBR, WØRD, WØRD + 3, and XYZ after the execution of the STØRE instruction.

The second technique can be exemplified in a procedure that automatically supplies a printout of the contents of the referenced location in any STØRE instruction. To accomplish this, the operation STØRE must be defined as a macro-instruction:

STØREZ	ØPSYN	STØRE
STØRE	MACRØ	A,T
	STØREZ	A,T
	JUMPSX	ØUTPUT,7
		FMT

(Continued)

```
        ZERØ      A,T
        MZERØ
        MACEND
```

If the tag is missing on a STØRE macro-call (actually, a STØRE instruction in the program), a blank is substituted for T within the macro-instruction, and tags are suppressed. Note that the MZERØ word is tagged also, utilizing the monitor convention on tagged calling sequences.*

These macro-instructions must be used with caution. As they are written, they destroy the contents of the accumulator and other registers; this is done by the ØUTPUT routine within the monitor program. If it is necessary that the accumulator not be affected, appropriate coding is needed within the macro-instruction. Note also that XR7 is modified by the JUMPSX instruction. If the tag on the STØRE instruction is 7, there may be trouble. This can be avoided if a simulated index register is used.

In the second approach of Example 17.13 it is not necessary to modify the coding in any way; we merely have to place the macro-instruction and ØPSYN cards ahead of the program. Most likely, several machine instruction names will have to be so modified. For example, a printout might be desired every time STØRE, STØREM, or STØRAD is executed. The additional coding is similar to that given here. The extra coding mentioned in the last paragraph to keep all registers intact is essential in general, for the added macro-instructions should not in any way affect normal program execution.

It might be desirable to provide the additional information not at every occurrence of a STØRE instruction, but rather only in certain regions of the program. This would be the case when certain portions were already debugged and the extra information was not needed in those portions. To provide this added flexibility, we can define TURNØN and TURNØF macro-instructions that "turn on and off" the printing feature.

Example 17.14 Write the TURNØN and TURNØF macro-instructions described.

To accomplish this the word STØRE must be used for both the normal machine instruction (when no printing is desired) and for the macro-instruction (when printing is desired). The TURNØN and TURNØF macro-instructions have the function of switching the significance (and interpretation) of the word STØRE back and forth between these two, the machine and macro-instructions. In this way the printing feature is "turned on and off."

The TURNØN and TURNØF macro-instructions have no arguments; their calls appear to be pseudo-operations.

The macro-definition is

```
     Location    Oper.    Var. Field

     STØREZ      ØPSYN    STØRE
     STØREX      MACRØ    A,T
              (Continued)
```

---

* The convention is that such tagged addresses are modified as are machine instructions; see Section 11.2.

```
                     STØREZ   A,T
                     JUMPSX   ØUTPUT,7
                              FMT
                     ZERØ     A,T
                     MZERØ
                     MACEND


          TURNØN   MACRØ
          STØRE    ØPSYN    STØREX
                   MACEND


          TURNØF   MACRØ
          STØRE    ØPSYN    STØREZ
                   MACEND
```

A short program, using these features, follows:

Location	Oper.	Var. Field
	TURNØN	
	SETXR	N,1
QQ	LØAD	LIST,1
	ADD	SIX
	STØRE	LIST,1
	LØØPXR	QQ,1,1
	TURNØF	
	LØAD	NUMBER
	STØRE	TABLE
	JUMPZE	ØUT

The sequence expands into the following machine instructions; note that the first STØRE expands into 5 instructions, including the output sequence, whereas the second STØRE does not:

```
               SETXR    N,1
          QQ   LØAD     LIST,1
               ADD      SIX
               STØREZ   LIST,1        )
               JUMPSX   ØUTPUT,7      )  EXPANSIØN ØF
                        FMT           )    "STØRE"
               ZERØ     LIST,1        )
               MZERØ                  )
               INCRXM   1,1           )  EXPANSIØN ØF
               XJUMP    QQ,1          )    "LØØPXR"
               LØAD     NUMBER
               STØRE    TABLE
               JUMPZE   ØUT
```

The distinction between assembly time operations and execution time operations must always be kept clearly in mind. This is particularly true in using macro-instructions and associated pseudo-operations. An example serves to emphasize the distinction in such use.

It is possible to provide additional information, such as the printing discussed in the last two examples, in a conditional manner. The TURNØN and

TURNØF macro-calls in Example 17.14 provide this feature.   Consider next two other conditions: (1) printing occurs at every third STØRE instruction in the program, and (2) printing occurs every third time a STØRE instruction is executed.   These two conditions are different, in general, and the counting must be performed in different ways.

In the first case the counting must be done at *assembly time,* since each STØRE instruction is assembled once, although executed an indefinite number of times.   In the second case counting must be done at *execution time,* since the number of executions is of concern.

Example 17.15   Write coding so that printing occurs (1) at every third STØRE instruction, and (2) at every third STØRE execution.

1. The STØRE macro-instruction of Example 17.13 is modified to provide for conditional assembly of the output calling sequence, using an IFZERØ pseudo-operation.   Because that operation refers only to one instruction, a nested macro-call for the subroutine call is used.   The symbol Q is used as a counter, increased by 1 each time the macro-instruction is called.   The IFZERØ variable field is similar to one given in Section 17.1 (page 355); assembly of PRINTW occurs every time Q is a multiple of 3.

Location	Oper.	Var. Field
Q	SET	0
STØREZ	ØPSYN	STØRE
STØRE	MACRØ	A,T
	STØREZ	A,T
Q	SET	Q+1
	IFZERØ	Q-Q/3*3
	PRINTW	A,T
	MACEND	
PRINTW	MACRØ	A,T
	JUMPSX	ØUTPUT,7
		FMT
	ZERØ	A,T
	MZERØ	
	MACEND	

2. Now counting must be done when the program is executed.   To achieve this, a sequence must be included that calculates the function $q - q/3*3$, where the contents of the counter is q (when the program is executed).   The routine follows.

Location	Oper.	Var. Field	
	LØAD	CNTR	Q+1 TØ Q
	ADD	ØNE	
	STØRE	CNTR	
	DIV	THREE	
	MULT	THREE	Q/3*3
	STØRE	TEMP	
	LØAD	CNTR	

(Continued)

```
        SUBT    TEMP            Q-Q/3*3
        SUBT    THREE           TEST FØR Q-Q/3*3 = 3
        JUMPNZ  NØPRNT
        JUMPSX  ØUTPUT,7        PRINT IF 3
        FMT
        ZERØ    A,T
        MZERØ
NØPRNT  BLØCK   0
```

Recursive Macro-instructions

Macro-instructions can be used to call on themselves in a *recursive* or iterative manner. This technique is appropriate if an operation to be performed is itself recursive. One such operation is the computation of $n!$ for some positive integer n. This quantity (factorial n) may be defined as follows:

$$\text{if } n = 0, \quad n! = 1$$
$$\text{if } n \neq 0, \quad n! = n(n-1)!$$

If n is positive, the second relation must be used repeatedly until n decreases to 0, when the first relation is used. In the following example this process is coded to occur at assembly time. (It can, of course, be equally well coded at execution time.)

Example 17.16 Write a macro-instruction that will cause a single word to be assembled, containing $n!$. The call is to be as follows:

FACTL   N

where N represents an integer to be supplied.

Two nested macro-instructions are used. In the inner macro-instruction (FACTLX) the actual recursion occurs. The macro-instruction repeatedly calls itself, each time computing one more factor in $n!$, as follows: $1 \cdot 2 \cdot 3 \cdot \cdots \cdot n$. At the same time, a "counter" Q is used for loop control; the counter runs from 1 to n. An IFNØNZ pseudo-operation is used to control the recursion; when the counter contains the value n, the process stops.

The outer macro-instruction is used to initialize both the counter Q (at 0) and the partial product F (at 1). If n is given as 0, a TØ pseudo-operation causes the inner macro-instruction to be bypassed, and F (which is $n!$) is set equal to 1. After the inner macro-instruction computes $n!$ (for $n \neq 0$), the word containing $n!$ is assembled. A flowchart of this process appears in Fig. 17.2.

Location	Oper.	Var. Field
FACTL	MACRØ	N
	CREATE	Z
Q	SET	0
F	SET	1
	IFZERØ	N

(Continued)

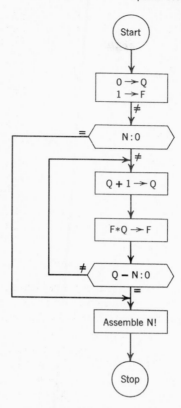

Fig. 17.2. Assembly time computation of N! (Example 17.16).

```
              TØ        Z
              FACTLX    N
        Z     DECML     F
              MACEND

        FACTLX MACRØ    N
        Q     SET       Q+1
        F     SET       F*Q
              IFNØNZ    Q-N
              FACTLX    Q
              MACEND
```

As an example of how this works, consider the call

                        FACTL   4

Following is a list of most of the pseudo-operations as they are generated in the assembly process during the recursive calling of FACTLX. The SET and conditional pseudo-operations are listed in the order of their generation:

Expansion of FACTL:	Q	SET	0
	F	SET	1
		IFZERØ	4

Expansion of FACTLX(1st time):	Q	SET	1
	F	SET	1
		IFNØNZ	−3

Expansion of FACTLX(2nd time):	Q	SET	2
	F	SET	2
		IFNØNZ	−2

Expansion of FACTLX(3rd time):	Q	SET	3
	F	SET	6
		IFNØNZ	−1

Expansion of FACTLX(4th time):	Q	SET	4
	F	SET	24
		IFNØNZ	0

| Expansion of FACTL: | ..001 | DECML | 24 |

This example offers a relatively simple use of macro-instructions in a recursive process. Examination of the accompanying flowchart (Fig. 17.2) indicates the great similarity between this process and a loop that might have been coded in Chapter 8 for computing $n!$ during program execution. In a similar manner, many processes normally performed during execution can be performed during the assembly process. The two approaches are not interchangeable, however, since assembly time computations are far slower than execution-time computations. On the other hand, assembly-time computations need be performed only once per assembly, whereas execution-time computations must be performed every time the program is run.

A Few Cautions

Although the use of macro-instructions can provide great flexibility and power in coding, they must be used with caution. Some aspects requiring careful consideration have already been pointed out. Another problem is concerned with relative addressing, which must be used carefully. Making a reference to WØRD + 13 leads to error if instructions between WØRD and WØRD + 13 are inserted. If macro-definitions cause the replacement of machine instructions with coding sequences, even harmless-looking coding causes serious errors. Thus, in the sequence

Oper.	Var. Field
JUMPPL	*+2
STØRE	SUM
LØAD	ABC

the expansion of STØRE into a sequence of three instructions invalidates the address ∗ +2 in the previous instruction. That reference is then to the wrong instruction. This difficulty is avoided by this sequence:

```
            JUMPPL   NEXT
            STØRE    SUM
   NEXT     LØAD     ABC
```

This transfer of control is unchanged regardless of whether STØRE is a macro-instruction or a machine instruction.

Summary

Macro-instructions, augmented by a series of special pseudo-operations, provide a flexible coding language. Flexibility is provided through means for conditional assembly of coding sequences, repetition of a coding structure with different parameters, creation of symbols, remote assembly of coding, setting desired equivalences to symbols, and the assignment of new names to machine operations. By these techniques, the programmer may to an extent "communicate" with the assembler during the assembly process, closely directing the manner in which a program is assembled.

Macro-instructions may be used in a number of special ways, including the development of special-purpose coding languages, the simulation of special features that are perhaps available on other computers, and the modification of an already coded program to provide extra information of a special nature while otherwise permitting normal program execution.

Along with the increased coding powers that macro-instructions provide comes a number of additional coding traps for the unwary programmer. Extra caution is needed as a result.

Notes

1. The macro-instruction special features and pseudo-operations that are available in BE-FAP are largely the work of D. E. Eastwood and M. D. McIlroy of Bell Telephone Laboratories.

PROBLEMS

Section 17.1

17.1. Write a routine to scan a macro-definition and produce a compact string of characters of the form described in the text; use the same $-sign conventions.

17.2. Write an expansion routine that the assembler could use to generate symbolic coding, being given a macro-call and the compact macro-definition format of the text.

17.3. Flowchart the macro-instruction processes of the assembly program, considering the following features, as described in the text: macro-definition packing, macro-expansion and coding generation, conditional-assembly pseudo-operations (IFSAME, IFZERØ, etc.), the REPEAT pseudo-operation, created symbols, and calls nested in macro-definitions. Code these routines.

17.4. Write a macro-instruction that will sum a variable number of quantities and then store the result either in a specified index register or the multiply register, or leave it in the accumulator. The call is to be of the following form:

VARSUM   (A,B,C,D),X

Any number of symbols may be placed in the parentheses, these being the names of words being summed, and X is XRi for index-register storage, MR for multiply-register storage, and AC for "storage" in the accumulator.

17.5. Write macro-instructions to perform the following operations, where numbers are "specified" by naming their locations:

(a) place the largest of three specified numbers in the MR;

(b) place the median (middle-valued) of 5 specified numbers in the AC;

(c) generate a calling sequence for the monitor INPUT subroutine of Section 11.2 (adopt a convenient macro-call format that allows for both individual words and blocks to be printed);

(d) store any specified bite of 1 word into a bite of the same size (although possibly different position) in another word, all other bits remaining unchanged.

17.6. Write conditional-assembly pseudo-operations with appropriate variable fields to cause conditional assembly of a particular instruction under the following conditions:

(a) if the equivalence of Q is at least 3 but no greater than 6;

(b) every fifth time the macro-instruction is called;

(c) if the equivalence of Q is 1, 2, 4, 8, 16, . . . ;

(d) if *any* of the macro-call's four arguments is the symbol YES;

(e) if exactly two or three of a macro-call's four arguments are blank.

17.7. Write a macro-instruction that evaluates *one* of the following three functions, depending on the number of call arguments given:

$$f_1 = 2x^2$$
$$f_2 = x^2 + y^2$$
$$f_3 = x + 2y^2 + z^2$$

The function f_1 is to be evaluated if one argument (x) is given (in the macro-call), f_2 is to be evaluated if two arguments (x, y) are given, and f_3 is to be evaluated if three arguments (x, y, z) are given.

Section 17.2

17.8. Example 17.10 describes five operations useful in the processing of data blocks. Write macro-instructions to perform the three operations not coded in the example:

(a) duplicating a block of words, placing the copy immediately after the original block in memory;

(b) reading a block of words from tape;

(c) printing out a block of words.

The macro-calls for these definitions should be those stated.

17.9. In Example 17.12 the LØAD instruction, with a tag as high as 100, representing the use of 100 index registers, is simulated with macro-instructions. Do the same for these instructions, following the techniques in the text where feasible: LØADXR, INCRXM, XJUMP, JUMPMI, and SETXR.

17.10. Write a macro-instruction that provides printing of information at a STØRE instruction, in the manner of Examples 17.13 through 17.15, whenever the effective address of the STØRE instruction lies between two specified symbolic or numeric limits.

17.11. Write recursive macro-instructions to assemble single words containing the following functions, evaluated for the particular value of n given in the macro-call:

$$(a)\ n^p \qquad\qquad (b)\ p^n \qquad\qquad (c)\ n!/[(p!)(n-p)!]$$

p is any desired constant.

17.12. Write recursive macro-instructions to assemble the following tables:

(a) a list of the numbers $1!, 2!, 3!, \ldots, n!$;

(b) a list of the first n powers of 2;

(c) a list of the first n perfect squares.

18

INTERPRETERS
AND SIMULATION

It is sometimes desirable to be able to write a program in the language of a particular computer and execute it on a different machine. In Chapter 17 we saw how a three-address computer could be simulated on a one-address computer through the use of macro-instructions. This was accomplished by an assembly process, the output of which is a program in the language of the machine on which it is then executed.

A completely different approach to the computer language simulation problem is the *interpretive* method. The program to be executed, written in any language, is stored in that form within a computer. An *interpreter* analyzes the program and executes it. This execution occurs by the action of instructions in the language of the computer being run, whereas the program remains in memory in the language of the simulated machine. The program being analyzed and executed actually may be written for an imaginary computer, since it is not being executed in its own language.

18.1 INTERPRETIVE PROGRAMS

Consider the following situation. A computer, called the *host computer* (*h-computer*), is available for program execution. It has its set of instructions (*h-instructions*), special registers, and other characteristics; its language is the *h-language*. A program, the *s-program,* is written in a language (the *s-language*) different from the language of the host computer; this is the language of a simulated computer, the *s-computer,* which itself has a set of instructions (*s-instructions*), special registers, and other characteristics.

The problem considered in this chapter is the realization and use of an *interpretive* program (or *interpreter*) which will analyze or *interpret* the *s*-program, stored in the *h*-computer, and "execute" it by means of the instructions of the *h*-computer. As the *s*-program is being executed, the interpreter must necessarily be present in the *h*-computer.

Example 18.1   To illustrate the interpretive approach, consider the three-address *s*-instruction

$$\text{ADD} \qquad \text{A,B,C}$$

which is present in an *s*-language, which means "Add the C(A) to the C(B) and store the sum in C." Let this instruction be stored in one word in the DELTA 63 in the following manner: bits 6–8 hold the operation code, bits 9–17 hold the A-address, bits 18–26 hold the B-address, and bits 27–35 hold the C-address. If the operation code for ADD is 1 in the *s*-language, the instruction might look as follows (in octal):

$$\text{00 1 345 222 775}$$

The interpreter must be able to analyze the instruction and execute it. To do this, it has to interpret the 1 in the operation code field as ADD and then it must, in DELTA 63 language, perform the indicated operation. The manner in which this might be done is described in Section 18.2.

The Purpose of Interpretation

A program that is executed interpretively will run relatively slowly, since the interpretation process must occur in addition to the program execution. There must then be a reason for using interpreters, one strong enough to outweigh this disadvantage.

The main reason for using an interpreter is that a program written in one language may be executed on another computer, without the need for the computer whose language was used. The *s*-computer may not be available at the place of execution; it may not even exist. A computer being designed or built can be programmed and the programs can be debugged by using an interpreter and a different machine. This technique is, in fact, sometimes used by computer manufacturers. In this way, by the time a computer is built, a set of programs may be ready to be run on it, working and debugged. In the case of assemblers and compilers this technique is particularly useful, since it is important that such programs be available for use when the computers for which they are written are available.

Writing s-Programs

A programmer codes in the s-language as though he were going to run the program on the s-computer. Most likely a symbolic coding language is available for the coding job. A special assembler would be required, of course, to produce the object deck for the s-computer. That assembler is probably very similar in structure to the h-computer's own assembler. The main difference is the manner in which the symbolic information is scanned and the format of the instruction is assembled. For example, if we examine the ADD instruction in Example 18.1, we see that a symbol table is required so that these equivalences can be obtained:

Symbol	Equivalence
A	345
B	222
C	775

In addition, an operation table is required for this equivalence to be obtained:

Operation	Code
ADD	1

An s-program object deck is produced by the special assembler on the h-computer; it is to be loaded into the h-computer memory for execution. Although the information within each s-instruction corresponds to the s-computer, the structure of each word is that of the h-computer.

In general, the object deck produced by the special assembler for interpretation on the h-computer is not usable on the s-computer. For example, if the h-computer is the DELTA 63, each program word has 36 bits. The s-computer might be the IBM 650, a decimal machine with 10 digits per word.

To summarize the several possibilities for assembly Table 18.1 is offered. The source language, the assembler, and the object language are given for four cases. The following examples illustrate these possibilities; the s-computer is the 650; the h-computer is the 63.

Case	Symbolic Instruction*		Assembled Machine Instruction
1.	LØAD	WØRD	001000033201(ØCTAL)
2.	RAU	WØRD	074000003671(ØCTAL)
3.	RAU	WØRD	6019770900(DECIMAL)
4.	RAU	WØRD	6019770900(DECIMAL)

* The 650 instruction RAU (reset add upper accumulator) is similar to the LØAD instruction.

TABLE 18.1 TYPES OF ASSEMBLY

	Symbolic Source Language	Assembler	Machine Object Language
1.	h-Language	Standard h-Assembler	h-Language
2.	s-Language	Special h-Assembler	s-Language, h-Format
3.	s-Language	Special h-Assembler	s-Language, s-Format
4.	s-Language	Standard s-Assembler	s-Language

A significant point to note here is that a symbolic source program may be assembled to produce a machine language object program on one computer, when both these languages apply to a different computer. This fact is not peculiar to the concept of interpretation, but proves to be useful in that context. Another point to note is that the assembled machine instructions must match in gross structure (word size, digit type) the machine that they will be loaded into. The manner of analysis of these instructions depends on whether an interpreter is used or not, so that their fine structure (size of operation and address fields) need not match the h-computer. If the s-computer and the h-computer have the same gross structure, the object s-program deck may possibly be used in both computers.

The Interpretation Process

The interpretation process is now considered in some detail. Assume that both the interpreter and the assembled s-program are located in the memory of the host computer. In order for the s-program to be executed, it is necessary to provide the interpreter with the starting location of that program. This starting location is placed in a simulated address register (SAR). Control is then considered to be at the instruction whose address is in the SAR. This is not strictly true, since control can never actually pass to the s-program; its instructions are not those of the h-computer and therefore cannot be executed by it. The starting instruction is then interpreted and executed and control "passes" to the next instruction. Control never leaves the interpreter; rather, the instruction that is to be executed is so identified by having its location address in the SAR. In this manner sequencing through the s-program is accomplished.

In order to interpret each instruction, the fields within the s-instruction word must be individually analyzed. As described in Example 18.1, this involves analysis of the operation code and three addresses for a three-address s-computer.

It may involve the analysis of a tag or other special fields if they are present in the s-instructions. Some computers are so structured that the address of the next instruction to be executed must be specified in each instruction. If such a computer is simulated, the new contents of the SAR is obtained from an analysis of the s-instruction. In any event, having analyzed the s-instruction fields, the interpreter supplies the information so obtained to appropriate subroutines where the s-instruction is executed.

Every register of the s-computer, including special registers, must be simulated by a set of h-computer memory words. The simulation is such that at the end of the interpretation and execution of one s-instruction, all the simulated registers contain exactly what they would contain within the s-computer in the same situation. The detailed steps during the simulation, however, may involve considerably different processes.

The manner of program sequencing and execution described here for the interpreter is very similar to the actions performed within the structure of any computer; the latter are described in Chapter 3. Within the computer the address register (AR) always indicates the instruction to be executed, and an analysis is performed on that instruction so that the operation will be performed on the indicated operands.

The three-address s-instruction in Example 18.1 was considered in Section 17.2, where it was simulated by a macro-instruction. Since there are at least two ways of realizing a three-address computer on a one-address computer, it is of interest to compare the two methods here, the assembler and the interpreter approaches.

The most significant difference between the two methods is in the speed of execution. In the assembler method, the program that is executed is the h-language and is executed at normal h-computer speed. In the case of interpretation, the program that is executed is in the s-language and must be interpreted and then executed. The latter process may be slower by a factor of 10. Another important difference lies in the space required for the two object programs. The three-address ADD instruction requires three memory words when expanded as a macro-instruction but only one word when left in three-address form for interpretation. More complex operations, some of which are considered in Section 18.2, may require many words when expanded as macro-instructions, yet still require a single s-instruction. In summary, the space advantage lies with the interpretive approach, whereas the time advantage lies with the assembler approach. The interpreter must be present during object program execution, however.

This comparison is frequently stated as being between the compiler and the interpreter approaches. All that was said in the last paragraph about assembly is true also about compilation. In both approaches an object program is produced in h-language and is executed in that language.

It should be noted here that the three addresses in the ADD instruction of Example 18.1 are only 9 bits each. It is possible to store three 11-bit addresses in a 36-bit word, provided three bits suffice for the operation. More likely, 10 bits would be used for an address. This contrasts with the 15-bit addresses of the DELTA 63 and most modern binary computers. The 3-to-1 space ratio quoted above must be modified to a 2-to-1 ratio if 15-bit addresses are required. The statement that the interpretive approach requires less room, however, still applies.

The use of arithmetic in symbolic expressions offers an illustration of an *s*-language that is executed interpretively. For example, consider the expression

NAME+37

The implied meaning here is "determine the sum of the equivalence of NAME and 37." That sum is then to be assembled into the instruction. The assembler must scan and analyze the expression; identify the operator, the symbol, and the integer; and perform the arithmetic. There is actually no *s*-computer intended; the *s*-language is purely artificial.

18.2 AN INTERPRETIVE PROGRAM

The problem stated at the start of this chapter, the realization of an interpretive program, is considered in this section. The DELTASIM 73, whose instructions were simulated with macro-instructions in Section 17.2, are now to be executed interpretively.

Example 18.2 The structure of the DELTASIM 73 is assumed to be slightly different from its earlier form (in Section 17.2); index registers are not present. The list of instructions follows, they are the same as previously used (see page 370).

HALT	
ADD	A,B,C
SUBT	A,B,C
MULT	A,B,C
DIV	A,B,C
MØVE	A,B,C
JUMP	A
JUMPPM	A,B,C

The format of each instruction is considered to be the same as in Example 18.1:

operation code: bits 6–8
A-address: bits 9–17
B-address: bits 18–26
C-address: bits 27–35

Each address, being 9 bits in size, can address only 512 or 1000_8 words in memory. The interpreter is to interpret each address relative to an *origin*, the address of which is placed in a standard location, 10000. If, for example, the origin is 32000, then the addressable portion of memory is from 32000 to 32777.

The action of the interpreter is illustrated in the flowchart in Fig. 18.1. In the flowchart SAR is the simulated address register.

The starting address of the program (L_0) is located in a second standard location, 10001. Initially, this is placed in location SIMAR, representing the SAR. The in-

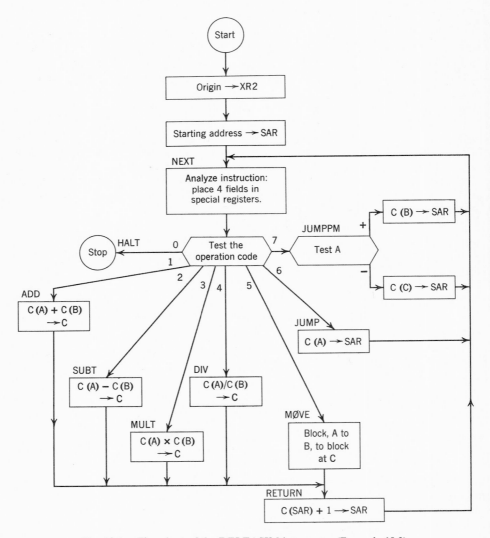

Fig. 18.1.   Flowchart of the DELTASIM interpreter (Example 18.2).

struction in location L_0 is then analyzed, each of the 4 parts of the instruction being placed in a different register:

<blockquote>
operation code: placed in XR1
A-address: placed in ADDRA
B-address: placed in ADDRB
C-address: placed in ADDRC
</blockquote>

The splitting of the instruction into these 4 portions is accomplished by masking; 3 masks are required (for the 3 address fields). Indirect addressing is used to obtain the contents of the instruction word, whose location address is in the SAR.

The s-instruction is executed by a transfer of control to 1 of 8 subroutines, representing the 8 s-instructions. The jump is dependent on the operation code, a number from 0 to 7. In each subroutine appropriate action is taken. In order to refer properly to an address relative to the origin, the C(10000) is placed into XR2; the locations ADDRA, ADDRB, and ADDRC are all tagged with 2, so that all addresses can be modified automatically to refer to the origin.

After a nonjump instruction is executed, the C(SIMAR) is increased by 1, so that the next instruction in sequence can be executed. After a jump instruction is executed, the C(SIMAR) is set to the address specified in the instruction, thereby effecting a change of control. It will be noted in the program shown below that control never leaves the interpreter. The program is sequenced through the addresses placed in SIMAR. In this program about 20 DELTA 63 instructions are required to interpret and execute most s-instructions; MØVE requires an indefinite number of instructions.

Following is the interpretive routine.

Location	Oper.	Var. Field	
	LØADXR	/0/10000,2	PUT ØRIGIN IN XR2
	LØAD	/0/10001	PUT STARTING ADDRESS
	STØRE	SIMAR	IN "SIMAR"
NEXT	LØADMK	AMASK	ØBTAIN A-ADDRESS BY MASKING
	LØAD*$	SIMAR	ØUT REST ØF INSTRUCTIØN...
	RSHIFT	18	PLACE IN "ADDRA"
	STØRAD	ADDRA	
	LØADMK	BMASK	ØBTAIN B-ADDRESS ...
	LØAD*$	SIMAR	
	RSHIFT	9	
	STØRAD	ADDRB	
	LØADMK	CMASK	ØBTAIN C-ADDRESS ...
	LØAD*$	SIMAR	
	STØRAD	ADDRC	
	LØADMK	ØPMASK	ØBTAIN ØPER.CØDE,
	LØAD*$	SIMAR	PUT IN XR1
	RSHIFT	27	
	PADDXM	0,1	
	JUMP*	SUBRT,1	JUMP ØN ØP.CØDE
SUBRT	HALTSR	0	
	ADDSR	1	
	SUBTSR	2	

(Continued)

```
                    MULTSR          3
                    DIVSR           4
                    MØVESR          5
                    JUMPSR          6
                    JPPMSR          7
        RETURN LØAD  SIMAR          MØDIFY C(SIMAR) BY 1
               ADD   ØNE
               STØRE SIMAR
               JUMP  NEXT


        HALTSR HALT
        ADDSR  LØAD* ADDRA
               ADD*  ADDRB
               STØRE* ADDRC
               JUMP  RETURN
        SUBTSR LØAD* ADDRA
               SUBT* ADDRB
               STØRE* ADDRC
               JUMP  RETURN
        MULTSR LØAD* ADDRA
               MULT* ADDRB
               STØRE* ADDRC
               JUMP  RETURN
        DIVSR  LØAD* ADDRA
               DIV*  ADDRB
               STØRE* ADDRC
               JUMP  RETURN
        MØVESR LØAD  ADDRA
               STØRAD MV1
               LØAD  ADDRC
               STØRAD MV2
               LØAD  ADDRB          FØRM SIZE ØF BLØCK (B-A+1),
               SUBT  ADDRA            PLACE IN XR3
               ADD   ØNE
               PADDXM 0,3
        MV1    LØAD  **,3           (A)...MØVE BLØCK
               STØRE **,3           (B)
               INCRXM 1,3
               XJUMP MV1,3
               JUMP  RETURN
        JUMPSR LØAD  ADDRA          FETCH NEW ADDRESS FØR SIMAR
               STØRE SIMAR
               JUMP  NEXT
        JPPMSR LØAD* ADDRA          TEST SIGN ØF C(ADDRA)
               JUMPPL JP1
               LØAD  ADDRC              HERE IF "-", PUT C-ADDRESS
               STØRE SIMAR              IN SIMAR
               JUMP  NEXT
        JP1    LØAD  ADDRB              HERE IF "+", PUT B-ADDRESS
               STØRE SIMAR              IN SIMAR
               JUMP  NEXT

        SIMAR                       SIMULATED A.R.
```

(Continued)

```
AMASK    ØCTAL    000777000000    MASKS
BMASK    ØCTAL    000000777000
CMASK    ØCTAL    000000000777
ØPMASK   ØCTAL    007000000000
ADDRA             0,2             REGISTERS FØR
ADDRB             0,2                THE 3 ADDRESSES
ADDRC             0,2
ØNE      DECML    1
```

The DELTA 63 and the DELTASIM 73 are quite similar, except for the facts that the former is a one-address computer and the latter is a three-address computer, and that there are many additional instructions and features on the 63. For this reason the coding required within the interpreter is relatively simple. If the s-computer is very different in structure from the h-computer, the interpreter coding is considerably more complex.

18.3 SELF-INTERPRETATION

Use of a Trace

Just as an interpretive program can execute an s-program written in another language, so can it interpret and execute a program written in the language of the host computer. The term *self-interpretation* or *tracing* is used for the latter function. Since interpretation may slow a program down by a factor of 10 to 20 compared to normal execution, there is no advantage to self-interpretation merely for program execution purposes. If, however, a program is to be studied by someone not familiar with it, an interpreter can be used to analyze each instruction and to provide printed information about actions that occur in the object program. A program that is complex and involves many decisions is usually difficult for someone other than its writer to follow; assemblers and compilers are examples of such programs.

Example 18.3   As an example of self-interpretation, consider the program coded in Example 15.1 (page 297) for the analysis of a symbolic expression. The program, which separated the parts of an expression and placed them in separate words of a block at NEWLST, is listed here again. The expression has previously been unpacked by characters, and is located in LIST. The program is now assumed to be loaded starting at location 00200; the location addresses are shown.

Address	Location	Oper.	Var. Field	
00200		LØADXR	ZERØ,1	0 TØ I
00201		LØADXR	ZERØ,2	0 TØ J
00202		LØADM	ZERØ	CLEAR MR
00203	NEXT	LØAD	LIST,1	FETCH 1 CHARACTER
00204		CØMPAR	BLANKT	TEST FØR BLANK
00205		JUMP	*+2	NØ

(Continued)

```
00206              JUMP      BLANK               YES
00207              CØMPAR    PLUS                TEST FØR "+"
00210              JUMP      *+2                 NØ
00211              JUMP      ØPER                YES
00212              CØMPAR    MINUS               TEST FØR "-"
00213              JUMP      *+2                 NØ
00214              JUMP      ØPER                YES
00215              LSHIFT    30                  HERE IF LETTER ØR DIGIT,
00216              RØTATE    6                      SHIFT TØ RIGHT ØF MR
00217              INCRXM    1,1                 I+1 TØ I
00220              JUMP      NEXT
00221    ØPER      STØREM    NEWLST,2            STØRE SYMBØL
00222              STØRE     NEWLST+1,2          STØRE ØPERATØR
00223              INCRXM    2,2                 J+2 TØ J
00224              INCRXM    1,1                 I+1 TØ I
00225              JUMP      NEXT-1
00226    BLANK     STØREM    NEWLST,2            STØRE SYMBØL
00227              HALT

00230    ZERØ      DECML     0
00231    BLANKT    ØCTAL     60
00232    PLUS      ØCTAL     40
00233    MINUS     ØCTAL     20
```

In the trace that follows one column is assigned to each of several registers in the computer; specifically, the contents of the MR, AC, XR1, and XR2 are listed. (Only the modifiers of the index registers are listed.) In addition, the address of each instruction executed is given at the left. The symbolic expression analyzed is

LX-5

We assume here that all the registers contain zero at the start. The contents of the registers *after* the instructions are executed as shown. The signs of the MR and AC are incorporated into the leftmost octal digit.

The sequencing of a program is as important as the contents of registers; this aspect of program execution is indicated by the series of addresses in the left-hand column. The several transfers of control are readily seen; they occur at and near the CØMPAR instructions and the JUMP instructions at 00220 and 00225. The results of the CØMPAR instructions vary as the BCD code of the letter being tested varies relative to the constants in the program (BLANKT, PLUS, and MINUS); the reader will note these variations in the list of addresses.

Location	C(MR)	C(AC)	C(XR1)$_m$	C(XR2)$_m$	
00200	000000000000	000000000000	00000	00000	INITIALIZE MR,XRS
00201	000000000000	000000000000	00000	00000	
00202	000000000000	000000000000	00000	00000	
00203	000000000000	000000000043	00000	00000	"L" TØ AC
00204	000000000000	000000000043	00000	00000	TEST THIS
00207	000000000000	000000000043	00000	00000	CHARACTER
00210	000000000000	000000000043	00000	00000	
00212	000000000000	000000000043	00000	00000	
00213	000000000000	000000000043	00000	00000	
00215	000000000000	430000000000	00000	00000	PUT LETTER IN

(Continued)

```
00216   000000000043   000000000000   00000   00000        RIGHT ØF MR
00217   000000000043   000000000000   00001   00000   INCREASE XR1
00220   000000000043   000000000000   00001   00000
00203   000000000043   000000000067   00001   00000   "X" TØ AC
00204   000000000043   000000000067   00001   00000
00207   000000000043   000000000067   00001   00000
00210   000000000043   000000000067   00001   00000
00212   000000000043   000000000067   00001   00000
00213   000000000043   000000000067   00001   00000
00215   000000000043   670000000000   00001   00000   PUT LETTER IN
00216   C00000004367   000000000000   00001   00000      MR..."LØ"
00217   000000004367   000000000000   00002   00000
00220   000000004367   000000000000   00002   00000
00203   000000004367   000000000040   00002   00000   "-" TØ AC
00204   000000004367   000000000040   00002   00000
00207   000000004367   000000000040   00002   00000
00210   000000004367   000000000040   00002   00000
00212   C00000004367   000000000040   00002   00000
00214   000000004367   000000000040   00002   00000   JUMP TØ "ØPER"
00221   000000004367   000000000040   00002   00000   STØRE "LX"
00222   000000004367   000000000040   00002   00000   STØRE "-"
00223   C00000004367   000000000040   00002   00002   INCREASE XR2
00224   000000004367   000000000040   00003   00002   INCREASE XR1
00225   C00000004367   000000000040   00003   00002
00202   000000000000   000000000040   00003   00002   CLEAR MR
00203   000000000000   000000000005   00003   00002   "5" TØ AC
00204   000000000000   000000000005   00003   00002
00207   000000000000   000000000005   00003   00002
00212   C00000000000   000000000005   00003   00002
00215   000000000000   050000000000   00003   00002   "5" TØ RIGHT ØF MR
00216   C00000000005   000000000000   00003   00002
00217   C00000000005   000000000000   00004   00002   INCREASE XR1
00220   000000000005   000000000000   00004   00002
00203   000000000005   000000000060   00004   00002   BLANK TØ AC
00204   000000000005   000000000060   00004   00002
00206   C00000000005   000000000060   00004   00002   JUMP TØ "BLANK"
00226   C00000000005   000000000060   00004   00002   STØRE "5"
00227   C00000000005   000000000060   00004   00002   HALT
```

Variations in Trace Information

The trace we have given contains a great deal of redundant information. It is not necessary to repeat the contents of a register if it does not change at the execution of an instruction. In fact, it may be more difficult to note changes in these words when repetitious information is not omitted. An alternative trace listing is the one following, where the printout of the contents of a register is suppressed if there was no change as the result of the execution of the latest instruction. This listing corresponds to the first half of the trace of the program given last.

Location	C(MR)	C(AC)	$C(XR1)_m$	$C(XR2)_m$
00200	000000000000	000000000000	00000	00000
00201				
00202				

(Continued)

```
00203                          000000000043
00204
00207
00210
00212
00213
00215                          430000000000
00216      000000000043        000000000000
00217                                                     00001
00220
00203                          000000000067
00204
00207
00210
00212
00213
00215                          670000000000
00216      000000004367        000000000000
00217                                                     00002
00220
00203                          000000000040
00204
```

This version of the trace is much easier to read than the earlier listing.

A self-interpreter may supply other information in a trace. For example, symbolic operation codes are frequently provided for the instructions executed. For this purpose the interpreter needs an operation table. Symbolic addresses cannot normally be provided, since the program being traced is in machine language. If an instruction is tagged, it is generally useful to know the effective address; the interpreter can supply this information. In the listing in Example 18.3, the LØADXR instructions are not indexable, whereas the LØAD instruction is indexable.* Tags would be provided in the case of tagged, nonindexable instructions. With these added items, the trace might begin as follows:

Location	Instruction	C(MR)	C(AC)	C(XR1)	C(XR2)
00200	LØADXR 00230,1	000000000000	000000000000	00000	00000
00201	LØADXR 00230,1	000000000000	000000000000	00000	00000
00202	LØADM 00230	000000000000	000000000000	00000	00000
00203	LØAD 00234	000000000000	000000000043	00000	00000
00204	CØMPAR 00231	000000000000	000000000043	00000	00000
00207	CØMPAR 00232	000000000000	000000000043	00000	00000
00210	JUMP 00212	000000000000	000000000043	00000	00000
00212	CØMPAR 00233	000000000000	000000000043	00000	00000
00213	JUMP 00215	000000000000	000000000043	00000	00000
00215	LSHIFT 00036	000000000000	430000000000	00000	00000
00216	RØTATE 00006	000000000043	000000000000	00000	00000
00217	INCRXM 00001,1	000000000043	000000000000	00001	00000
00220	JUMP 00203,1	000000000043	000000000000	00001	00000
00203	LØAD 00235	000000000043	000000000067	00001	00000

A Self-Interpreter

The *s*-language that is interpreted in Section 18.2 consists of eight instructions. In this section we consider the *h*-language, which consists of several dozen in-

---

* An *indexable* instruction is one whose operand address is modifiable by an index register. LØADXR is not in this category. (Refer to Section 8.1.)

structions. The interpreter required here therefore must contain several dozen subroutines for interpretive execution of all instructions. In addition, it must be able to interpret tag fields, indirect addressing, and masking operations. Instead of using actual registers, the interpreter would contain simulated index registers, a simulated accumulator, etc. The actual registers would be required by the interpreter for carrying out its functions. It is interesting to consider the coding required within some of these subroutines.

Example 18.4 Write routines for a self-interpreter for the DELTA 63 to simulate the instructions INCRXM, JUMPSX, and XJUMP.

In the self-interpreter the address and tag portions of the instruction being executed interpretively are placed in ADDR and TAG (in the address fields of those two words) before control goes to the individual routines. In addition, the SETTAG routine is executed at that time. Its purpose is to set into a memory location the tag of the instruction being executed; the address field of that word contains the address SIMXR. SIMXR heads a block of eight words; SIMXR$+j$ represents the simulated XRj. An indirect address reference to that word thus references the proper simulated XR. The tally and modifier of the XR are located in the leftmost and rightmost 15 bits of the simulated XR, respectively.

Location	Oper.	Var. Field
SETTAG	LØAD	BSIMXR
	ADD	TAG
	STØRE	REFXR
	• • •	• • • •
REFXR		
BSIMXR		SIMXR

In the following routines, SIMAR, RETURN, and NEXT serve the same purpose as in the interpreter in Example 18.2. Control passes to RETURN if a jump is not executed; control passes to NEXT if a jump is executed.

INCRXM:	LØAD*	REFXR	INCREASE C(SIMXR+J)
	ADD	ADDR	
	STØRE*	REFXR	
	JUMP	RETURN	

JUMPSX:	LØAD	SIMAR	PLACE LØCN. ØF INSTR.
	STØRE*	REFXR	IN SIMXR+J
	LØAD	ADDR	PLACE ADDRESS PØRTIØN ØF
	STØRE	SIMAR	INSTR. IN SIMAR,
	JUMP	NEXT	EFFECTING "JUMP"

XJUMP:	LØAD*	REFXR	FETCH SIMXR+J
	STØRAD	XJTEMP	STØRE MØDIFIER ØF XRJ TEMP.
	RSHIFT	21	SHIFT TALLY TØ RIGHT
	CØMPAR	XJTEMP	CØMPARE TALLY, MØDIFIER
	JUMP	XJ1	JUMP IF TALLY GREATER
	JUMP	RETURN	EQUAL
	JUMP	RETURN	LESS THAN
XJ1	LØAD	ADDR	HERE IF TALLY IS GREATER,
	STØRE	SIMAR	PLACE ADDR. PØRTIØN ØF
	JUMP	NEXT	INSTR. IN SIMAR

Interpretive program execution is slow, as we have seen. It should be used only in special situations, as in following a complex program or finding an error in coding. The latter use is discussed in Section 19.4. Although interpretation alone may slow a program down by a factor of 20, the process of writing the trace information on tape may further slow program execution by a factor of 200 or more. Self-interpretation or tracing always requires tape-writing if it is to be useful and hence is extremely slow, whereas normal interpretation usually involves only execution of the *s*-program, without tape-writing. It is possible to effect partial tracing, that is, tracing of specified portions of a program. This approach then only slows down the program where tracing information is needed; other portions of the program run at normal speed. This technique is also described in Section 19.4.

Summary

Interpretation is a method of program execution that involves the analysis of a program written in a language different from that of the computer being operated. The language used may be any at all, even that of an imaginary or yet-to-be-designed machine. This method may be applied to a program written in the language of the host computer; the term self-interpretation or tracing is then used. Tracing permits the detailed study of all or part of a program. This is useful for understanding a complex program or for debugging. Since tracing is a very slow process, it must be used with caution and only under appropriate circumstances.

PROBLEMS

Section 18.1

18.1. Consider the macro-instruction-aided compiler and the interpreter approaches to the following problems, and compare the relative merits of each; decide on the better approach in each case.

(*a*) Simulation of floating-point operations in a computer not having them;

(*b*) multiplication of complex numbers, assuming any convenient format for expressing the operations, and assuming the existence of any required subroutines;

(*c*) simulation of an indefinite number of index registers;

(*d*) simulation of a three-address computer.

18.2. Discuss the feasibility and usefulness of assembling and compiling programs for a nonexistent computer and subsequently running such programs by interpretive methods.

Section 18.2

18.3. Add routines to the DELTASIM 73 interpreter to permit the following instructions:

JUMPZE	A,B,C	Jump to B if the $C(A) = 0$; otherwise, jump to C.
CLEAR	A,B	Clear the block from A to B.
LARGST	A,B,C	Put the largest of the numbers in the block from A to B in location C.
SHIFTR	A,B	Shift the $C(A)$ right B bit positions.
FILL	A,B,C	Fill the block from A to B with the $C(C)$.

Section 18.3

18.4. Write routines in the manner of Example 18.4 for a self-interpreter for the DELTA 63 to simulate the instructions SETXR, SETXRI, and STØRXR.

18.5. Write a routine for the self-interpreter to suppress the printing of repeated words in a column.

18.6. Consider the partial tracing of a program. How might this be accomplished?

19

PROGRAM DEBUGGING
AND TESTING

Because so much time in the development of a computer program is spent debugging it, sometimes as much as 90% of the total time, it is important that the programmer learn of the techniques available to help him in this area. Many of the coding errors made are obvious or easily discovered, but others are obscure. The programmer should first attempt to unearth the errors by inspecting the program, but he should not ignore the help that the computer can give him through debugging routines.

This chapter offers a guide to preliminary checking of a program before it is run; a list of some of the more common errors is given. The use of the computer in debugging is described. The type of information made available by each of several debugging approaches is considered, and the use of each is described.

19.1 PRELIMINARY CHECKING

Manual Checking

When a programmer prepares a program, it is possible that he will make errors at every step: original analysis, flowcharting, and coding are all susceptible. It is invariably surprising to the beginning programmer that he makes as many errors as he does. If he proceeds carefully through a rough analysis, then a more detailed one, and then finally the coding, he tends to minimize his errors. By so proceeding, he gradually translates the mathematics of his problem to the language of the computer. That language is relatively strange, even to an experienced programmer, and slow, steady progress through a programming job is an important factor in the minimization of errors.

We now consider the job of manually checking the several steps in the programming process, prior to putting the program on the computer. Care here may save much expensive computer time.

Initially, the statement of the problem should be verified. Sometimes the programmer is not the originator of a problem, and it is possible that the wrong problem is coded. It must be perfectly clear to the programmer just what the problem is, what results are wanted, and in what form the results are to be provided. Even if he programs his own problems, this verification is important.

The method for solution must be carefully chosen. An error made here is usually one of poor judgment. As an example, there may be several iterative methods for the solution of a problem in calculus. Of these, some may converge rapidly for the problem at hand, whereas others may converge much more slowly. If the latter type is chosen, a great deal of computer time may be wasted.

The flowchart (or an equivalent analysis) must be carefully checked. The boxes used in the chart have a definite structure, regardless of the conventions used. For example, all decision boxes have at least two paths leaving them, whereas all boxes have one entering path. All lines in the chart must run from one box to another, except for those indicating the start and end of the program. In addition to being structurally correct, a flowchart must correspond to the original problem. It is necessary to trace all paths of flow to see that they are taken under the correct conditions and that all conditions have corresponding paths. Special attention must be paid to the exceptional situations; all possible conditions must be accounted for. The merge points and decision boxes in a flowchart are especially important places to check.

Loops are often particularly troublesome. Each must have the following characteristics: initialization, an operation to be performed, at least one test for termination, and a jump either to the start of the loop or out of the loop. It is important to check the number of cycles that will actually occur to see if this number is correct.

An excellent way to verify the flowchart is to draw it a second time from the statement of the problem; this is best done a day or two after the first drawing. This technique serves to verify both the chart and the coding.

Errors made in problem analysis are usually called *logical* errors. Though these are among the rarest errors, they are frequently the most serious. They tend to be overlooked, because they occur so early in the program-writing process. Furthermore, they may result from a misunderstanding of the method, an error difficult to detect.   More likely, they occur through carelessness; an example is the omission of one of several conditions that occur.

Finally, an instruction-by-instruction check of the coding is one of the best methods for finding errors, provided this is done in correspondence with a flowchart.   A simple, informal trace of the program can be written during this process.   This method of checking can be tedious, but it pays off, since it can find many errors.

It is extremely helpful if a second person can assist in the preliminary checking procedures.   When he makes an error an individual sometimes tends to look at the error without seeing it.   Another person will not be blind to the same error, generally.   If the second person redraws the flowchart from the coding, for example, an exact match between his chart and the original chart almost certainly indicates accuracy of the flowchart.   A verbal explanation of the analysis and the coding to the second person is also almost a sure way for logical errors (and sometimes coding errors) to be detected.

Physical errors are those involving the deck or other input medium; most commonly, they are due to the interchange of program decks and monitor control cards and to the omission or mispunching of required cards.   If other input media are used, there may be corresponding errors.

In order to avoid a common source of errors, a programmer should be very careful in keeping his decks and program listings up to date.   Old listings of a program should be discarded and replaced by new ones or should at the very least be dated.   The same should be done with old versions of program decks.

Common Errors

We can list thousands of errors in programming and coding, but most of these would be quite specialized and peculiar to certain computers or classes of problems.   A list is given here of some of the more common errors, listed in a semiarbitrary order.

Logical errors
  1. Interchange of two of the paths leaving a decision box.
  2. Use of an improper test for the termination of a loop.
  3. Inclusion of an improper number of loop cycles.
  4. Improper or omitted loop initialization.
  5. Failure to take into account all situations that may occur in the data or in the calculations.

Coding errors
  6. Omission in the coding of one or more flowchart boxes.
  7. Improper or omitted address modification.
  8. Reference to an undefined symbol.
  9. Use of a symbol defined at two or more locations.

10. Transposition in a symbol or operation code, as INCXRM for INCRXM.

11. Omission of coding to set addresses to be supplied during execution.

12. Omission of resetting counters to initial values.

13. Use of relative addressing to refer to a location beyond coding that is subsequently changed.

14. Failure to save and restore an index register in a sequence of coding that uses that register for another purpose.

15. Making references to absolute locations which are changed during reassembly, without correcting references.

16. Use of floating-point instructions for fixed-point calculations, and vice versa.

17. Use of an improper format statement for reading or printing data.

18. Improper use of a subroutine calling sequence.

19. Omitted or improper tag in an instruction, or use of a tag where none is required.

20. Failure to clear accumulator or multiply register before shifting information into it for unpacking or packing.

21. Failure to set a program switch properly.

22. Coding a return from the end of a loop to the instruction that sets the index register for the loop, resulting in an endless loop.

23. Storage of information in locations where needed information was previously stored.

24. Failure to rewind tapes before writing or reading, resulting in the possible loss of information or the reading of improper information.

25. Failure to take into account all the effects of a program change, possibly resulting in undefined symbols, references to wrong locations, or many other errors.

26. Use of incorrect number system, as octal for decimal, or vice versa (in some machines).

27. Failure to allow for accumulator overflow as the result of an addition or shifting operation.

28. Coding a jump or reference to the wrong location, be it an instruction, a constant, or an item of data.

29. Failure to reserve sufficient space for calculations, resulting in the overflow of a data block and the overwriting of information just beyond the block.

Physical errors

30. Omission of data cards.

31. Use of wrong data format on cards.

32. Interchange of the several program decks in a deck of cards.

33. Interchange of individual cards within a program deck.

34. Omission or mispunching of monitor control cards.

35. Failure, when using a reassembled deck, to discard correction cards that apply to the older version.

36. Reference to an old program listing when using a new deck.

19.2 DEBUGGING AND TESTING ON THE COMPUTER

Assembler Aids

Sometimes a coded program, as written, will fail to assemble correctly. Most assemblers supply, with the program listing, a number of *error flags* adjacent to the instructions containing certain errors; in this way some errors can be easily detected. These errors include the following.

1. Use of an undefined or multiply defined symbol.
2. Use of an illegal operation code.
3. Improper use of certain pseudo-operations, such as use of an 8 or 9 on an octal data card.
4. Illegal use of operators in a symbolic expression.
5. Improper or omitted address.

The flags are generally single letters; if an instruction contains two errors that can be flagged, two letters appear.

Example 19.1 The following letters are used by the HAP assembler to flag the errors we have indicated.

> U: undefined symbol
> M: multiply defined symbol
> Ø: illegal operation code
> N: improper field on an ØCTAL card
> S: incorrect symbolic expression
> A: improper address

Following is a program coded with several errors. The program is taken from Example 8.7 (page 155). The octal listing is given and a number of error flags are shown. Portions of the octal word are omitted where errors occur.

	Location	Contents				Location	Oper.	Var. Field
	00200						ØRIGIN	/Ø/200
Ø	00200	0		0001	03720		SETXKI	2000,1
	00201	0	01	0001	00226	NEWØNE	LØAD	LIST,1
U	00202	0	07	0000			DIV	TEN
	00203	0	37	0002	00000		PADDXM	0,2
S	00204	0	01	0002			LØAD	CTABLE+,2
A	00205	0	04	0000			ADD	
	00206	0	02	0002	00214		STØRE	CTABLE,2
	00207	0	33	0001	00001		INCRXM	1,1
U	00210	0	34	0001			XJUMP	NEWØN,1
A	00211	0	30	0007	53324		JUMPSX	SUBR,7
	00212	0	00	0000	00000		HALT	
	00213	+000000000001				ØNE	DECML	1
	00214					CTABLE	BLØCK	10
	00226					LIST	BLØCK	2000
A						SUBR	SET	55000

The errors made were (1) mispunching of SETXRI as SETXKI, (2) failure to define the constant TEN, (3) insertion of an extraneous plus sign in the instruction at 00204, (4) omission of the ADD address, (5) mispunching of NEWØNE as NEWØN, resulting in an undefined symbol, (6) omission of octal qualifier /Ø/ in the last instruction, resulting in the computation of the octal equivalent of 55000, which is 153324. Since this last number is larger than any machine address, the instructions containing SUBR as a symbol are flagged. Note that an omitted qualifier would not always result in an A flag, as in an address below memory size.

In the event that part or all of a word cannot be assembled because of an error, the HAP assembler leaves blanks for erroneous operation or address fields. The resulting program deck has zeros in all such fields. Thus, at location 00204, this word is assembled into the deck:

$$001000200000$$

which corresponds to

$$\text{LØAD} \qquad 0,2$$

A program deck might not be assembled when there is an error that can be flagged, unless the programmer specifically makes an unconditional request for a deck. Often, some "errors" are considered to be *nonfatal;* these are possible errors that may be intentional, such as the omission of an address. These conventions vary from one assembler to another.

The errors made in the program in Example 19.1, like all coding errors, can be corrected by the use of correction cards, described in Section 11.1, or by reassembly.

Example 19.1, Continued The following octal correction cards will correct the errors made in the program. They would be added at the end of the object deck.

Location	Oper.	Var. Field
00200	ØCTAL	032000103720
00202	ØCTAL	007000020000
00204	ØCTAL	001000200214
00205	ØCTAL	004000000213
00210	ØCTAL	034000100201
00211	ØCTAL	030000755000
20000	ØCTAL	000000000012

Most of these cards are easily understandable. Note that a word containing 10 (12_8) has been established at location 20000, a location outside the region of the program.

Another feature that is sometimes available with an assembly listing is a *symbol reference table,* which lists all the symbols defined in the program, the locations where they are defined, and all references to them.

Example 19.2 The symbol reference table for the program coded in Example 8.7 is as follows.

Location	Symbol	References
00214	ØNE	00205
00213	TEN	00202
00227	LIST	00201
55000	SUBR	00211
00215	CTABLE	00204,00206
00201	NEWØNE	00201

The list of symbol references is useful in debugging or revising a program. For example, if a change to correct an error must be made at a location where a symbol is defined, it is important that all the references to that symbol be checked. Special care is required when a coding sequence is deleted, since it may contain symbols in location fields.

Compiler Aids

Compilers can provide information to the programmer on the presence of some errors in the program. These are generally printed with the listing, and make reference to particular statements, if possible. Following is a partial list of the comments (called *diagnostics*) provided by FORTRAN during a compilation.

Diagnostics on individual statements
1. An illegal symbol was used. (There may be too many characters, the first character may be a digit, etc.)
2. An arithmetic is mixed, that is, contains both fixed- and floating-point variables in an illegal manner.
3. An error in the use of parentheses has been made. (There may be an unequal number of left and right parentheses, etc.)
4. An illegal expression is present. (Incorrect arithmetic operators may be present, two operators may have been used in succession, etc.)
5. A fixed-point variable is subscripted.

Diagnostics on interaction of two or more statements
6. A referenced statement is not present or is unnumbered.
7. A DIMENSIØN statement for a subscripted variable is omitted.
8. A variable that appears in an arithmetic expression (on the right side of an arithmetic statement) does not appear earlier in the program.

Diagnostics on capacity of words or of memory
9. A table has been exceeded. (FORTRAN, during compilation, uses a number of tables; if one of these is exceeded, because the programmer has too many statements or certain other features, this comment is given.)
10. The program exceeds the memory capacity.
11. A number is used that is less than 10^{-38} (greater than 10^{38}). These limits vary from computer to computer; the limits stated are typical of 36-bit binary words.)

Diagnostics on logic of program

12. Flow cannot reach at least one portion of a program. (If, because of jump statements, control cannot pass to at least one executable statement, this comment is given.)

13. A jump occurs to within a DØ loop from outside the loop.

14. There are too many levels of nested loops. (The limit depends on the computer; it is usually determined by the number of index registers present.)

Clearly, a number of these diagnostics would apply to any algebraic-language program; these are 3, 4, 6, 8, 9, and 10. Others are peculiar to FORTRAN and may be peculiar to other compilers; with sufficient coding incorporated into the compilers, they would not apply; these are 1, 2, 5, 7, 11, 13, and 14. Diagnostic 12 is provided primarily as an aid to the programmer; although it indicates an error, the program may run very well despite it. The diagnostics called *logical* do not refer to errors in the same category as the logical errors stated earlier in this chapter; these diagnostics are peculiar to the compiler and the indicated errors may even be correct in terms of the original problem.

Help at the Console

Once a program has been checked and has been assembled or compiled correctly (that is, with no error flags or diagnostics), it is placed on the computer. When this is done, one of the following things occurs.

1. It will run through to completion, yielding correct results.
2. It will run through to completion, yielding wrong results.
3. It will stop before completion.
4. It will continue indefinitely, in an endless loop.

Other possibilities exist, but these four are of the greatest interest to us.

Let us consider the four cases in reverse order. First, if the program loops indefinitely, it is extremely useful to note the location of the loop. Either the programmer himself or the computer operator should note the location addresses involved, producing comments such as

"looping through 00457, 00460, 00461, 00462, 00463, 00457, . . ."

if the loop is a short one, or

"looping from 02301 through 02442"

if the loop is a long one. Sometimes this little information will reveal the cause of the error; it serves to direct the attention of the programmer directly to the trouble.

For the operator to identify a loop, he must be able to sequence through the program at a speed slow enough for him to read the contents of the AR (address register), displayed on the console. Computers have *manual* operating modes, in which each instruction is executed either on a command from the operator or

automatically at a very low speed.   Because of the high cost of computer operation, manual stepping is done entirely for loop identification or for other
information on sequencing.

Second, if the computer stops it does so either because it encounters a HALT
instruction or because it encounters an illegal operation code.   Some computers
continue operating in the latter case; their action at that time is frequently unpredictable.   If a monitor program is used to control the running of programs, as described in Section 11.1, then HALT is never used under normal circumstances.   In
such cases, therefore, a stop is always an error.   Here, too, it is very important
to know where the stop occurred.   The location of the stop is in the AR and
should be noted.

Knowing where the computer stopped is not always sufficient information for
finding the error, since what is probably really needed is information on how
control got to the HALT; such information is not directly available.   If a post-
mortem dump is used, this information may be indirectly available.   A bit of
detective work may reveal the information, as this example shows.

Example 19.3   Suppose a stop occurs at location 02345.   A dump reveals the contents
of the console registers: the accumulator, multiply register, mask register, and the index
registers.   Suppose the modifiers of the XR's contain the following (octal) numbers:

XR1: 00000   XR2: 00222   XR3: 00000   XR4: 00111   XR5: 00000
XR6: 00000   XR7: 00000

It is possible that the address 02345 is the effective address of a tagged jump instruction;
if so, either XR2 or XR4 modified that address. (All other XR modifiers are zero.)   The
direct address was then either 02123 (02345 − 00222) or 02234 (02345 − 00111), so that
the instruction causing the jump was possibly one of the following:

Oper.	Var. Field
JUMP	02123,2
JUMP	02234,4

An examination of all the instructions in the dump may reveal one of these instructions.

Another possibility for the error in the case of a stop exists if the operation
code for HALT is 00, as in the DELTA 63.   The dump may reveal a sequence of
coding that is in good condition until it terminates abruptly and is followed by
words of zeros, the first of which caused the stop.   In this case, a block-clearing
routine might have zeroed a block of words incorrectly; all such routines should
be checked.

There are, of course, many reasons why a computer stops; these are only two
possibilities.   They are presented to indicate the kinds of errors that may lead
to a stop.

The third condition, a run to completion with wrong answers, is probably the most common situation in a program with errors.   The causes are
extremely numerous and cannot readily be characterized.   Examination of the

results obtained often points out the trouble when the programmer has an idea of what the correct answers are.

The fourth condition, the proper working of the program, obviously evokes no further comment here.

Program Testing

In order to test a program, it is necessary to apply a set of test data to the program. Generally such data should be simple, so that hand calculations can be used to check the results. For example, if we have written a program to solve for the unknowns in a set of linear algebraic equations, the test data might consist of a set of three equations. To make the hand-checking process even simpler, we can begin with a set of solutions and then write equations that will yield the assumed results. The resulting equations are satisfactory for checking purposes.

A check on all possibilities of flow of control in the program is essential. Every path in the program, as well as all special routines to handle exceptional cases, should be traversed with a variety of data. Therefore, once the test data have successfully passed through the program, revealing the absence of gross errors, variations on these data should also be used. Finally, continued use of the program using actual data proves out the program. It is surprising how common it is that a program can be used dozens or even hundreds of times with success, only to fail later when an "unusual" set of data is used. A program, unless quite simple, is rarely ever known to be absolutely correct.

If a program is written in segments, as suggested in Section 12.2, it is important that errors in each segment be removed before a check is made on the following segments. The test data should be applied, and the intermediate results produced at the end of each segment should be checked.

Restarting After an Error

If a long program, perhaps 4 hours long, fails as the result of errors "external" to the program after completing 90% of its calculations, it is extremely wasteful of computer time to restart it from the beginning. By an "external" error is meant one not in the program. Some examples are machine malfunctions, operator errors, and errors in the data.

To avoid wasting time in the event of such failures, it is prudent to incorporate a sequence of checks, perhaps one at the end of each segment. If any check reveals an error up to that point, calculations should cease and be restarted at the last point that was known to be correct.

If a program is to be restarted at an intermediate point, either because of an error check stop or machine or operator mishap, it is necessary to save information about the status of the program at that point. Such information includes the contents of all memory storage areas, internal and external. If the program is unchanged in any way, it need not be saved. More likely, instructions will have been modified by address modification. Counters, indicators, switches, and storage areas must be saved. All intermediate results must be saved.

One approach is to dump all of memory at every check point, always saving the latest dump. In this way the program status at the latest possible time is always available. On restarting, this information can be reloaded, and the program can continue. There will invariably be some overlap, with calculations being done that were previously done; failures rarely occur exactly at check points. Sometimes it is more convenient to have intermediate results punched on cards (or put on a tape for later punching) at check points. Whatever method is used, the procedure of checking and saving the program status is an invaluable aid for starting programs and avoiding a great deal of wasted time.[1]

Programs for Debugging

If manual checking and console debugging procedures have been used and errors still remain, the next step is to turn to the use of special-purpose computer programs for debugging help. Generally we use these programs to provide information on the contents of specified memory words or registers during or after program execution. By examining such information in a sequence that follows the running of the program, the programmer can attempt to track down the cause of his errors.

With enough information of this type provided at the proper points in the program, any error can be located. It is not, however, always easy to locate the proper points, nor is it easy to know what information to request.

Program dumps were extensively described in Section 11.3 and little more will be said about them here, except by way of review. Other debugging techniques are described in later sections.

19.3 THE USE OF DUMPS

A memory dump provides a block of information—the contents of a sequence of locations in memory. Snapshot dumps indicate information existing at specified times during execution; post-mortem dumps indicate information existing after a program has stopped, either through error or by intention.

Snapshot dumps are useful when the programmer has little or no idea where his errors are located. If he has segmented his program, it is relatively easy to localize at least the earliest error, identifying the segment in which it occurs. Then the snapshot dumps are useful for checking the coding within each segment in turn. As errors are localized, snapshots are used more densely and over smaller memory areas. As a general rule, it is advisable, when debugging, to provide a post-mortem dump of *all* the memory (except possibly the monitor system). Since the effects of errors are unpredictable, it is very often helpful to see the complete picture while debugging.

To be able to print snapshot dump information, the monitor must gain control temporarily from the program being debugged (the object program). A common way for this to be done, on computers containing the feature, is to use a *trap*. The trap is simply a means whereby control passes to a specified memory location within the monitor program. Since it is necessary for control to be returned to the object program, some means for a return is required.

When the monitor program encounters debugging control cards in the deck, it must place the means for the trap to occur at the specified locations. Unless the trap provides it, the location from which control went to the monitor must be noted.

In the DELTA 63 a special trapping feature is provided. If bit position 1 of any instruction being executed has a 1-bit (called a *trap* bit), then that instruction will not be executed. Instead control will go directly to location 00001, and the C(AR), the location of the instruction with a trap bit, is placed in the address field of location 00000.* In this manner the monitor gains control.

As the program deck is loaded, the SNAP cards are also loaded. As these are encountered by the monitor, the information on them is stored within the snapshot routine. A snapshot table is established with a list of addresses where snapshots are requested and with other appropriate information. The monitor places a trap bit in all locations where snapshots are to occur.

When control passes to one of the instructions containing a trap bit, a trap occurs and control goes to 00001. At that location, a JUMP instruction sends control to the snapshot routine. There a search is made of the snapshot table, and if a dump was requested at the address in location 00000, the dump is given. It is possible that control might go to a location in the object program that has 1 in bit 1 which is not a trap bit; for that reason, a dump cannot be given unconditionally when a trap occurs. The address in 00000 (the address that has 1 in bit 1) is sought in the snapshot table; if it is not found, the 1 cannot be a trap bit.

In any event, the instruction from which control came to the monitor must be executed. After that is done, control returns to the object program, either at the next instruction or, if a jump or skip was executed, at the indicated instruction.

To assist the programmer when his program unintentionally sends control outside the block of executable instructions and associated constants, the monitor, just prior to loading a program, places trap bits in all memory words (except for the monitor area). Programs loaded into memory of course write over some of these bits, but the areas not so covered retain them; this includes areas set aside by BLØCK pseudo-operations. If, then, control passes to a word outside the program, a trap occurs, and the monitor, now recognizing the fact that no snapshot was requested at that location, stops the program, supplying information on where control went.

---

* The STR (store location and trap) instruction on the IBM 7090 is very similar to this feature.

The special trap feature of the DELTA 63 and its monitor provides two services: (1) snapshot dumps at any specified location, and (2) an automatic stop of the program when control passes incorrectly to a word outside the program or in its storage space (provided nothing was stored there) with information about the location of the stop. Other computers have similar features. When a program clears a storage block and control later inadvertently passes to a location in that block, the trap cannot occur. An operation code of 00, however, corresponds to a HALT instruction in some computers; in that case, the computer stops. The computer operator, noting this, can read the console and inform the programmer of the location of the stop.

Symbolic Dumping

Some assemblers provide for dumping through the use of symbolic location designations. For example, we might be permitted to use the following control card:

Location	Oper.	Var. Field
LØØP	SNAP	Ø,LIST,NUMBER+30

This card designates that locations LIST through NUMBER + 30 inclusive are to be dumped in octal form whenever control passes to LØØP.

The advantages of this approach are apparent when we consider the advantages of symbolic coding over machine language coding. If changes are made in the program, a card such as the one just given need not be modified as it might if it were written using absolute locations.

In order for symbolic dumping to work, the symbol table associated with the program being debugged must be present in memory. The debugging routine must then convert the symbols on the SNAP cards to absolute locations (considering relocation, if necessary).

19.4 THE USE OF TRACING

Tracing was described in Section 18.3, where we saw that it is useful for studying a program or for debugging a program. While a program is executed a trace provides the contents of the console registers as each instruction is executed and also lists the sequencing of the program. Thus two types of information are provided: the contents of words and registers as they are modified, and the order in which instructions are executed.

A complete program trace is very slow, as noted in Section 18.3, and can produce an enormous amount of printout. On a high-speed computer that executes about 200,000 instructions per second, a complete trace would produce over

3000 pages of printout in the equivalent of 1 second of normal running time. Therefore it is almost essential that conditional tracing facilities be available. There are a number of possibilities.

1. A single trace at each instruction in a loop, so that a loop is traced only once;
2. tracing in specified portions of a program;
3. tracing at specified types of instructions.

Each of these is considered briefly.

Since loops are repetitious, it is usually not necessary to have a trace of every instruction execution; frequently, one trace of each instruction in the loop is sufficient. Almost always three or at the most five are required. If an error exists in a loop, it will most likely be revealed in that many cycles. In order for the tracing program to be able to suppress tracing after n loop cycles, it is necessary for it to contain a "history" of locations traced and a set of counters. Thus a check can be made to see if an instruction was already traced n times. The additional information, the history and the counts, require a great deal of room, which makes their use somewhat prohibitive if space is a problem. In any event, each instruction must be interpreted, but time waste is avoided through suppression of printing.

If only certain portions of the program are to be traced, it is desirable that all the other portions run at normal speed, so that no time will be wasted. To accomplish this, the interpreter must relinquish control to the executed program during the noninterpreted portions and later recover control for the interpreted portions. The trap feature of the computer can be used for this purpose. Prior to giving control to the object program initially, trap bits are placed throughout the program at those points where control is to return to the interpreter. In this case, the monitor must relinquish control to the interpreter on obtaining it at location 00001.

The trap feature can also be used to trace only certain operations. Here the trap bits are placed at the indicated instructions. Before giving up control to the executed program initially, the interpreter must locate all those instructions; it can locate them by a search for appropriate operation codes. Thus, if JUMP, JUMPPL, and JUMPMI are specified, the operation codes 20, 21, and 22 are sought.

Because of the trap feature the processes of normal and interpretive execution can both occur, since control can zigzag back and forth between the executed program and the interpreter. This is highly advantageous because it results in time savings.

Tracing provides information of a different kind from that contained in a snapshot dump. In the latter, a large amount of information is usually provided at relatively few locations in the program. In the former, a small amount of information is provided at relatively many locations.

19.5 THE USE OF MACRO-INSTRUCTIONS

A method that we studied in Section 17.2 used macro-instructions to provide information during the running of a program in addition to that normally supplied. That technique is very useful for debugging purposes; the additional information is used to find errors. This information can appear in the same form as dumps or lines of trace. Macro-calls are placed in the program to provide the information instead of using the trap feature or interpretation.

Examples 17.13, 17.14, and 17.15 (pages 372–375) show the use of a modified STØRE instruction to provide the printout of information. This information can be very helpful in debugging since an indication is given of every number stored in memory. If an error that causes an improper number to be stored exists, this information might disclose the error. If the STØRE instruction is located within a many-cycle loop, conditional printing is needed; Example 17.15 indicates two ways in which this can be accomplished. The TURNØN-TURNØF feature of Example 17.14 permits printing only in certain portions of the program.

More common than the macro-instructions just described, where existing machine instructions are modified by macro-definitions to supply information, is the *insertion* of macro-calls into the program for debugging purposes. The PRTBLK macro-instruction of Example 17.10 (page 365) is of this type; a similar call is

Oper.   Var. Field

PRTBLK   BLØCK,N

which means, "Print on the output tape a record from the block at BLØCK of size C(N)." For debugging, only writing on the output tape is useful, so the third field (TAPE) of Example 17.10 is unnecessary. An alternate form is

PRTBLK   A,B

which means "Print on the output tape the block from A through B inclusive." For completeness, it might be necessary to designate a format: octal, decimal, floating-point, or BCD.

These macro-instructions expand into coding that calls on the monitor output routines, which do the tape writing. If loops are required, they are also generated by the macro-instruction.

As with other forms of debugging-information production, the macro-instructions should contain features for conditionally writing the desired information. A typical macro-call that provides for a format designation and conditional dumping follows.

Oper.   Var. Field

PRTBLK   Ø,LIST,LIST+199,UNTIL,20

This means, "Print in octal format the block from LIST through LIST + 199 every time until the twentieth." That is, provide a dump the first twenty times that control passes through this location.

Example 19.4   Write a short program containing a loop into which a debugging macro-call is placed.

The program is

Location	Oper.	Var. Field
	SETXRI	100,1
START	LØAD	SUM
	ADD	NUMBRS,1
	STØRE	SUM
	PRTBLK	Ø,SUM,SUM,UNTIL,5
	LØØPXR	START,1,1
	HALT	

The resulting printout, which merely shows the contents of SUM, might appear as follows.

```
000000000010
000000000034
000000000055
000000000067
000000000102
```

The next example shows a more complex printout, the dump of two different blocks.

Example 19.5   Consider Example 8.6, which sorts a list of 1000 numbers into two blocks, PØSLST and NEGLST. Assume that the following two cards are inserted in the program immediately following the instruction at MØD:

```
PRTBLK   D,PØSLST,PØSLST+3,UNTIL,4
PRTBLK   D,NEGLST,NEGLST+2,UNTIL,3
```

This requests a decimal output, assumed to be given with three or four words to a line. The resultant output might be as follows:

+23498	0	0	0
0	0	0	
+23498	0	0	0
−232	0	0	
+23498	0	0	0
−232	−86001	0	
+23498	+77	0	0

Note that four dumps of PØSLST (four numbers on a line) were given, whereas three dumps of NEGLST (three numbers on a line) were given.

The use of macro-instructions to provide dumps requires reassembly in order to incorporate the extra coding, a step not necessary with the other two debugging methods described. This method has at least two advantages over the others. First, references to locations or blocks to be dumped are made *symbol-*

ically, in the language of the program; this is a significant advantage. If there are coding changes, there is usually no need to change the macro-calls; with snapshot control cards, such changes are necessary since locations at which they are placed are absolute.* Second, the programmer can readily devise any sort of dump that he wishes, dump-like, trace-like, any combination of the two, or any other form. All macro-instructions for dumping purposes are quite simple in structure, primarily involving coding for a loop, for the output calling sequence, and for the storage of certain registers.

Example 19.6 Write a macro-instruction that will provide the following information, all in octal, when control passes to it.

1. The C(MR) and the C(AC);
2. contents of any three specified index registers;
3. contents of any three specified words in memory;
4. contents of a block of any size in memory.

A typical call is

Oper.	Var. Field
DUMP	2,3,6,WØRD,XXX,SUM,LIST,LIST+10

which means "Dump the MR, the AC, XR2, XR3, and XR6, locations WØRD, XXX, and SUM, and the block from LIST through LIST + 10."

In the macro-instruction that follows, the index registers are first saved and later restored. The C(MR) and the C(AC) are stored in two locations, so that they can be referenced in the output subroutine calling sequence. The format (FMT) used by the macro-instruction is not shown.

The macro-instruction is

Location	Oper.	Var. Field	
DUMP	MACRØ	T1,T2,T3,A,B,C,L,M	
	STØRXR	Q,T1	
	STØRXR	Q+1,T2	STØRE THE 3 XRS
	STØRXR	Q+2,T3	
	STØREM	Q+3	STØRE MR, AC
	STØRE	Q+4	
	JUMPSX	ØUTPUT,7	
		FMT	
	MZERØ	Q	PRINT C(XRS),C(MR),C(AC)
	MZERØ	Q+4	
	ZERØ	A	PRINT 3 WØRDS
	ZERØ	B	
	ZERØ	C	
	MZERØ	L	PRINT BLØCK
	MZERØ	M	
	MZERØ		

(Continued)

---

* This is not true, of course, if symbolic dumping is used.

```
        LØADXR   Q,T1            RESTØRE XRS
        LØADXR   Q+1,T2
        LØADXR   Q+2,T3
        LØADM    Q+3             RESTØRE MR, AC
        LØAD     Q+4
        MACEND
        • • •    • • • • •
  Q     BLØCK    5
```

The dump may include symbolic information for ready identification of words and registers; this is possible because symbolic information may be assembled into format statements. The sample printout in Fig. 19.1 indicates the usefulness of this approach. The dump shown would result from the use of the sample call for DUMP in this example.

Not only are such macro-instructions as the one in Example 19.6 easy to write, but almost any type of conditional dumping can also quite readily be incorporated. The various conditions under which snapshot dumps are executed (listed in Section 11.3) or under which tracing occurs (Section 19.4) can be considered. The reason that writing such macro-instructions is easier than writing the appropriate coding for a monitor system snapshot routine or an interpreter is that the latter two must be completely general and every piece of information must be stored in tables or left in instructions to be interpreted. In the use of macro-instructions, the coding is specific to the task at hand and remains in readily executable form within the macro-call expansion.

19.6 THE USE OF COMMENTS

It is possible to make use of comments built into a program to indicate the course of execution. These are generally placed at the conclusion of segments of the program and may either indicate that everything is all right or that trouble exists. To ascertain whether the latter is true, a number of tests might be necessary. Comments can also be used to indicate the overflow of storage blocks or a diverging series of values. Typical comments are:

> THE SERIES ØF ESTIMATES IS DIVERGING
>
> THE TWØ CØUNTS DØ NØT AGREE
>
> THE BUFFER STØRAGE IS FULL
>
> PART 3.4 HAS BEEN CØMPLETED

The first comment results from a continual testing of new estimates within an iterative process. If the series of estimates diverges at a rate larger than a predetermined value, the comment is provided and the program stops.

The second comment results from a check in the program at an appropriate point after some processing has occurred. For example, a list of numbers might

```
MR = +000000222675   AC = -000111000234
XR2 = 00000 00000   XR3 = 00000 00270   XR6 = 00100 00052

WØRD = 000000021025    XXX = 400000000002    SUM = 024132560147

LIST THRØUGH LIST+10
000000000000 000000000012 000034000102 400000011010
423016532013 000001100000 000000000000 000004700111
212223335556 000000022222 000000000001
```

Fig. 19.1. Example of macro-instruction dump.

be sorted into several classes and the counts of each class later checked against an original count. In the case of disagreement, the comment is printed.

The third comment results from the filling of an allotted block of storage. For this purpose, a counter is increased every time an entry is made into the block and its contents are checked each time.

The fourth comment results from the completion of "Part 3.4," after which the comment is printed. Probably it would be more useful if this were done only if the part was successfully completed.

In this manner comments that indicate both desirable and undesirable conditions can be provided. They can be scattered in any way throughout the program to indicate its progress. Use of such comments does not constitute debugging in the usual sense, since they may give indications of success. They are very useful, however, in indicating errors that can later be determined by other methods. If, for example, a comment like the last one we have given is printed after each part of the program is successfully completed, we can see at a glance which parts have worked and know where not to look for trouble.

Summary

Debugging, the tracking down of errors in a computer program, is a necessary step in the development of that program. Although we may be painstakingly careful in the development, errors can still creep in. There are a number of ways of locating errors, all of which in general should be applied in a given case.

Prior to running the program on a computer, it is advisable to check it carefully. This involves a check of the problem statement and its analysis, including the flowchart. When that is done, the assembly process may identify some errors. Errors in coding will be revealed during an actual run, although the sources of errors are often well concealed. For testing purposes, sample data should be used, and the results should be checked manually.

A number of computer programs and programming techniques are available for the determination of mistakes. The principle behind all of them is to provide information about a specified portion or portions of the program as control passes through specified instructions. Depending on the nature of the effect of the error, the amount and location of the information will both vary. The several debugging approaches provide varying kinds of information.

Notes

1. The subject of restarting (rerunning) programs is discussed in the following book.

D. D. McCracken, H. Weiss, and T. H. Lee, *Programming Business Computers,* Wiley, 1959, Chapter 17.

PROBLEMS

Section 19.1

19.1. Discuss the possible consequences of each of the "common errors" listed in the text.

19.2. List other errors that might be made at any stage of program-writing process, in addition to those stated.

Section 19.2

19.3. Flowchart the portion of an assembler that detects the errors listed in the text. Code a routine for this purpose.

19.4. Flowchart the portion of a compiler that detects the errors listed in the text. Code a routine for this purpose.

Section 19.3

19.5. Write a snapshot routine to provide the dumping facilities described in Sections 11.3 and 19.3. Include symbolic dumping facilities. It is to be assumed that the routine is in memory during the execution of the object program.

Section 19.4

19.6. Describe ways in which the self-interpreter (trace program) of Example 18.3 could be modified to yield conditional tracing under the following conditions.

(*a*) Tracing of certain portions of the object program only;

(*b*) tracing of certain instructions only;

(*c*) tracing only once at any instruction;

(*d*) tracing *n* times at one instruction (where *n* may vary from one instruction to another).

Section 19.6

19.7. Discuss the relative advantages and disadvantages of each of the several debugging approaches described in this chapter. What are some other approaches?

APPENDIX 1

THE DELTA 63

The DELTA 63 is the hypothetical computer used throughout this book for illustrative and instructional purposes. Its characteristics have been described in several chapters and are summarized here for reference purposes. A complete list of its instructions, with the descriptions appearing in the book, is also given.

A1.1 GENERAL FEATURES

The DELTA 63 is a binary computer having a memory of 32,768 36-bit words. These words are generally considered to be addressed octally, from 00000 through 77777. Bits in memory words are labeled S, 1, 2, . . . , 35. The S-bit holds the sign, so that a signed, 35-bit integer can be stored in each word. A positive sign is stored as 0.

A floating-point number is stored in two parts: bits 1–8 hold the characteristic, which is 128 (200_8) greater than the exponent to the base 2; bits 9–35 hold the fraction, which is multiplied by the indicated power of 2. The binary point of the fraction is assumed to be immediately to the left of bit 9.

Special registers include the accumulator, the multiply register, and seven index registers. The accumulator has 36 bits and is used for addition and subtraction, sums and differences being accumulated there. Its contents may be tested for certain conditions and jumps may occur if these conditions are met. The multiply register is an adjunct to the accumulator. It also has 36 bits and is used with the accumulator for multiplication and division. For this purpose, the two registers sometimes act as a single 72-bit register.

The seven index registers are numbered 1, 2, . . . , 7. Associated with most instructions is a tag which specifies one of these registers, if it is nonzero. Each index register contains two 15-bit fields, the modifier and the tally. If XRj is specified in the tag field of an instruction, then the effect is that the operand address is temporarily increased by the contents of the XRj modifier, forming an effective address.

Automatic masking is available on the DELTA 63; it is indicated in an instruction by the presence of a 1 in bit 11. If that 1 is present, then only those bits which correspond to the presence of 1's in the bits of the 36-bit mask register are transmitted between memory and the accumulator by a LOAD or STORE instruction.

Indirect addressing is available; it is indicated in an instruction by the presence of a 1 in bit 14. If that 1 is present, the operand address of the instruction is the location in which will be found (in the address field) the address of the operand of the instruction.

Within the computer, BCD (binary-coded-decimal) bites are used as encodings of all digits, all letters, and a number of arithmetic and punctuation marks. Each code occupies 6 bits, so that six codes can be stored in one 36-bit word. A list of the codes and their equivalents appears on page 209.

The console of the computer contains a number of switches and indicators. One purpose of these switches is to enter information manually into the computer; the keys, 36 in number, are used for this purpose. Each key can be set or reset, corresponding to a 1 or 0 bit. When the "load keys" button on the console is pushed, the binary number stored in the keys is placed in location 00000 and control passes to that location. This feature is useful for loading programs into memory.

Eight magnetic tape units are connected to the computer, and it is possible to read information from and write information on any of them. For these purposes, there are tape-reading and -writing instructions. Single records of information are read either from memory onto tape or from tape into memory on execution of one of these instructions.

Information is placed on tape in a binary manner. Seven bits are placed across the width of the tape, of which one is a check bit. Six such rows constitute a word (36 bits) of information. A group of words stored on tape with no gap constitutes a record. A record of information, as we have noted, is read or written during one instruction execution; the tape read-write head stops only between records. Records are separated by record gaps. A group of records constitutes a file, which is terminated by an end-of-file mark, a special short record.

The amount of information read from a tape depends on the size of the record or on a number present in the tape-reading instruction, whichever is smaller. The amount of information written on tape depends on a number present in the tape-writing instruction and constitutes one record. The particular tape unit involved depends on another number present in either of the tape instructions.

The on-line card reader, connected to the computer, reads information from a binary card into memory. Twenty-four binary words are read into memory, unless a particular smaller number is present in the card-reading instruction. The off-line card reader reads information from binary or symbolic cards onto tape, the contents of one card filling one tape record.

The off-line card punch and off-line printer place information from magnetic tape on cards (punched) and on paper (printed), respectively.

A1.2 INSTRUCTIONS

Each computer instruction is placed in one 36-bit memory word. The parts of the instruction word are as follows:

Bits 3–8:	operation field
Bit 11:	mask bit
Bit 14:	indirect-addressing bit
Bits 18–20:	tag field
Bits 21–35:	address field

In the three input-output instruction words, the parts are as follows:

Bits 3–8:	operation field
Bits 9–14:	count
Bits 18–20:	tag field
Bits 21–35:	address field

The other bits are not used.

In the descriptions that are given next, the following sequence of information is given: the instruction name in full, an abbreviated form for the instruction, the numerical operation code, and the description. The symbol Y in the descriptions refers to the effective address of the instructions.

Arithmetic Instructions

ADD (ADD Y) (04). The C(Y) is added algebraically to the C(AC), and the sum is placed in the AC. The C(Y) is unchanged.

SUBTRACT (SUBT Y) (05). The C(Y) is subtracted algebraically from the C(AC), and the difference is placed in the AC. The C(Y) is unchanged.

MULTIPLY (MULT Y) (06). The C(Y) is multiplied algebraically by the C(AC), and the product is placed in the AC and the multiply register. The less significant half of the product is placed in the AC, and the more significant half of the product is placed in the MR. The sign of the product is placed in the signs of both registers.

DIVIDE (DIV Y) (07). The C(AC) is divided algebraically by the C(Y), and the quotient is placed in the AC. The remainder is placed in the MR.

FLOATING ADD (FLADD Y) (14). The C(Y) is added algebraically to the C(MR), and the sum is placed in the MR and the AC; the more significant half of the sum is placed in the MR. The characteristic of the AC is adjusted so that it is 27 less than the characteristic of the MR. The C(Y) is unchanged.

FLOATING SUBTRACT (FLSUBT Y) (15). The C(Y) is subtracted algebraically from the C(MR), and the difference is placed in the MR and the AC; the more significant half of the difference is placed in the MR. The characteristic of the AC is adjusted so that it is 27 less than the characteristic of the MR. The C(Y) is unchanged.

FLOATING MULTIPLY (FLMULT Y) (16). The C(Y) is multiplied algebraically by the C(AC), and the product is stored in the MR and the AC; the more significant half of the product is stored in the MR. The characteristic of the AC is adjusted so that it is 27 less than the characteristic of the MR. The C(Y) is unchanged.

FLOATING DIVIDE (FLDIV Y) (17).   The C(AC) is divided algebraically by the C(Y), and the quotient is placed in the AC.   The remainder is placed in the MR.   The C(Y) is unchanged.

Logical Arithmetic Instructions

ACCUMULATOR RIGHT SHIFT (RSHIFT Y) (42).   The C(AC), including the sign, are shifted right Y bit positions.   Bits shifted out at the right are lost; vacated bits are filled with zeros.

ACCUMULATOR LEFT SHIFT (LSHIFT Y) (43).   The C(AC), including the sign, are shifted left Y bit positions.   Bits shifted out at the left are lost; vacated bits are filled with zeros.

LONG RIGHT SHIFT (LRSHFT Y) (44).   The C(MR) and the C(AC), considered as a single 72-bit word, are shifted right Y bit positions.   Bits shifted out at the right are lost; vacated bits are filled with zeros.

LONG ROTATE LEFT (ROTATE Y) (45).   The C(MR) and the C(AC), considered as a single 72-bit word, are shifted left Y bit positions in an "end-around" fashion.   Bits shifted out of the leftmost bit position (the MR S-bit) reappear at the right (the AC-35 bit). No bits are lost.

COMPLEMENT ACCUMULATOR (COMPL) (40).   Every bit of the accumulator that is 1 is changed to 0, and every bit that is 0 is changed to 1.   The sign is also changed.

Data Transmission Instructions

LOAD ACCUMULATOR (LOAD Y) (01).   The C(Y) replaces the C(AC).   The C(Y) is unchanged.

STORE ACCUMULATOR (STORE Y) (02).   The C(AC) replaces the C(Y).   The C(AC) is unchanged.

STORE ADDRESS (STORAD Y) (03).   The contents of the address field of the AC, that is, bits 21–35, replaces the contents of the address field of Y.   The C(AC) and the other bits in Y are unchanged.

LOAD MULTIPLY REGISTER (LOADM Y) (10).   The C(Y) replaces the C(MR). The C(Y) is unchanged.

STORE MULTIPLY REGISTER (STOREM Y) (11).   The C(MR) replaces the C(Y).   The C(MR) is unchanged.

LOAD MASK REGISTER (LOADMK Y) (46).   The C(Y) replaces the C(MK). The C(Y) is unchanged.

STORE MASK REGISTER (STORMK Y) (47).   The C(MK) replaces the C(Y). The C(MK) is unchanged.

CLEAR STORAGE (CLEARS Y) (13).   The C(Y) is set to zero and its sign is set plus.

Control and Decision Instructions

JUMP (JUMP Y) (20).   The computer takes its next instruction from location Y and proceeds in sequence from there.

JUMP IF PLUS (JUMPPL Y) (21). If the sign of the AC is positive, the computer takes its next instruction from location Y and proceeds from there. If the sign is negative, the next instruction in sequence is taken.

JUMP IF MINUS (JUMPMI Y) (22). If the sign of the AC is negative, the computer takes its next instruction from location Y and proceeds from there. If the sign is positive, the next instruction in sequence is taken.

JUMP IF ZERO (JUMPZE Y) (23). If the magnitude of the C(AC) is zero (regardless of sign), the computer takes its next instruction from location Y and proceeds from there. If the magnitude of the C(AC) is nonzero, the next instruction in sequence is taken.

JUMP IF NONZERO (JUMPNZ Y) (24). If the magnitude of the C(AC) is nonzero, the computer takes its next instruction from location Y and proceeds from there. If the magnitude of the C(AC) is zero, the next instruction in sequence is taken.

COMPARE ACCUMULATOR WITH STORAGE (COMPAR Y) (41). If the C(AC) is algebraically greater than the C(Y), the computer executes the next instruction in sequence. If the C(AC) equals the C(Y), the computer skips the next instruction and proceeds from there. If the C(AC) is algebraically less than the C(Y), the computer skips the next two instructions and proceeds from there.

HALT (HALT) (00). The computer stops on executing this instruction.

Indexing Instructions

SET INDEX REGISTER (SETXR Y) (31). The operand address of location Y replaces the contents of the tally of the specified index register, and the modifier of that index register is cleared. The C(Y) is unchanged.

SET INDEX REGISTER IMMEDIATE (SETXRI Y) (32). The operand address Y in this instruction word replaces the contents of the tally of the specified index register, and the modifier of that index register is cleared.

INCREASE INDEX REGISTER MODIFIER (INCRXM Y) (33). The operand address Y in this instruction word is added to the contents of the modifier of the specified index register, and the sum is placed in the modifier.

INDEX JUMP (XJUMP Y) (34). If the modifier of the specified index register is less than the tally of that index register, the computer takes its next instruction from location Y and proceeds from there. If the modifier equals or exceeds the tally, the next instruction in sequence is taken.

LOAD INDEX REGISTER (LOADXR Y) (35). The leftmost 15 bits (bits S, 1–14) and the rightmost 15 bits (the address field) of the C(Y) replace the tally and modifier, respectively, of the specified index register. The C(Y) is unchanged.

STORE INDEX REGISTER (STORXR Y) (36). The contents of the tally and the modifier of the specified index register replace the leftmost 15 bits and the rightmost 15 bits, respectively, of the C(Y). The middle 6 bits (bits 15–20) of the C(Y) are cleared. The contents of the index register are unchanged.

PLACE ADDRESS IN INDEX REGISTER MODIFIER (PADDXM) (37). The contents of the address field of the accumulator replaces the contents of the modifier of the specified index register. The C(AC) and the index register tally are unchanged.

JUMP AND SET INDEX (JUMPSX Y) (30). The location address of this instruction is placed in the modifier of the specified index register, and the computer takes its next instruction from Y and proceeds from there. The index register tally is unchanged.

Input-Output Instructions

WRITE TAPE X (WRITEX Y) (70–77).   A single record of information is written on tape X from the block of words starting at location Y. If a nonzero integer m appears in bits 9–14 of this instruction word, the m words from locations Y through $Y+m-1$ form a record on tape.   The number m cannot exceed 63.   If $m = 0$, it is interpreted as though it were 64.

READ TAPE X (READTX Y) (60–67).   A single record of information is read from tape X into the block of words starting at location Y.   If a nonzero integer m appears in bits 9–14 of this instruction word, the first m words of the record are read into the m words from locations Y through $Y+m-1$, provided at least m words are present.   If n is the number of words present, and $m > n$, then n words are read into locations Y through $Y+n-1$.   If bits 9–14 contain 0, the entire record is read into locations Y through $Y+n-1$.   If the tape reading head is positioned at an end-of-file mark, the computer continues in sequence to the next instruction; otherwise, the next instruction is skipped.

READ CARD (READC Y) (57).   The contents of a binary card (24 words) are read into locations Y through $Y+23$, unless a nonzero integer m appears in bits 9–14 of this instruction word.   If the integer m appears, the first m words on the card are read into locations Y through $Y+m-1$; if $m > 24$, only 24 words are read.   If no further cards are present in the on-line card reader, the computer continues in sequence to the next instruction; otherwise, the next instruction is skipped.

A1.3 THE HAP ASSEMBLY LANGUAGE

The language of the HAP assembler permits a programmer to write programs for the DELTA 63 in a convenient form.   The significant characteristics of this language are described in this section.

The symbolic instruction consists of three fields, as follows:

> Location field: symbol (name of instruction word)
> Operation field: symbolic operation
> Variable field: symbolic address, tag, count

Symbols consists of a sequence of 1 to 6 nonblank characters, each of which is a letter, a digit, or a period, and at least one of which is not a digit; symbols may be chosen at random by the programmer.   Symbolic operations are selected from a list whose entries correspond to the machine instructions on the computer.   Symbolic addresses are either symbols or arithmetic combinations of symbols and integers.   Tags refer to index registers.   Counts apply only to input-output instructions.   The three subfields in the variable field are written so that they appear in the order shown, separated by commas with no intervening blank spaces.

Indirect addressing in an instruction is indicated by the use of an asterisk (*) immediately following the symbolic operation in the operation field.   Masking in an instruction is indicated by the use of a dollar sign ($) in the same position.   If both characters are required, they may be placed in either order.

The following pseudo-operations are available in HAP.

ØRIGIN.   The variable field of this pseudo-operation indicates the address to be assigned to the next instruction. The assembler then assigns successive instructions to successive memory location unless directed otherwise.

END. The use of this pseudo-operation signals the end of the symbolic program. Its variable field contains the location at which the program starts, that is, the address of the first executable instruction.

ØCTAL. The octal numbers in the variable field of this pseudo-operation are assigned to successive locations in memory at the point in the program at which this card occurs. Numbers are separated by commas with no intervening blank spaces.

DECML. The decimal numbers in the variable field of this pseudo-operation are assigned to successive locations in memory at the point in the program at which this card occurs. Numbers are separated by commas with no intervening blank spaces. If any numbers contain decimal points, they are converted to floating-point form by the assembler; in such numbers the character E may be used to indicate numbers written with exponents (powers of 10).

BLØCK. A block of words of the size indicated in the variable field of this pseudo-operation is set aside for later use at the point in the program at which this card occurs.

SET. If a symbolic card contains a symbol S in the location field and a symbolic expression T in the variable field, then the use of this pseudo-operation assigns the value of T to the symbol S. All the symbols in T must be defined earlier in the program.

BCD. The first character in the variable field of this pseudo-operation is a decimal digit n, from 1 to 9. The following BCD string of characters (after a comma) of $6n$ characters is stored in the n successive computer words in memory at the point in the program at which this card occurs.

ZERØ. This pseudo-operation directs the assembler to assemble 0-bits into bits S and 1–8 of a computer word. If an address and tag are given in the variable field, they are assembled as on an instruction card.

MZERØ. This pseudo-operation directs the assembler to assemble 1 into the S-bit (a minus sign) and 0-bits into bits 1–8 of a computer word. If an address and tag are given in the variable field, they are assembled as on an instruction card.

Normally, an integer that appears in the variable field of a symbolic card is treated as a decimal number. If it is desirable to write an octal number, a qualifier may be used. The characters /Ø/ are used immediately prior to any numbers intended to be octal.

Macro-instructions may be defined and later called. The pseudo-operations MACRØ and MACEND begin and end, respectively, a sequence of coding that comprises a macro-definition. Any number of dummy arguments, to be subsequently substitutable, are identified by listing them in the variable field of the MACRØ card. Later usage is made of these definitions by macro-calls, which consist of cards containing the names of the macro-instructions in the operation field and the arguments that are to be substituted in the variable field. These call arguments must correspond in position to the dummy arguments. Several pseudo-operations are available for use within macro-definitions for providing flexibility in coding.

APPENDIX 2

BIBLIOGRAPHY

A2.1 BOOKS

The following list of books provides further information on the topics mentioned. This list cannot be exhaustive, but an attempt has been made to include most books on computer programming that are of a general nature. All the books cited in the text, at the ends of chapters, are listed; the chapters in which they are cited are mentioned.

General Programming

Evans, G. W., II, and C. L. Perry, *Programming and Coding for Automatic Digital Computers,* McGraw-Hill, 1961.
> This is an introductory text on programming, using a three-address computer coded in a semisymbolic manner. Cited in Chapters 3 and 13.

Grabbe, E. M., S. Ramo, and D. E. Wooldridge, *Handbook of Automation, Computation, and Control,* Vol. 2, Wiley, 1959.
> Volume 2 of this three-volume set is concerned with all phases of computer usage. Chapter 2 is an extensive study of advanced programming techniques. Cited in Chapters 3 and 16.

Jeenel. J., *Programming for Digital Computers,* McGraw-Hill, 1959.

> This introductory text uses absolute-address coding for a hypothetical computer. Much space is devoted to storage allocation, flowcharting, and program sequencing. Cited in Chapters 2 and 9.

Ledley, R. S., *Programming and Utilizing Digital Computers,* McGraw-Hill, 1962.

> This book is largely devoted to automatic-programming languages, particularly ALGOL and COBOL, and to data-processing techniques.

Leeds, H. D., and G. M. Weinberg, *Computer Programming Fundamentals,* McGraw-Hill, 1961.

> Although this book uses the IBM 7090 computer for coding illustrations, its subject matter is of general interest. It is an introductory book, using symbolic language. Cited in Chapters 2, 3, and 7.

McCracken, D. D., *Digital Computer Programming,* Wiley, 1957.

> This is an introductory text, using absolute-addressing techniques. A wide range of topics is discussed.

McCracken, D. D., H. Weiss, and T. H. Lee, *Programming Business Computers,* Wiley, 1959.

> Despite the word "business" in the title, this book covers many general-programming topics, besides several that are of a business nature. Cited in Chapters 16 and 19.

Specialized Programming

The books listed here are more specific in their subject matter than those just listed. The degree of speciality varies widely.

Andree, R. V., *Programming the IBM 650 Magnetic Drum Computer and Data-Processing System,* Holt, 1958.

Chapin, N., *Programming Computers for Business Applications,* McGraw-Hill, 1961.

> This book is largely concerned with COBOL.

Chorofas, D. N., *Programming Systems for Electronic Computers,* Butterworths, 1962.

> This book is concerned with techniques for writing automatic-programming languages.

Goodman, R. (ed.), *Annual Review of Automatic Programming,* Vols. 1 and 2, Pergamon, 1960 and 1961.

> These anthologies cover assemblers and compilers for a variety of computers.

Halstead, M. H., *Machine-Independent Computer Programming,* Spartan, 1962.

> NELIAC, a dialect of ALGOL, is described. The routines within NELIAC, written in NELIAC itself, are listed.

IBM Corporation, *Flowcharting and Block Diagramming Techniques,* 1961 (C20-8008-0).

Cited in Chapter 2.

————, *General Information Manual—FORTRAN,* 1961 (F28-8074-1).

Cited in Chapter 14.

————, *The COBOL Translator,* 1960 (F28-8053).

Leeson, D. N., and D. L. Dimitry, *Basic Concepts and the IBM 1620 Computer,* Holt, 1962.

McCracken, D. D., *A Guide to FORTRAN Programming,* Wiley, 1961.

Cited in Chapter 14.

————, *A Guide to ALGOL Programming,* Wiley, 1962.

Cited in Chapter 14.

Nathan, R., and E. Hanes, *Computer Programming Handbook, A Guide for Beginners,* Prentice-Hall, 1961.

This book treats a number of programming topics by reference to four existing computers.

Newell, A. (ed.), *Information Processing Language—V Manual,* Prentice-Hall, 1961.

Cited in Chapter 15.

Wrubel, M. H., *A Primer of Programming for Digital Computers,* McGraw-Hill, 1959.

This book is concerned with the IBM 650 computer.

Digital Computers

The books listed here cover several topics on digital computers, such as their design, structure, and operation. Programming is discussed briefly in some of these books.

Alt, F. L. (ed.), *Electronic Digital Computers,* Academic Press, 1958.

Much of this book is devoted to programming and the analysis of numerical problems.

Arden, B. W., *An Introduction to Digital Computing,* Addison-Wesley (preliminary edition), 1962.

About half of this book is devoted to numerical methods. The MAD compiler language, of the University of Michigan, is used primarily as the coding language.

Bowden, B. V. (ed.), *Faster than Thought,* Pitman, 1953.

This book describes a number of British and American computers and has a large section on computer applications. Cited in Chapter 1.

Chapin, N., *Introduction to Automatic Computers,* Van Nostrand, 1957.

Flores, I., *Computer Logic: the Fundamental Design of Digital Computers,* Prentice-Hall, 1960.

> This book is concerned with the structural details of computers, particularly the mathematical aspects. Cited in Chapters 1, 3, and 15.

IBM Corporation, *General Information Manual—Introduction to IBM Data Processing Systems,* 1960 (F22-6517).

> This manual is primarily concerned with IBM equipment.

Siegel, P., *Understanding Digital Computers,* Wiley, 1961.

> Computer devices and structural units are the main topics in this book.

Smith, C. V. L., *Electronic Digital Computers,* McGraw-Hill, 1959.

> Cited in Chapter 3.

Stibitz, G. R., and L. A. Larrivee, *Mathematics and Computers,* McGraw-Hill, 1957.

> Cited in Chapter 1.

Numerical Analysis and Computers

Hamming, R. W., *Numerical Methods for Scientists and Engineers,* McGraw-Hill, 1962.

> This book was written for people who will use digital computers to solve numerical problems.

Ralston, A., and H. S. Wilf, *Mathematical Methods for Digital Computers,* Wiley, 1960.

> Cited in Chapter 13.

Todd, J. (ed.), *Survey of Numerical Analysis,* McGraw-Hill, 1962.

> Cited in Chapter 13.

Stanton, R. G., *Numerical Methods for Scientists and Engineers,* Prentice-Hall, 1961.

> Cited in Chapters 2 and 14.

Other Books

Gotlieb, C. C., and J. N. P. Hume, *High-Speed Data Processing,* McGraw-Hill, 1958.

Huskey, H. D., and G. A. Korn (eds.), *Computer Handbook,* McGraw-Hill, 1962.

> Half of this book is devoted to digital computers, from nearly all points of view. Cited in Chapter 16.

Ledley, R. S., *Digital Computer and Control Engineering,* McGraw-Hill, 1960.

> A wide variety of topics is covered, including programming and coding at several levels. Cited in Chapter 16.

Martin, E. W., Jr., *Electronic Data Processing,* Irwin, 1961.
Cited in Chapters 3 and 16.

Richards, R. K., *Arithmetic Operations in Digital Computers,* Van Nostrand, 1955.
Cited in Chapter 4.

A2.2 PAPERS

A complete list of papers on digital-computer programming would be nearly impossible to compile and maintain; the number of such papers may increase annually by the hundreds. Listed here, therefore, are simply those papers cited in this book.

Several journals publish programming articles and some of these review many other published articles, as the following list indicates.

Communications of the Association for Computing Machinery regularly publishes many papers on programming. Cited in this book are the following special issues:

> April, 1960: symbol manipulation. Cited in Chapter 15.
> January, 1961: compilers. Cited in Chapter 14.
> October, 1961: storage allocation. Cited in Chapter 12.
> May, 1962: COBOL. Cited in Chapter 16.

Each issue of the *Communications* also contains several programs in ALGOL.

Journal of the Association for Computing Machinery, IRE Transactions on Electronic Computers, Datamation, and *Computers and Automation,* although primarily devoted to other aspects of digital computers, have several papers on programming.

Computing Reviews (published by the Association for Computing Machinery) and *IRE Transactions on Electronic Computers* contain reviews and abstracts of programming papers (among others). This journal published, in early 1963, a programming bibliography covering the years 1955–1961.

The list of papers cited in this book follows.

Bar-Hillel, Y., "The Present Status of Automatic Translation of Languages," in *Advances in Computers,* Vol. 1 (ed. by F. Alt), Academic Press, 1960, pp. 91–163.
Cited in Chapter 15.

Bottenbruch, H., "Structure and Use of ALGOL 60," *J. Assoc. Computing Machinery,* **9** (1962), pp. 161–221.
Cited in Chapter 14.

Bouton, C. L., "Nim, a Game with a Complete Mathematical Strategy," *Ann. Math.,* series 2, **3** (1901–2), pp. 35–39.
Cited in Chapter 15.

Gelernter, H., J. R. Hansen, and D. W. Coveland, "Empirical Explorations of the Geometry Theorem Machine," *Proc. Western Joint Computer Conference,* May 1960, pp. 143–150.

Cited in Chapter 15.

Green, B. F., Jr., "Computer Languages for Symbol Manipulation," *IRE Trans. Electronic Computers,* **EC-10** (1961), pp. 729–735.

Cited in Chapter 15.

Highleyman, W. H., "Linear Decision Functions, with Application to Pattern Recognition," *Proc. IRE,* **50** (1962), pp. 1501–1514.

Cited in Chapter 15.

McCarthy, J., "Recursive Functions of Symbolic Expressions and their Computation by Machine, Part I," *Comm. Assoc. Computing Machinery,* **4** (1960), pp. 184–195.

Cited in Chapter 15.

Naur, P. (ed.), "Report on the Algorithmic Language ALGOL 60," *Comm. Assoc. Computing Machinery,* **3** (1960), pp. 299–314.

Cited in Chapter 14.

Perlis, A. J., and K. Samelson, "Preliminary Report—International Algebraic Language," *Comm. Assoc. Computing Machinery,* **1** (1958), pp. 8–22.

Cited in Chapter 14.

Phillips, N. A., "Numerical Weather Prediction," in *Advances in Computers,* Vol. 1 (ed. by F. Alt), Academic Press, 1960, pp. 43–90.

Cited in Chapter 1.

Rabinowitz, I. N., "Report on the Algorithmic Language FORTRAN II," *Comm. Assoc. Computing Machinery,* **5** (1962), pp. 327–337.

Cited in Chapter 14.

Samuel, A. L., "Programming Computers to Play Games," in *Advances in Computers,* Vol. 1 (ed. by F. Alt), Academic Press, 1960, pp. 165–192.

Cited in Chapter 15.

Serrell, R., M. M. Astrahan, G. W. Patterson, and I. B. Pyne, "The Evolution of Computing Machines and Systems," *Proc. IRE,* **50** (1962), pp. 1039–1058.

Cited in Chapter 1.

Shannon, C. E., "Programming a Computer for Playing Chess," *Phil. Mag.,* **41** (1950), pp. 256–275.

Cited in Chapter 15.

Sherman, P. M., "Table-Look-At Techniques," *Comm. Assoc. Computing Machinery,* **4** (1961), pp. 172–173, 175.

Cited in Chapter 8.

INDEX

Page references in **boldface** indicate definitions; page references in *italics* indicate computer programs; a reference of the form 234n. indicates a footnote.

433